Blue Book of
Modern Black Powder Values
Third Edition

by John Allen
Photography & Editorial by Dennis Adler
Feature Editorial by R.L. Wilson
Edited by S.P. Fjestad

$24.95

Publisher's Softcover
Suggested List Price

$39.95

Publisher's Hardcover
Suggested List Price

Blue Book of
Modern Black Powder Values™
Third Edition

Publisher's Note:

This book is the result of nonstop and continual research obtained by attending shows and events, in addition to communicating with dealers, collectors, company historians, contributing editors, and other knowledgeable industry professionals worldwide each year. This book represents an analysis of prices for which collectible black powder models have actually been selling during that period at an average retail level. Although every reasonable effort has been made to compile an accurate and reliable guide, prices may vary significantly (especially auction prices) depending on such factors as the locality of the sale, the number of sales we were able to consider, and economic conditions. Accordingly, no representation can be made that the models listed may be bought or sold at prices indicated, nor shall the author or publisher be responsible for any error made in compiling and recording such prices and related information.

All Rights Reserved
Copyright 2003
Blue Book Publications, Inc.
8009 34th Avenue South, Suite 175
Minneapolis, MN 55425 U.S.A.

Orders Only: 800-877-4867
Phone No.: 952-854-5229
Fax No.: 952-853-1486
Email: bluebook@bluebookinc.com
Web site/home page: http://www.bluebookinc.com

Published and printed in the United States of America

ISBN No. 1-886768-40-4

Library of Congress ISSN number - 1529-7349

About the Cover

Author and photographer Dennis Adler and Val Forgett, III, teamed up to create this historic montage of Navy Arms literature, photos, and guns for the cover of the Third Edition *Blue Book of Modern Black Powder Values*. Shown are Reb 1, the first Navy Arms 1851 Navy revolver, an early Colt Blackpowder Arms 1851 Navy prototype, and an engraved LeMat, one of the great Civil War era guns that Val Forgett, Jr. had recreated by F.LLI Pietta in Italy. Photo by Dennis Adler.

Back Cover

The most elaborate contemporary longrifle ever produced, this highly embellished flintlock with gold and silver inlays was handcrafted in Alaska by artisan gunmaker Jud Brennan over a period of three and a half years. It is flanked by a matching pipe ax, also by Brennan, and a pair of flintlock pistols built by renowned gunmaker Keith Casteel. The matched pistols are fashioned after the Simon Lauck school of design from Winchester, Virginia, c. 1800. The petal star for the silver escutcheons, acorn finials on the trigger guards, and the line engraving on the pistols are all features of the Winchester school. Photo by Dennis Adler.

CONTENTS

GENERAL INFORMATION

While many of you have probably dealt with our company for years, it may be helpful for you to know a little bit more about our operation, including information on how to contact us regarding our various titles, software programs, and other informational services.

Blue Book Publications, Inc. contact information:
Mailing Address:
Blue Book Publications, Inc.
8009 34th Avenue South, Suite 175
Minneapolis, MN 55425   U.S.A.
Phone No. 952-854-5229 • Orders Only (domestic and Canada): 800-877-4867
Fax No. 952-853-1486 (available 24 hours a day)
Web site: http://www.bluebookinc.com
Email: bluebook@bluebookinc.com – we check our email at 9am, 12pm, and 3:30pm M-F (excluding major U.S. holidays). **Please refer to individual email addresses listed below with phone extension numbers.**

To find out the latest information on our products (including availability and pricing) and related consumer services, and up-to-date industry information (trade show recaps with photos/captions, upcoming events, feature articles, etc.), please check our web site, as it is updated on a regular basis. Surf us – you'll have fun!

Since our phone system is equipped with voicemail, you may also wish to know extension numbers which have been provided below:

Ext. No.: 11 - Tom Stock (toms@bluebookinc.com)	Ext. No.: 17 - Zach Fjestad (zachf@bluebookinc.com)
Ext. No.: 12 - John Andraschko (johnand@bluebookinc.com)	Ext. No.: 18 - Katie Sandin (katies@bluebookinc.com)
Ext. No.: 13 - S.P. Fjestad (stevef@bluebookinc.com)	Ext. No.: 19 - Cassandra Faulkner (cassandraf@bluebookinc.com)
Ext. No.: 14 - Honored Guest	Ext. No.: 20 - Honored Guest
Ext. No.: 15 - Clint Schmidt (clints@bluebookinc.com)	Ext. No.: 22 - Heather Mohr (heatherm@bluebookinc.com)
Ext. No.: 16 - John Allen (johna@bluebookinc.com)	Ext. No.: 25 - Beth Marthaler (bethm@bluebookinc.com)

Office hours are: 8:30am - 5:00pm CST, Monday - Friday.

Additionally, an after-hours answering service is available for ordering. All orders are processed within 24 hours of receiving them, assuming payment and order information is correct. Depending on the product, we typically ship either UPS, Media Mail, or Priority Mail. Expedited shipping services are also available domestically for an additional charge. Please contact us directly for an expedited shipping quotation.

All correspondence regarding technical information/values on guns or guitars is answered in a FIFO (first in, first out) system. That means that letters, faxes, and email are answered in the order in which they are received, even though some people think that their emails take preference over everything else.

Online subscriptions and individual downloading services are available for the *Blue Book of Gun Values*, *Blue Book of Modern Black Powder Values*, *Blue Book of Airguns*, *Blue Book of Electric Guitars*, *Blue Book of Acoustic Guitars*, and the *Blue Book of Guitar Amplifiers*.

GENERAL INFORMATION

As this edition goes to press, the following titles/products are currently available, unless otherwise specified:

Blue Book of Gun Values, 24th edition by S.P. Fjestad (ISBN 1-886768-39-0 1,792 pages)

Parker Gun Identification & Serialization compiled by Charlie Price and edited by S.P. Fjestad (ISBN 1-886768-37-4)

Colt Black Powder Reproductions & Replicas by Dennis Adler (ISBN: 1-886768-11-0)

3rd edition *Blue Book of Airguns* by Robert D. Beeman and John B. Allen edited by S.P. Fjestad(ISBN: 1-886768-40-4)

Blue Book 3-Pack CD-ROM (includes the databases from 24th edition *Blue Book of Gun Values*, 3rd edition *Blue Book of Modern Black Powder Values,* and 3rd edition *Blue Book of Airguns* (ISBN 1-886768-41-2)

Blue Book of Electric Guitars, 8th edition, by Zach Fjestad, edited by S.P. Fjestad (ISBN 1-886768-26-9, available Sept., 2003)

Blue Book of Acoustic Guitars, 8th edition, by Zach Fjestad, edited by S.P. Fjestad (ISBN 1-886768-33-1, available Sept., 2003)

Blue Book of Guitar Amplifiers, 2nd edition, by Zach Fjestad, edited by S.P. Fjestad (ISBN 1-886768-42-0, available Sept., 2003)

Blue Book of Guitars CD-ROM (ISBN: 1-886768-43-9, available Sept., 2003)

Blue Book of Guitar Amplifiers CD-ROM (ISBN: 1-886768-44-7, available Sept., 2003)

We would like to thank all of you for your business in the past – you are the reason(s) we are successful. Our goal remains the same – to give you the best products, the most accurate and up-to-date information for the money, and the highest level of customer service available in today's marketplace. If something's right, tell the world over time. If something's wrong, please tell us immediately – we'll make it right.

FACES BEHIND THE PHONE

Many of you may want to know what the person on the other end of the telephone/fax/email looks like, so here are the faces that go with the voices.

John Allen – Author & Firearms Researcher

S.P. Fjestad – Editor & Publisher

Cassandra Faulkner – Executive Assistant Editor

Tom Stock – CFO

Zach Fjestad – Author & Guitar Researcher

Clint Schmidt – Art Director

John Andraschko – Technology Director

Beth Marthaler – Operations Manager

Katie Sandin – Operations

Heather Mohr – Operations

ACKNOWLEDGEMENTS

David Kosowski
Paolo Amadi of Euroarms Italia S.r.l.
David Meredith of Blackpowder Products, Inc.
Dennis Russell
Doug Evans of Austin & Halleck Gun Crafters
Drew Herbst of Knight Rifles
Gurney Brown of Cherry's Fine Guns
George "Butch" Winter of Dixie Gun Works, Inc.
James Bruno of Traditions Performance Firearms
Jerry Bowe
John Stimson Jr.
Karen Griffin of Lyman Products Corp.
Kevin Cherry of Cherry's Fine Guns
Mike Wills of Whie Rifles LLC
Phil Spangenberger of Guns & Ammo
Robert Millington of ArmSport LLC
Roger Renner of Pacific Rifle Co.
Tanya Dosher of Cimarron F.A. Co.
Val Forgett III of Navy Arms

DEDICATION

In Memory of Val Forgett
who gave us all something to write about
- Dennis Adler -

FOREWORD

S.P. Fjestad (c), Editor & Publisher of the *Blue Book of Modern Black Powder Values*, R.L. Wilson (r), noted firearms authority and historian, and photojournalist Dennis Adler (l), at the 2003 Orlando NRA Show.

Welcome to the greatly expanded Third Edition *Blue Book of Modern Black Powder Values*! For those of you who have followed this project all the way back to its humble beginnings in 1983 – a whopping 8½ page section in the back of the 4th Edition *Blue Book of Gun Values*, the Modern Black Powder Guns section finally outgrew the gun book and was broken out after the 18th Edition. In 1998, the section was integrated into the award-winning *Colt Black Powder Reproductions & Replicas* by Dennis Adler. During 2000, the Modern Black Powder guns section was released, and with the Third Edition, this book has quickly evolved into the most important single publication available within the modern black powder industry.

So what's new for this edition? As you can already see, the format has been enlarged to 8½ x 11 inches, and the color sections have also been extended to 40 pages. For the first time, a color section (pages 169-176) on identifying popular modern black powder revolvers will make it a lot easier for both novices and budding collectors to immediately identify these most popular revolver configurations. Maybe more important than anything else however, is that John Allen has greatly expanded the A-Z sections to include not only all the currently manufactured makes and models, but also many additional discontinued and out of production black powder replicas/reproductions, produced after 1959.

In this new Third Edition, we are very pleased to offer you important and significant black powder editorials by R.L. Wilson, Dennis Adler, and Al Raychard. R.L. Wilson, one of the world's most recognized firearms authorities and historians, has written a definitive article on the conversion from flintlock to percussion ignition – don't miss a word. Well known photojournalist Dennis Adler once again has provided us with a dazzling array of stunning color images – this year, with the concentration being on modern flintlocks, and last but certainly not least, Al Raychard contributing editor for *Muzzle Blasts* magazine, keeps us right up-to-date with all the most recent technological innovations on in-line ignition systems.

With each edition of the *Blue Book of Modern Black Powder*

Values, we address a different segment of the black powder hobby, and this Third Edition features flintlocks. This is a term that immediately conjures up childhood memories of stories about Davy Crockett and mountain men, or the adventures of Lewis & Clark and their Journey of Discovery, which began 200 years ago in 1803, and most certainly that indelible image of Daniel Day Lewis clutching one flintlock in each hand as he dashes through the woods in the film classic *The Last of the Mohicans*. Outside of the guns of the American Civil War, and the legendary Colt Peacemaker, no firearm in history is more popularized than the flintlock.

Within the various black powder collector associations, perhaps the strongest and most organized body of enthusiasts are the collectors of original and reproduction flintlocks. There are more reenactments of American history involving flintlocks than any other period, French and Indian War and Revolutionary War reenactments for example, which take place all across the nation throughout the spring, summer, and fall, in historic sites like Valley Forge, Pennsylvania, and across the states comprising the original 13 colonies.

Organizations like the Contemporary Longrifle Association (CLA) have further strengthened the depth and breadth of this hobby through the promotion of America's artisan gunmakers, who specialize in recreating authentic renditions of the historic European and American flintlock pistols and longrifles of the 17th, 18th, and early 19th centuries. These are the firearms we see in films like *The Last of the Mohicans* and *The Patriot*, the fine, handcrafted, and expensive longrifles displayed at CLA shows around the country. Each is a work of art, painstakingly built in the old world tradition by gunmakers who are also historians, antiquarians, and teachers. The average artisan reproduction is more costly today than the average original flintlock!

The Third Edition pays tribute to these talented craftsmen who have kept the history of America's past alive through their remarkable work. While you may find this special section of the Blue Book short on words, as Fred R. Barnard wrote in *Printers Ink* back in 1927, "One picture is worth a thousand words," and our featured section "Flintlocks by America's Artisan Gunmakers" speaks volumes.

Certainly not to be overlooked is the revised and greatly expanded Trademark Index. This is the most up-to-date listing available on both domestic and international black powder manufacturers, importers, distributors, and repair centers.

Thank you again for your help and support on this project, and we look forward to providing you with up-to-date and reliable modern black powder information for many editions to come.

S.P. Fjestad
Editor & Publisher
Blue Book Publications, Inc.

Dennis Adler
Photojournalist
Blue Book Publications, Inc.

INTRODUCTION

Knight Rifles DISC Extreme in hand with the muzzle loader hunter's secret (ready for the next test ride) standing up in the back, the (Original) DISC rifle.

Welcome to the 3rd Edition *Blue Book of Modern Black Powder Values*. My name is John Allen, and I have been working at Blue Book Publications, Inc., as an editor for a little over 11 years. Other than proof reading past editions, my involvement in this book has been rather limited, but from now on the A-Z sections fall into my area, so if something is missing I want to hear about it.

My introduction to black powder arms started about 20 years ago with putting together a CVA .50 caliber percussion Hawken pistol kit (still haven't shot it). Next came a 2nd Generation Colt 1861 Navy revolver, but the real initiation came with an invitation to hunt elk with a muzzle loader in New Mexico back in 1997. A friend loaned me his .50 caliber Remington M-700ML, and the education began.

The following year (1998) with Knight Rifles new DISC rifle in hand and the right load, three 50 grain Pyrodex pellets and Knights' 300 grain jacketed soft point Saboted bullet, a nice 5x6 bull was in the bag. These things really shoot, 1.5 inches outside to outside at 100 yards, and it wasn't just luck. Five years later two elk and four whitetail have learned the muzzle loader

hunter's secret. They are not safe on their own turf. There is nothing more fun than showing a bunch of friends with their jacked-up center fire rifles how to shoot 1.5 inch groups with a muzzle loader. Well, maybe it was the looks on their faces after letting them take it for a test ride (it will back you up).

This brings us to 2003 and the 3rd Edition *Blue Book of Modern Black Powder Values*, back to the 8.5 by 11 inch format of the *Colt Blackpowder Reproductions & Replicas* book, with plans to add black and white images of different models in future editions. Also added to this edition are great new editorials by noted authors, "Modern In-Line Muzzleloaders" by Al Raychard, "The Transition from Flintlock to Percussion Ignition" by R.L. Wilson, "Flintlocks by America's Artisan Gunmakers" by Dennis Adler, and all the new black powder arms that appeared at the SHOT (Shooting, Hunting, Outdoor Trade) Show in February. A "Guide to Black Powder Resources" has been added for the internet savvy, as an introduction to what may have been missed on different web sites, while surfing the net.

This book is a work in progress (WIP, I hate these letters), we plan on expanding the A-Z sections, and would like to hear from you on what you are looking for. The firearms library here at Blue Book Publications, Inc. is full of information, and we have access to some of the most knowledgeable people in the industry. A short list of additions (FIE, H & R, Hopkins & Allen, Interarms, Intercontinental Arms, Kassnar, Parker-Hale, etc.) is in the development process, with all the information available out there to answer your question. Your input is always welcome, so don't hold back, and let us know what you are looking for.

John B. Allen
Author – *Blue Book of Modern Black Powder Values*

HOW TO USE THIS BOOK

The prices listed in this Edition of the *Blue Book of Modern Black Powder Values* are based on national average retail prices for most black powder reproductions and replicas. **This is not a wholesale black powder pricing guide. More importantly, do not expect to walk into a gun/pawn shop or gun show and think that the proprietor/dealer should pay you the retail price listed within this text for your black powder reproductions/replicas.** Resale offers on most models could be anywhere from near retail to 20%-50% less than the values listed, depending upon locality, desirability, dealer inventory, and profitability. In other words, if you want to receive 100% of the price (retail value), then you have to do 100% of the work (become the retailer, which also includes assuming 100% of the risk).

Percentages of original condition (with corresponding prices) are listed between 95%-100% for most reproductions and replicas. **Since this edition is 256 pages, it may be easier to zero in on a particular model by referring to the updated Index on pages 253-255.** On trademarks/companies with various ignition types, individual category names are listed alphabetically. If you have any questions regarding grading and/or the Photo Percentage Grading System, it is suggested to look at pages 46-111 of the 24th Edition *Blue Book of Gun Values* (now online also) for more information (including color photos of condition factors).

To find a model in this text, first look under the name of the manufacturer, trademark, brand name, and in some cases, the importer (please consult the Index if necessary). Next, find the correct category name(s) (Pistols: Percussion, Rifles: Flintlock, Shotguns: Percussion & Flintlock, etc.). Once you find the correct model or sub-model under its respective subheading, determine the specimen's percentage of original condition and find the corresponding percentage column showing the price.

For the sake of simplicity, the following organizational framework has been adopted throughout this publication.

1. Alphabetical names are located on the top of right-facing, odd-numbered pages and appear as follows:

S SECTION

2. Trademark, manufacturer, brand name, importer, or organization is listed in bold face type alphabetically, i.e.,

LYMAN PRODUCTS CORP.

3. Manufacturer information is listed directly beneath the trademark heading, i.e.,

Current manufacturer located in Middletown, CT. Lyman Products Corp. also carries a complete line of black powder accessories. Dealer and consumer direct sales.

4. Manufacturer notes may appear next under individual heading descriptions and can be differentiated by the following typeface, i.e.,

Faber Brothers is currently marketing customized C.V.A. (see Connecticut Valley Arms) and InvestArms Hawken rifles. These rifles come drilled and tapped for scope with offset hammers and chrome bores. Faber Brothers rifles may command a slight premium over similar configurations from C.V.A. & InvestArms.

5. Next classification is the category name (normally, in alphabetical sequence) in upper case (inside a ruled screened box) referring mostly to the type of black powder ignition, i.e.,

REVOLVERS: PERCUSSION

6. A further sub-classification may appear under a category name in both upper and lower case, as depicted below. These are sub-categories of a major category name, and again, appear in alphabetical order whenever possible.

"C" Series Revolvers

7. Following a category or sub-category name, a category note may follow to help explain the category, and/or provide limited information on models and values. They appear as follows:

Colt 2nd Generation Percussion models are listed in Series order as produced by Colt Firearms.

8. Model names appear flush left, are bold faced, and capitalized either in chronological order (normally, with the original year of manufacture listed first) or alphabetical order (sometimes, the previous model name and/or close subvariation will appear at the end in parentheses) and are listed under the individual category names, examples include:

1858 REMINGTON .36 NAVY

9. Model descriptions are denoted by the following typeface and usually include information, i.e.,
- calibers, gauges, ignition type, barrel lengths, finishes, weight, and other descriptive data are further categorized adjacent to model names in this typeface. This is where most of the information is listed for each specific model including identifiable features and possibly some production data (including quantity, circa of manufacture, discontinuance date, if known).

10. Variations within a model appear as sub-models. They can be are differentiated from model names by an artistic icon (*) prefix, are indented, and are in upper and lower case type, i.e.,

  ✳ *1851 Navy Klay–Colt Engraved*

and are usually followed by a short description of that sub-model. These sub-model descriptions have the same typeface as the model descriptions, i.e.,

- additional sub-model information that could include special/limited edition items, finishes, calibers, barrel lengths, special order features, and other production data specific for that sub-model.

11. Manufacturer and other notes/information appear in smaller type, and should be read since they contain both important and other critical, up-to-date information, i.e.,

  This revolver is also known as "The Shooter."

12. Extra cost features/special value orders and other value added/subtracted features are placed directly under individual price lines or in some cases, category names. These individual lines appear bolder than other descriptive typeface, i.e.,

  Add $150 for custom nickel finish.
  Add $150 for premium nickel finish (highly polished).
  Add $350 for silver plating.

  On many variations which are less than 15 years old, these add/subtract items will be the last factory MSR price for that option.

13. On black powder cartridge conversions and Open Tops requiring FFLs for legal transfer, the following line will appear:

  This firearm must be purchased through an FFL dealer.

  Since this configuration is defined as a firearm by the BATF, normal county, state, and federal regulations apply to its sale/resale.

14. On many discontinued models/variations after 1985, a line may appear under the price line, indicating the last manufacturer's suggested retail price flush right on the page, i.e.,

  Last MSR was $325.

15. A grading line will normally appear at the top of each page. The most commonly encountered grading line (shown with discontinued price line - w/o MSR) in this text is from 100%-60%, i.e.,

GRADING	100%	98%	95%	90%	80%	70%	60%
	$360	$300	$240				

16. Pricing format is as follows - when the price line shown below (with proper grading line) is encountered,

GRADING	100%	98%	95%	90%	80%	70%	60%
MSR $355	$310	$265	$220				

it automatically indicates the reproduction/replica is currently manufactured and the manufacturer's retail price is shown left of the 100% column. Following are the 100%-95% values. This 100% price is the national average price a consumer will typically expect to pay for that model in NIB unfired condition. 100% specimens without boxes, warranties, original paperwork, etc., that are currently manufactured must be discounted slightly (5%-20%, depending on the desirability of make and model). This 100% price also assumes not previously sold at retail on currently manufactured black powder reproductions and replicas (i.e., must have warranty card). Values for reproductions and replicas in 90% or less condition are typically shooters only with little collector value (except Colts), and are priced 15%-35% less than the 95% figures listed.

On 2nd Generation Colts, the following grading line has been used throughout the section:

GRADING	NIB	98%	95%

100% prices are not specifically listed, since values listed are for NIB (New in Box) specimens. This NIB condition factor is the most commonly encountered condition when buying, selling, or trading the very collectible 2nd Generation Blackpowder Colts. Subtractions have to be made for 100% specimens without cases, accessories, paperwork, damaged packaging, etc. (please refer to section for specifics).

Also included in this edition *Blue Book of Modern Black Powder Values* is an updated Trademark Index (pages 249-252), which lists current manufacturer, trademark, and/or importer information, as well as 2nd Generation Colt & Pietta Serialization. When using this Serialization section, make sure your 2nd Generation Colt/Pietta model is listed and find the serial number within the yearly range listings.

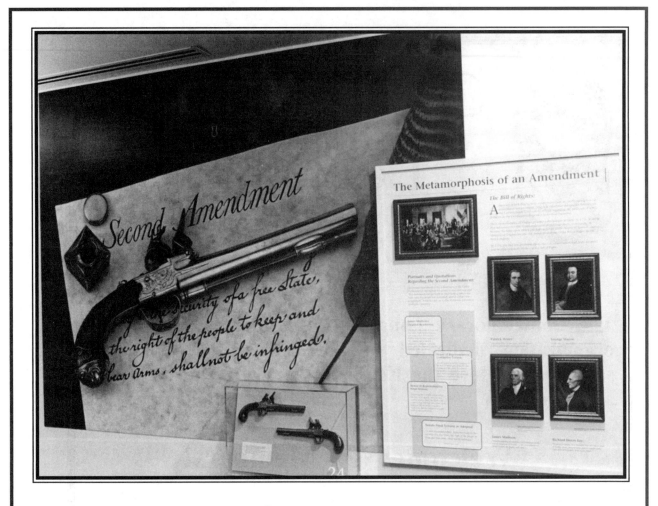

DEFENDING YOUR SECOND AMENDMENT RIGHT TO OWN GUNS, HUNT, SHOOT, PROTECT YOURSELF AND SO MUCH MORE...

For nearly 130 years the National Rifle Association has been the leader in defending our Second Amendment right to keep and bear arms as well as protecting our hunting rights and traditions. We're fighting the gun banners and animal rights fanatics on all fronts. By joining the NRA, or renewing your existing membership, you will help to keep our unique American traditions alive.

When you join NRA you will receive these great benefits:

- NRA Black and Gold Shooters Cap
- A no-annual-fee NRA Visa card (for qualified individuals)
- Your choice of NRA monthly publications, *America's 1st Freedom*, *American Hunter* or *American Rifleman*
- $10,000 Personal Accident Insurance
- $1,000 in ArmsCare Firearm Insurance
- Hotel, Car Rental and Interstate Moving Discounts
- Discounts at local Gun Stores and other Retail Outlets

And much, much, more...

NATIONAL RIFLE ASSOCIATION

☐ 1 Year Regular.........$35   ☐ 3 Year Regular.........$85
☐ 5 Year Regular.........$125   Date_____

NRA Recruiter #X012415

If renewal, give ID# ☐☐☐☐☐☐☐   Payment Information:

Mr./Mrs./Ms. _____   ☐ Check/Money Order

Street: _____ Apt.#: _____   Charge to: ☐ MC ☐ VISA ☐ Amex

City: _____ State: ____ Zip ____   ☐ Discover   Expiration Date ☐☐☐☐

Daytime Phone: (____)_____   Credit Card#

Choose ONE Magazine: ☐ America's 1st Freedom   ☐☐☐☐☐☐☐☐☐☐☐☐☐☐☐☐

☐ American Rifleman ☐ American Hunter   Member Signature _____

Contributions gifts or membership dues made or paid to the National Rifle Association of America are not refundable or transferable and are not deductible as charitable contributions for Federal Income Tax purposes.
Mail with payment to: NRA, 11250 Waples Mill Rd., Fairfax, VA 22030

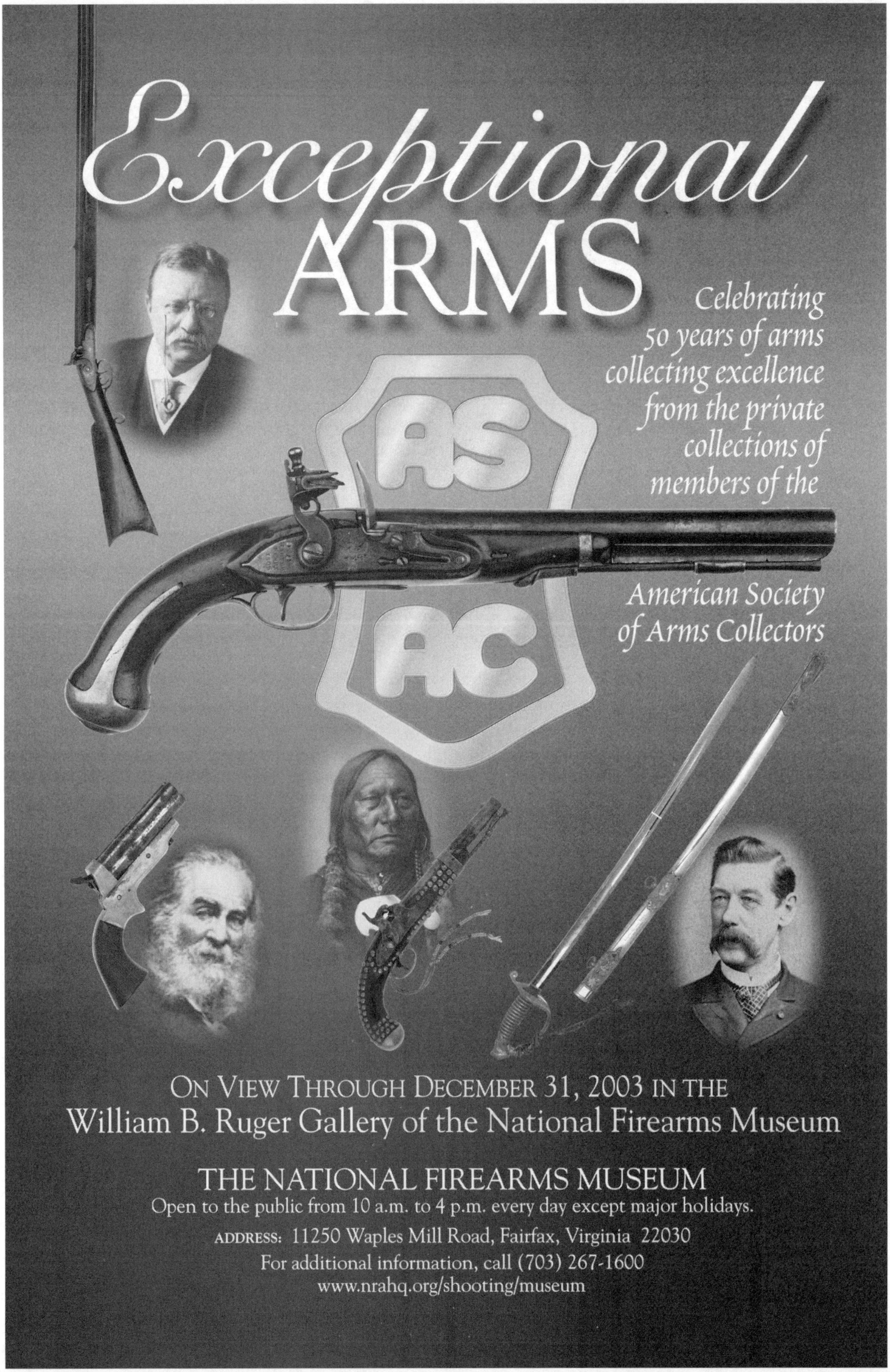
Exceptional
ARMS
Celebrating 50 years of arms collecting excellence from the private collections of members of the
AS AC
American Society of Arms Collectors
ON VIEW THROUGH DECEMBER 31, 2003 IN THE
William B. Ruger Gallery of the National Firearms Museum
THE NATIONAL FIREARMS MUSEUM
Open to the public from 10 a.m. to 4 p.m. every day except major holidays.
ADDRESS: 11250 Waples Mill Road, Fairfax, Virginia 22030
For additional information, call (703) 267-1600
www.nrahq.org/shooting/museum

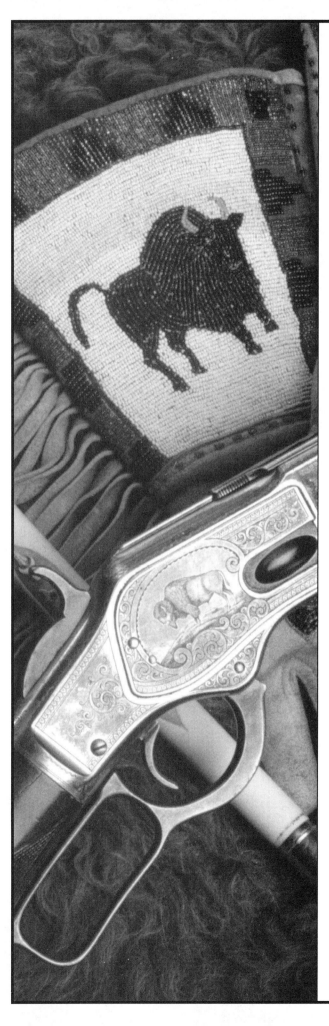

1.) Since the 1600s, there have been three principal ignition systems for black powder pistols and longarms. Pictured from left to right, the flintlock c.1620 to 1836, the percussion lock c. 1807 to 1868, and percussion cylinder c. 1836 to 1871. There was a continual overlap of these designs; flintlocks were still being used during the Civil War, and single shot and percussion revolvers well into the 1870s.

It began with a loud boom! The first black powder pistol was a hand cannon developed in the late 14th century, and the soldier firing one of these devices, essentially a barrel on a stick, was as likely to take his own life as that of his intended target. Historian Claude Blair notes that development of a true pistol, a one-handed gun, was inhibited by two factors:

1. Firearms were regarded essentially as infantry weapons to be used en masse. Various attempts to arm horsemen with firearms are recorded during the later Middle Ages, but these appear to have been intended to function as mounted infantry. There was therefore no known tactical reason for the development of the pistol.

2. No purely mechanical system of ignition existed.[1]

The invention of the matchlock in the early 15th century, essentially a barrel on a better stick, fitted with a burning rope or match for ignition of the powder, was just slightly less precarious of a device than the hand cannon. The matchlock remained in use for more than 100 years going through various design improvements, though none safer or more reliable. Then in the early 16th century, the wheel lock design appeared. This very complex, clockwork-like mechanism assured a safe and reliable ignition of the powder charge, and by the mid to late 1500s the first practical pistols were being developed in Europe.

The wheel lock reigned supreme in the world of firearms design for more than a century. Then in the 1600s, a new, more reliable and less costly ignition system was devised. The flintlock.

This is the first of the examples pictured (image 1 (left) and image 2), and is typical of all flintlock designs utilizing a cock (hammer) to hold the flint, a pan to retain a small amount of priming powder, and a steel (frizzen) which was hinged to close over the pan and provide a metal surface against which the flint was struck, simultaneously creating a spark and igniting the powder in the pan, which in turn flashed through a small hole in the side of the barrel, igniting the

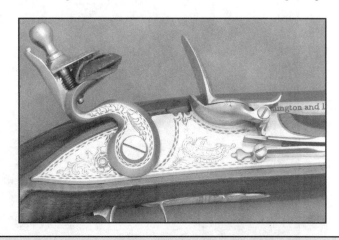

2.) This is a good example of a c.1776 American flintlock design. Note the style of the cock (hammer) and the jaws to retain the flint, the pan and steel, and feather spring for the steel and pan cover.

larger powder charge within, and discharging the firearm. This all happened in a split second, and with a good flint, it was a very reliable means of ignition. So much so, that the flintlock remained in popular use until the 1830s!

There are various tales about the development of the first percussion lock in the early 1800s, but none is more inspirational than the story of the Reverend Alexander Forsyth, minister of Belhelvie, Aberdeenshire, and an avid hunter, who, displeased with his flintlock, sat down and designed an improved means of ignition in 1805 that eliminated the momentary delay between the drop of the hammer and the ignition of the powder charge in the barrel. The good reverend reasoned that if the spark went directly into the main powder charge, rather than being ignited second handedly by the ignition of the powder in the priming pan, the gun would be more efficient, faster to load, and most important of all, would not require the ignition of the priming pan which often alerted his intended dinner before the shot was fired.

The part of the firearm pictured in image 3 is a typical percussion lock of the early 1800s. The guns themselves changed little from flintlock to percussion lock, and in many instances old flintlocks were refitted for the new ignition system. Gun makers simply continued to make the same models but with percussion locks.

As is shown in image 3, the cock (now officially the hammer) was used to strike the percussion cap seated on top of the nipple, which was threaded into the breech of the barrel. Thus when the fulminating mercury in the cap was ignited by the impact of the hammer, the flame went directly into the powder charge at the breech and boom…instantaneous ignition. With a good eye and a clean shot, Reverend Forsyth's dinner was in the bag.

The single shot percussion lock was the most short-lived of all firearms ignition systems[2] but the concept was carried forth beginning in 1837 into an entirely new type of firearm, the revolving cylinder pistol.

The idea of a revolving cylinder is nearly as old as the matchlock, but making it work was something altogether different. Flintlock revolvers with a manually rotated cylinder were produced as far back as the 1600s, and there were various multi-barreled pistols, such as

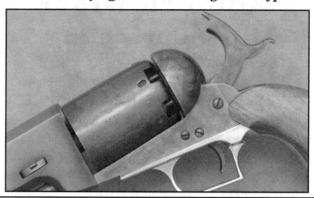

4.) The basic style of pistol did not change significantly with the advent of the percussion lock in the early 1800s. The cock (hammer) was now designed to strike the top of the nipple, which was threaded into the breech and fitted with a percussion cap (not shown).

the early percussion Pepperbox, introduced by the Darling Brothers of Massachusetts in 1836, and the double action Pepperbox models developed by Ethan Allen. But these were all heavy, unwieldy designs. Then young Sam Colt came along and changed everything.

On February 25, 1836 twenty-one year old Samuel Colt received his third patent for the revolving cylinder pistol, (he had already received a British patent on October 22, 1835 as well as a French patent) and began final development of what would become the Paterson revolver introduced in the fall of 1837.

Though Colt's first revolvers were not a huge success, nor was the Patent Arms Mfg. Co. of Paterson, New Jersey (which went out of business in 1842), the Colt design reemerged in 1847 as the massive .44 caliber Walker revolver, the most powerful and successful handgun of its time, and the wellspring for 156 years of Colt's Patent Firearms Manufacturing Company production.

The third type of ignition illustrated then is the Walker pistol. The cylinder has six chambers, each nipple capped with a percussion cap, (not shown). A loaded chamber rotates into battery each time the hammer is cocked. Pull the trigger and up to 60 gr. of black powder backing a .44 caliber lead ball are unleashed with a thundering roar. The Texas Rangers of the 1840s and 1850s swore by them, as did many others in the U.S. military during the war with Mexico from 1846 to 1848.

The Walker revolver, designed by Sam Colt and Capt. Sam Walker, brought forth a revolution in firearms design. Followed by the Colt Baby Dragoon, First through Third Model Dragoons, the 1851 Navy and 1860 Army, among others, Colt's design was copied by countless arms manufacturers after his patent extension expired in 1858. The Colt design became the most popular ignition system of the black powder era. And even with the advent of the metallic cartridge in the late 1860s, the venerable Colt cap-and-ball revolvers remained popular among lawmen, gunslingers, and pioneers during the post Civil War era and settling of the American West.

Whether you pour your black powder down the barrel or into the chambers of a cylinder, use a flint or a percussion cap, the principals of black powder longarms and pistols changed very little from the late 17th century to the mid 19th century. It still ended in a loud boom! ∎

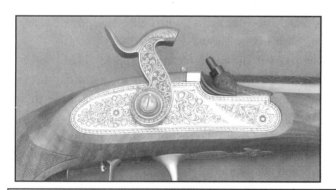

3.) The basic style of pistol did not change significantly with the advent of the percussion lock in the early 1800s. The cock (hammer) was now designed to strike the top of the nipple, which was threaded into the breech and fitted with a percussion cap (not shown). Lock designs were essentially the same, as were trigger guards and triggers. The percussion lock was a much more elegant design with fewer exposed components and a far superior seal against the elements.

[1] *Handguns of the World* by Edward C. Ezell, 1981 Barnes & Noble Books, New York.
[2] The single shot percussion pistol, principally the Henry Deringer designs, and various single shot percussion boot pistols, principally underhammer designs, remained in use well into the 1860s.

Modern Black Powder Proofmarks
Unraveling The Mystery Of Icons

When you purchase either a 2nd or 3rd Generation Colt Blackpowder Arms revolver it bears the Colt patent stamping on the frame and the Colt address on the top of the barrel. There is also a serial number stamped on the bottom of the frame, again on the bottom of the barrel lug, trigger guard and buttstrap. The serialization indicates the year or period of manufacture, and this is as straightforward as model identification gets. Even though many of the Colt parts for the 2nd Generation, and all of the Colt parts for the 3rd Generation were cast in Italy, the guns were finished and assembled in the United States by Colt or the Colt Blackpowder Arms Company, and Colt pistols, regardless of the origin of their components, bear only Colt markings.

The same model gun, an 1860 Army for example, manufactured in Italy and sold by Uberti or F.LLI Pietta, is stamped with a variety of markings – Italian Proof House devices, manufacturer's symbols and an encoded date of manufacture. It is usually a combination of heraldry and letters, which need to be decoded. The same is true of flintlock and percussion lock pistols and long rifles manufactured by Uberti, F.LLI Pietta, ArmiSport, Davide Pedersoli, Armi San Paolo SRL (Euroarms), and Palmetto, which comprise the major Italian manufacturers currently in production.

The Italian proof houses in Gardone and Valtrompia have been around for a very long time but as far as reproduction black powder arms are concerned, the dating begins in 1954. Prior to 1954 the year of proof was indicated in full Arabic numerals.

Following is a chart displaying the year of proof symbols used from 1954 to 2003. These are traditionally found within a box next to the individual proof house symbols. From 1954 through 1970 Roman Numerals were used. Roman Numerals and Arabic Numerals were combined in 1971, 1972, and 1973, and Roman Numerals were used again in 1974. Since 1975 two capital letters have been used exclusively.

As to the placement of proof house symbols, it depends upon the model of gun, and the level of embellishment, the latter often dictating a discrete location on the underside of the barrel or frame on highly engraved examples.

Symbol	Year of Proof	Symbol	Year of Proof	Symbol	Year of Proof
X	1954	XX7	1971	AT	1988
XI	1955	XX8	1972	AU	1989
XII	1956	XX9	1973	AZ	1990
XIII	1957	XXX	1974	BA	1991
XIV	1958	AA	1975	BB	1992
XV	1959	AB	1976	BC	1993
XVI	1960	AC	1977	BD	1994
XVII	1961	AD	1978	BF	1995
XVIII	1962	AE	1979	BH	1996
XIX	1963	AF	1980	BI	1997
XX	1964	AH	1981	BL	1998
XXI	1965	AI	1982	BM	1999
XXII	1966	AL	1983	BN	2000
XXIII	1967	AM	1984	BP	2001
XXIV	1968	AN	1985	BS	2002
XXV	1969	AP	1986	BT	2003
XXVI	1970	AS	1987		

There are two standardized proof house marks. The first is the provisional Gardone proof, consisting of a star surrounded by eight lands and grooves over a coat of arms featuring a hammer and anvil and crossed bayoneted rifles; the second is a star surround by eight lands and grooves over the capital letters PN. All firearms produced in Italy since 1950, regardless of type, receive the first stamping. The second, also instituted in 1950, is the first black powder proof for Gardone and Brescia, and is only used on black powder arms. Thus all black powder arms must bear both proof house symbols.

Finally, there is the manufacturer's mark. This is often confusing unless one is familiar with the manufacturers' insignia. Most use their logo, while some combine their name and logo, or use an abbreviation as their logo. Earlier guns generally bear only their manufacturers' mark, while more recent production has been seen using both an emblem and company name.

Davide Pedersoli, one of Italy's oldest manufacturers has had three logos since 1957. The earliest was a diamond inside a circle. This is rarely seen. This mark was followed by the image of an anvil with PEDERSOLI above it in capital letters and the initials DAP inside the anvil. This again is rarely seen, except on very early models. The company logo, a lowercase dp within an oval, has been used for more than 40 years. This logo is often fol-

These are the three standard stampings on every Italian-made black powder revolver, pistol, rifle and shotgun. From left to right: year of manufacture, Gardone V.T. black powder proof house stamping, and Gardone proof house stamping. The year of manufacture is?

The underside of this screw barrel deringer manufactured by Pedersoli shows only the dp logo. Both proof house marks are present and a boxed BL denoting the year of manufacture as 1998.

Aldo Uberti S.r.l. was founded in 1959 and has always used a capital U surrounded by an octagonal device, which is actually the muzzle of an 1851 Navy (their first gun) with six lands and grooves and the front sight. This photo of a Paterson barrel has a boxed AZ indicating a manufacturing date of 1990.

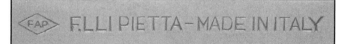

F.LLI Pietta always uses its diamond logo with the initials FAP. This is the barrel from a Le Mat revolver and it also bears the company name and country of origin. The proof house marks and manufacturing code are stamped elsewhere on the gun.

Here is an example of a manufacturer using two different styles. The standalone Palmetto palm tree logo on this screw barrel derringer, and the logo and company name on the barrel of this 1851 Navy.

Arms originally manufactured by Armi San Paolo S.r.l. or Euroarms S.r.l., now the proprietary name, bear the DGG emblem representing the company's founders, Grassi, Doninelli, and Gazzola.

Armi Sport uses a circular device with the capital letters AC.

lowed by the DAVIDE PEDERSOLI or PEDERSOLI name in capital letters. In short, there is no mistaking a Pedersoli product!

The same is true of Aldo Uberti, S.r.l, which has used the same logo since its founding in 1959 – a capital U contained within an octagonal barrel device.

For Fratelli Pietta, another of Italy's leading manufacturers of black powder pistols and long arms, the initials FAP contained within a horizontal diamond identify F.LLI Pietta; often followed by F.LLI PIETTA in capital letters.

Palmetto, which manufactures a variety of black powder arms distributed primarily through Dixie Gun Works, uses a very recognizable palm tree within a circle as their company logo.

Armi San Paolo S.r.l., established in 1970, uses the last names of the original founders Grassi, Doninelli, and Gazzola as a symbol, DGG, usually contained within a circle. Beginning December 31, 2001, Armi San Paolo officially became Euroarms Italia S.r.l. The same logo is used on all Euroarms models.

Armi Sport, which produces an exceptional line of single shot percussion pistols like the French Le Page, Sharps rifles, and the popular Spencer rifle for Taylor's & Co., uses an AC within a circle, (AC for Armi Chiappa founder Rino Chiappa's last name).

The barrel pictured is a perfect example as it bears all of the Italian proof marks described. This is from a Deluxe engraved Pedersoli Le Page pistol, and all of the stampings are on the underside of the barrel. From left to right (upside down) are the test house and black powder proof house stampings, followed by a boxed BM, denoting a manufacturing date of 1999, then the gun's serial number, a dp oval manufacturer's mark, as well as the PEDERSOLI name, pistol caliber and notification that the gun is for black powder only. This warning appears on the barrel or barrel lug of all black powder arms manufactured in Italy.

Armed with this information it is now possible to identify the maker and year of manufacture on any black powder rifle, shotgun, pistol, or revolver produced since 1950. ∎

MODERN IN-LINE MUZZLELOADERS

by Al Raychard

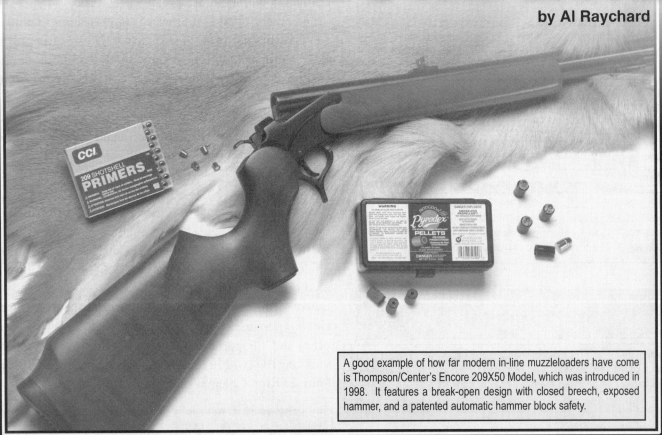

A good example of how far modern in-line muzzleloaders have come is Thompson/Center's Encore 209X50 Model, which was introduced in 1998. It features a break-open design with closed breech, exposed hammer, and a patented automatic hammer block safety.

Things might have been somewhat different in our neck of the woods had Native Americans been in possession of the modern in-line muzzleloader. Of course, had that been the case, the first Europeans to these shores and early settlers would have had them too, and chances are the end result would have been the same considering the eventual overwhelming odds. But considering their knowledge of home turf, unparalleled and in some cases superior fighting skills, determination, and spirit, had the modern in-line and its many attributes been available, the playing field undoubtedly would have been a bit more even.

The interesting thing is, it could have been. Well, almost. Contrary to common belief, the in-line ignition system just didn't appear out of nowhere, and the concept itself is far from being anything new. Various patents date back to 1808 when the first was issued in Switzerland for an in-line rifle to inventor Jean Samuel

Pauley. The design was continuously improved upon in the years that followed, and was actually used by Paul Mauser for his classic Model 1868 cartridge rifle and later for the 1903 Springfield (see footnote 1). According to Doc Carlson in his contribution to the *1996 Gun Digest*, "The In-Line Muzzleloader" (see footnote 2) the Paczelt flintlock in-line existed "long before the telephone," and Sam Fadala states in his *Complete Blackpowder Handbook* (see footnote 3) both the underhammer and sidehammer systems are based on the idea of "introducing the flame of a percussion cap into the breech of the frontloader by tapping a hole directly into the barrel and inserting a nipple." The plunger idea, the system upon which many modern muzzleloaders are based, whereby a plunger-like striker is propelled forward by a powerful main spring slamming into a percussion cap tapped directly "in-line" with the breech is merely an off-shoot.

It has often been said there really isn't much new in the

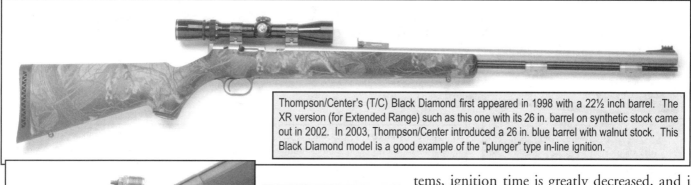

Thompson/Center's (T/C) Black Diamond first appeared in 1998 with a 22½ inch barrel. The XR version (for Extended Range) such as this one with its 26 in. barrel on synthetic stock came out in 2002. In 2003, Thompson/Center introduced a 26 in. blue barrel with walnut stock. This Black Diamond model is a good example of the "plunger" type in-line ignition.

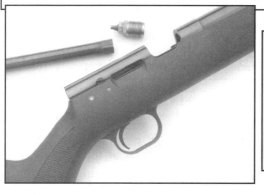

Like most "plunger" type in-line muzzleloaders, T/C's Black Diamond XR has a removable universal breech plug that allows easy and fast cleaning and is supplied with three interchangeable ignition systems for Number 11 caps, Musket caps, or 209 shotgun primers.

world of muzzleloader ignition; what is generally considered new or innovative is really old in some way, and many of the in-line designs we have today have been simply brought up-to-date. That statement has a certain level of truth to it, but regardless, one thing is certain. The in-line rifle as we know it today started and has maintained a craze in muzzleloading shooting and hunting unprecedented in modern times. In recent years in particular, in order to take advantage of this tide of popularity, manufacturers that historically specialized in more traditional sidelock muzzleloaders and some of our most respected and best known builders of more conventional arms such as Remington, Winchester, Ruger, Savage, even Austin & Halleck have jumped on the bandwagon with their own offerings. Whatever the name on the barrel and cosmetic variations, the ignition system used falls within one of three general categories: the striker or plunger type which is the design that started it all (also referred to as the "pullcock" system), the bolt-action, and the "disc" type or closed breech/pivoting breech. Each system has its fan club based upon personal preference and opinion but the bottom line is each system works extremely well and is a sound choice for those just getting into the sport or upgrading from more traditional systems.

This is because each system is based on a rather simple principle of throwing spark from a percussion cap and nipple directly into the breech. Because of the relatively close proximity of the cap and nipple to the main charge, and because spark not only travels a shorter distance, but straight in, rather than turning a corner as in sidelock sys-

tems, ignition time is greatly decreased, and is almost instantaneous. Because of these two attributes, more spark is also delivered to the main charge, greatly increasing reliability at the same time. This speed and reliability is in part what quickly made an in-line the muzzleloader of choice when it first appeared on the scene and what has kept it there for nearly two decades. This fast and reliable ignition has only been enhanced in recent years with the use of so-called hot shot nipples and standard No. 11 percussion caps, musket caps, or 209 shotgun primers all designed to provide more spark into the breech. Several in-line models, such as Thompson/Center's (T/C) Black Diamond, the HunterBolt from Connecticut Valley Arms, and the original Lightning Bolt from Traditions, came with interchangeable breech plugs allowing the use of all three types of caps or primers in the same rifle. Today, with "magnum" loads quite popular, the 209 shotgun primer seems to lead the pack and is standard on many in-line models, but a number still offer either interchangeable plugs or nipples to accommodate the 3-way option.

The basic outlines and features offered on many models are quite familiar to a modern hunter used to centerfire rifles. Some, like Winchester's new Apex Magnum 209 include a Monte Carlo cheek piece, raised checkered pistol grip, and beavertail comb, just like many of Winchester's cartridge rifles. Ruger's 77/50 muzzleloader incorporates a three-position manual safety like its famous Model 77 centerfire, and Remington's Model 700ML bolt-action in-line for all practical purposes is the same rifle in appearance, and to a certain degree mechanically as well, as its legendary Model 700. The safety, sight and scope mounting systems, ventilated recoil pads, sling mounts, general appearance, balance of these rifles look and feel familiar, like rifles many of us started out with.

For many enthusiasts, however, even more important is the fact modern in-lines are user-friendly. Removable breech plugs for easy and straight-through cleaning are

Winchester introduced its Apex Magnum 209 in 2003. This model features a simplified, short, "swing action" breech which allows using a 30-inch barrel without the rifle feeling "barrel heavy." The breech opens by swinging the trigger guard mechanism forward for easy access priming. Once equipped with a 209 shotgun primer, the trigger mechanism swings back, closing the breech for a weather-tight seal. The rebounding hammer is low profile with an internal hammer block for safety, reliability, and ultra-fast ignition. The Apex 209 is available in both .50 caliber and the increasingly popular .45 caliber as well. Synthetic stock options include a black fleck finish or Mossy Oak New Break-Up pattern with blued steel or stainless steel barrel.

standard these days. Walnut and laminated stocks are still available from most manufacturers for those who prefer them. Nearly all in-line muzzleloaders are also built on synthetic stocks, easing and decreasing the cleaning and maintenance.

THE STRIKER, PLUNGER OR PULLCOCK SYSTEM

The modern muzzleloader era started in 1985 when Knight Muzzleloading introduced its MK-85. It was a pullcock design that was cocked to firing position by pulling straight back on the striker or plunger mechanism. When the trigger was pulled, the striker, or plunger, was forced forward hitting a percussion cap placed on the nipple mounted into a stainless steel breech plug. This system utilized a standard No.11 percussion cap positioned on an "open" or "exposed" nipple, which afforded two safeties – one on the rear part of the pullcock that screwed in and out from safety to firing position, in addition to a traditional thumb lever located on the side of the receiver. Up to that time, the muzzleloading industry relied predominantly on more traditional sidelock designs. The great success of the MK-85 clearly made everyone in the trade sit up and take notice, however, and within a decade or so, numerous offerings from other manufacturers incorporating the striker or plunger concept were on the market. The Fire Hawk from Thompson/Center, first introduced in 1995, is a prime example. The nipple was "open" and the breech plug was fixed. Others along the same basic lines include White's Whitetail Series and Super 91, and Gonic's GA-87.

Because of fewer moving parts, low manufacturing costs, time-tested dependability, and in spite of other designs that have recently come on the scene, the strik-

er/plunger design remains popular and a mainstay within the industry, although with some improvements. Even the earliest models started incorporating a side handle that was used to position the striker or plunger in "safe" or "fire" position, rather than pulling straight back on the striker as with the Knight MK-87. Removable breech plugs for easy cleaning soon became standard fare, quickly followed by interchangeable breech plugs or interchangeable nipples with catchy names like universal and 3-way allowing the use of No.11, musket caps, or 209 shotgun primers. The most recent trend with some of the newest models from certain makers seems to be exclusive use of the 209 shotgun primer.

In 2002, for example, Traditions introduced its Tracker 209 in-line. Available in .45 and .50 caliber it can accommodate 150 grains of Pyrodex pellets. That same year CVA introduced its Eclipse 209 Magnum, available in both 45. and 50 caliber, and its Stag Horn Magnum, that comes presently only in .50 caliber. Knight's new Wolverine 209 is a bit different than most striker or plunger designs in that it retains the same basic pullcock system as its original MK-85, but each of these offerings rely on the hot and reliable 209 shotgun primer for ignition. The 209 shotgun primer has increased in popularity of late overall, and seems to be the most popular source of ignition even among rifles accommodating universal or 3-way systems. This is undoubtedly due to the popularity of heavy or so-called magnum powder charges that require a hotter spark for a uniform and complete burn, but it is also popular among those using standard powder loads who desire more spark and reliability when pulling the trigger.

THE BOLT ACTION 209 CRAZE

The bolt action ignition design has really taken the muz-

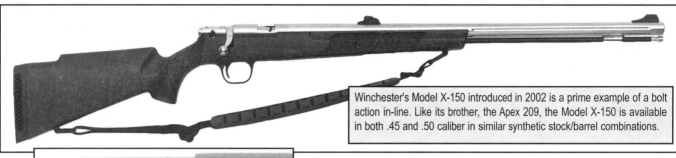

Winchester's Model X-150 introduced in 2002 is a prime example of a bolt action in-line. Like its brother, the Apex 209, the Model X-150 is available in both .45 and .50 caliber in similar synthetic stock/barrel combinations.

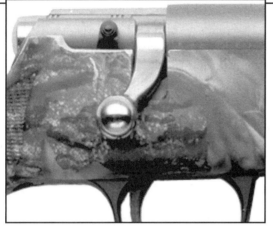

zleloader industry by storm. In 1993 when Thompson/Center introduced its Thunder Hawk, one of the first bolt actions on the scene and the company's second in-line, its appearance was like that of a modern styled bolt action centerfire, and its balance, the way it pointed and carried afield was like one as well. It's been nowhere but up for the bolt action design since. Today, nearly all of the best known and principal players in the trade including Thompson/Center, Traditions, Connecticut Valley Arms, White, Knight, Winchester, Remington, Savage, Sturm Ruger, and Austin & Halleck, along with some lesser knowns are building and offering bolt action muzzleloaders.

And for good reason. Among the many design attributes is a comparatively short stroke of the firing mechanism. The flame path through the nipple/breech assembly, whether one piece as is the case with the Ruger Model 77/50, or segregated as with the Hunter Bolt from CVA, which has interchangeable nipples screwing into the breech plug, is also short. Once the trigger is pulled, both design features contribute to an extremely quick ignition time, faster even than their striker or plunger counterparts, and by most accounts, the fastest of all muzzleloader ignition designs currently on the market.

But this is not the only thing the bolt action has going for it. These same design qualities also make this a most reliable and dependable ignition system, due in part to more consistent seating and alignment of the cap or primer on the nipple, which is due to the design of the bolt. In a world that is rarely idyllic, hunters also appreciate the sealed waterproof nipple/breech assembly all bolt systems seem to offer these days. Essentially, once the nipple is primed, as the bolt is closed into firing position, it slides over the nipple and breech sealing it against rain, snow, and other undesirables, practically eliminating misfires on properly maintained guns. The key words here, however, are "properly maintained."

Sealing of the nipple and breech is a big plus, but over time it can also present problems by not allowing sufficient amounts of exhaust gases from the cap or primer, and breech area to escape. While some models have been designed with ports or vent liners specifically for this purpose, and while the problem is negligible in the short term or with occasional shooting, over time and after repeated shooting, residue builds up inside the bolt body, and can make it difficult to work the mechanism. Because blackpowder and Pyrodex are both hydroscopic, attracting moisture from the air, rusting in the bolt and nipple/breech area can also occur. The use of non-hydroscopic propellants such as Clear Shot from Goex and Triple-Seven from Hodgdon can greatly reduce this problem in bolt action muzzleloaders, and despite synthetic stocks, stainless barrels and ignition assemblies and other features that make today's modern muzzleloaders user-friendly and somewhat less dependent on a religious maintenance program, all muzzleloaders, even bolt actions, need a complete and thorough cleaning from time to time, hopefully on a regular basis. With that in mind, after continued use, once the hunting season closes and before prolonged storage a thorough cleaning of the bolt and nipple/breech assembly with any of the modern solvents is the best bet. With everything considered, however, bolt action muzzleloaders are a fine offering and a sound investment that will provide years of satisfactory use.

Like some of its predecessors, bolt action muzzleloaders might use standard No. 11 percussion caps, musket caps, or 209 shotgun primers, depending upon the maker and

Connecticut Valley Arms Hunter Bolt 209 Magnum.

model. Ruger's Model 77/50 has used the No. 11 cap since it first appeared in 1997, but CVA's Hunter Bolt with its interchangeable breech plugs and nipples will accommodate all three. The same is true for Traditions new Evolution Premier, introduced in April 2003. The Evolution Premier is equipped with a 26-inch, 1:28 twist stainless steel barrel in .50 caliber. When Savage designed and built its Model 10ML-11 in 2000, the first muzzle-loader capable of shooting blackpowder, Pyrodex, or smokeless powder, and subsequently its list of offshoots including the 10ML-II, 10ML-IIXP (with scope), 10MLSS-II, 10MLSS-II Camo, 10MLBSS-II and 10MLSS-IIXP (with scope), the company went exclusively with the 209 shotgun primer for ignition. So did Winchester when it introduced its Model X-150 in 2002. As with many of its newest cousins using the striker or plunger and 209 primer combination, a number of the newest and retooled bolt action offerings seem to be following the same trend.

Connecticut Valley Arms is now offering its flagship FireBolt and its brother, the HunterBolt in 209 Magnum versions. The barrel length on the HunterBolt has been extended two full inches in 2003 to 26-inches, same as the FireBolt, to better accommodate magnum loads and long range shooting. Both guns are available in .45 and .50 caliber, 1:28 twist and CVA's Quick Release Bolt. Winchester is expanding its Model X-150 line in 2003 with a Mossy Oak New Break-Up/Stainless steel barrel combination. It is a most handsome offering, and like the others in the X-150 line-up it is available in both .45 and .50 caliber with a 1:28 twist and powered by a 209 primer.

Also from Traditions in 2003 is the Thunder Bolt. It sports a 24-inch, 1:28 twist barrel in .45 or .50 caliber and its magnum receiver can accept up to 150 grains of powder. Completing the Evolution lineup is the Evolution with its 24-inch nickel plated barrel bored to .50 or .54 caliber, and the Evolution LD (Long Distance) with its slightly longer 26-inch barrel, available in either .45 or .50 caliber. Each of these come equipped for 209 shotgun, magnum sized nipples for sure-fire, super hot ignition with Pyrodex pellets or loose powder. All Evolution models come with Traditions new Ultra Guide Bolt System, advertised as "the easiest bolt-action muzzleloader to cock and close on the market today."

THE CLOSED BREECH/PIVOTING BREECH REVOLUTION

Modern closed breech in-line muzzleloaders relying on a hammer for ignition have been around for a few years now. Thompson/Center introduced one of the first in 1991 in the form of the Scout, actually the famous builder's first in-line ignition muzzleloader. Since then several others have appeared on the scene over the years including the Colorado, Black Bear, Brown Bear, and Bear series of muzzleloaders from Markesbery, all of which offer a uniquely designed modern version of a system which appeared in the mid-1800s, (near the end of the muzzleloading era), based on an exposed center-mounted hammer that swings through an arc to hit the nipple.

The modern pivoting breech or break open breech isn't

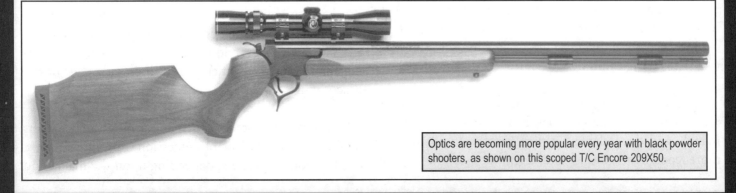

Optics are becoming more popular every year with black powder shooters, as shown on this scoped T/C Encore 209X50.

Thompson/Center released its Omega Model in 2002 in .50 caliber, and followed it up a year later in .45 cal. Contemporary in basic design, the Omega is a prime example of a sealed, pivoting breech muzzleloader using the trigger spur to open the mechanism. This model has a removable breech plug, and an exposed hammer with patented trigger and hammer mechanism, which makes it simple to operate, faster and easier to clean. It is also extremely reliable, even in the worst weather conditions. Utilizing a 209 shotgun primer for ignition, the Omega can handle 150 grains of loose powder or pellets, and when combined with its 28 in. barrel, the Omega produces higher velocities over standard length barrels translating into flatter trajectories and increased down range energy.

T/C's Omega action is operated by applying forward motion on the triggerguard spur, which pivots the breech block downward. Once opened, access to the 209 primer is easy. When primed, the triggerguard is pulled backward, which raises the breech block and also seals the breech mechanism.

quite as new, but recently it has been incorporated with the closed breech and hammer design and has been coming on strong. One of the best examples is T/C's Encore 209X50 introduced in 1998. It is a closed breech break open design with an exposed hammer featuring a patented automatic hammer block safety, 26-inch, 1:28 twist barrel in .45 and .50 caliber with removable breech plug. T/C kept the basic design alive in 2002 with its Omega which offered a unique sealed pivoting breech. The Omega, like the Encore, operates by using the forward motion of the trigger guard to pivot the breech block downward, allowing easy access to the primer pocket. Once primed, the lever is pulled back, or rearward, raising the breech block and sealing the breech from the elements. Cleaning is as easy as pivoting the breech down and unscrewing the removable breech plug. Originally the Omega was available only in .50 caliber, but given its popularity a .45 caliber was introduced in early 2003.

Also in 2003, Thompson/Center introduced the G2 Contender 209X45. This is a .45 caliber that operates much the same way as the larger Encore 209X50 Magnum and Omega – the action breaks open by a trigger guard release. Also like the Encore, the G2 209X45 has a patented automatic hammer block safety preventing the hammer from making contact with the firing pin until the trigger has been pulled full rearward. Each of these offerings uses a 209 primer for main ignition.

Also along these lines and new in 2003 are the Optima 209 Break Action and its big brother the Optima Pro 209

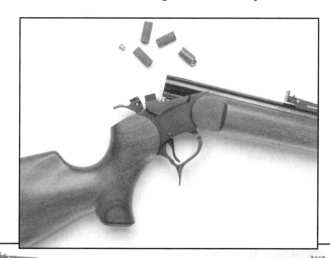

T/C's 209 X 45 Contender is new for 2003. Overall length is 37 3/4 inches and total weight is just 5 1/2 pounds. The barrel length is 26 inches with a 1 in 28 twist. Barrels for the G2 are interchangeable, making it possible to covert the muzzleloader to rimfire or centerfire in a matter of seconds. The G2 accepts magnum charges for long range shooting and when loaded with 150 grains of FFg black powder or three 50 grain .45 caliber Pyrodex pellets, muzzle velocities of approximately 2,400 fps are produced.

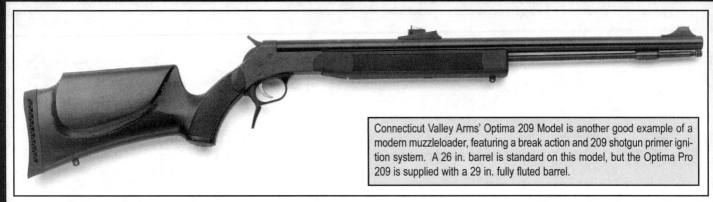

Connecticut Valley Arms' Optima 209 Model is another good example of a modern muzzleloader, featuring a break action and 209 shotgun primer ignition system. A 26 in. barrel is standard on this model, but the Optima Pro 209 is supplied with a 29 in. fully fluted barrel.

Break Action from Connecticut Valley Arms, both of which use a 209 shotgun primer. The break action operates by swinging open or closing the trigger guard. Unlike conventional in-line muzzleloaders there is no receiver on the Optima series. The Pro comes with a 29-inch fully fluted barrel for magnum loads, and while the barrel on the Optima 209 is shorter at 26-inches, but it is also designed for magnum loads. Both are available in .45 and .50 caliber, and designed to switch barrels allowing choice of caliber and barrel length for various game and shooting conditions.

And then there is the new Apex Magnum 209 from Winchester. It offers a swing action trigger guard that opens the breech allowing easy priming and clean up. When closed, the breech seals tight against the weather, and its rebounding hammer offers an extremely low profile. Overall the Apex has the same graceful lines as its sister, the Model X-150. It comes in 45 and .50 caliber, 1:28 twist with either black or camo synthetic stock.

As they have from the beginning, the modern in-line has continued to evolve, and will no doubt continue to do so. Those available today are already light years ahead of their predecessors. Where the future takes them is only bounded by imagination, practicality, and what the market will demand. During this evolutionary process, it will be exciting and interesting to see how changes affect the basic attributes that have made the in-line so popular in today's black powder marketplace. With fewer parts to worry about, removable breech plugs, bolts and plungers, many of which are stainless steel to resist corrosion and easy maintenance, stainless steel barrels and composite stocks, today's modern in-lines are more user-friendly and easier to clean than any of us ever imagined possible. Although regular attention remains the best policy, the time and effort to clean today's modern in-line is minimal. Considering how far black powder technology has come in the past 25 years, the question is, where will they go from here? Truly, we are living in the golden age of modern muzzleloading.

Al Raychard is the author of *The Complete Guide to Blackpowder Hunting*, The Lyons Press, New York, New York, and the "Muzzleloading Afield" columnist for *MuzzleBlasts Magazine*, the official publication of the National Muzzle Loading Rifle Association in Friendship, Indiana. ■

Footnotes:
(1) **Blue Book of Modern Black Powder Values** *by Dennis Adler, Edited by S.P. Fjestad, published by Blue Book Publications, Minneapolis, MN.*

(2) **"The In-line Muzzle Loader"** *by Doc Carlson, 1996* **Gun Digest**, *DBI Books, a division of Krause Publications, Iola, WI.*

(3) **The Complete Blackpowder Handbook** *by Sam Fadala, DBI Book, a division of Krause Publications, Iola, WI.*

The Passing of a Giant

Remembering Valmore Forgett, Jr.

by R.L. Wilson and Dennis Adler

Even as a young man in 1960, Val Forgett had the same bearing that became familiar to firearms collectors and black powder enthusiasts for nearly half a century.

Firearms design, manufacture, embellishment and performance, rate amongst the most intriguing subjects in the annals of civilization. Down through the centuries, the world of firearms has been graced with giants, men – and occasionally women – who have greatly influenced this captivating and far-reaching field. In our own time, among those giants, have been William B. Ruger, Gene Stoner, Sam Cummings, Mikhail Kalashnikov, Roy Weatherby, and subject of the present tribute, Valmore J. Forgett, Jr.

Born into a family, which supplied flamethrowers for the front in World War II, Val grew up enamored with guns and shooting. Though best known for his extraordinary impact on the replica firearms market – as exemplified by the Navy Arms Co. – his main business was

Always fond of cannons, Val was always ready to touch off the big guns in N-SSA reenactments. He also participated in an early recording of the sounds of Civil War armament.

the Service Armament Co. Little known is the fact that his import and export business in surplus firearms, and in modern militaria and gunmaking, made Val one of the most influential of the world's gunmen.

Val was so respected within the munitions field that when the CIA played a role in the overthrow of the Fulgenico Batista dictatorship in Cuba, the clandestine agency supplied vast quantities of arms and ammunition to Val, so he and his agents could clandestinely supply them to Fidel Castro.

Val's expertise was not only from being born with a rifle in his crib, but drew from his army service at Aberdeen Proving Ground. He knew about secret Russian weaponry long before others had a clue, and his identity was known to Russia's KGB – he was listed in their files (the Soviets always respected knowledge, experience, and power).

Not only did Val master the design and function of military armaments, he was an expert in the allied field of ammunition. Once when a self-styled authority claimed the originality and superiority of the Dardick "tround," Val reached into his desk drawer at Aberdeen and produced a cartridge, which predated the Dardick by decades. Of course, the "expert" was totally ignorant of that historic predecessor!

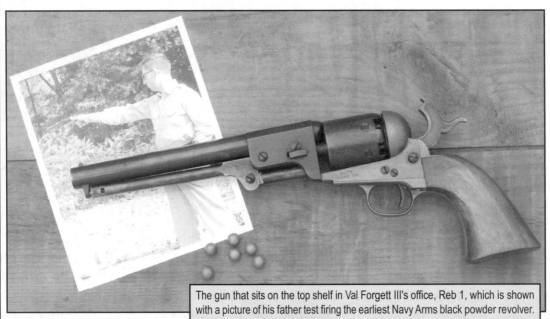

The gun that sits on the top shelf in Val Forgett III's office, Reb 1, which is shown with a picture of his father test firing the earliest Navy Arms black powder revolver.

I well remember first meeting Val on the occasion of the "Samuel Colt Presents" exhibition, when I was a rookie in the employ of the Wadsworth Atheneum

Museum of Art, Hartford, Connecticut (1961), on leave from my senior year at Carleton College.

Two busloads of collectors came to the Atheneum from the New Jersey Arms collectors – among them Val Forgett, already a highly respected authority. The following year we met again, during an Ohio Gun Collectors Association meeting (Columbus), as well as in Washington, D.C., for my first NRA Annual Meeting and Exhibition. Over the years we would renew our friendship at meetings of the Armor and Arms Club of New York, as well as at Val's palatial setup in Ridgefield, New Jersey, headquarters of Navy Arms Co.

Most of the public and the shooting, hunting and collecting world knew Val through his brilliant creation and management of Navy Arms Co. With his old friend William B. Edwards, research had been done in the gun manufacturing centers of Europe, seeking a supplier or suppliers who could build replica guns, to satisfy the demand for celebrations of the Civil War centennial.

Forgett finally decided on Italy as the best place for manufacture – most specifically at the ancient arms making center of Gardone, Val Trompia. There he discovered the talent he needed to develop what became the Navy Arms empire. In the process, Val breathed new life into the Italian firearms industry. The demand for replicas of Colt, Remington, Springfield and Harpers Ferry Armory, and other firearms, led to an epidemic of manufacturers, including Euroarms, Pedersoli, and Aldo Uberti.

Beginning his arms career as a draftsman at Beretta, and ably assisted by the support of his wife Giuseppina Moretti (a cousin of Carlo and Pier Giuseppe Beretta – uncles of Ugo Gussali Beretta), Aldo Uberti launched his own business, thus building most of the first products ordered by Val Forgett and Navy Arms.

Uberti quickly became the premier manufacturer of replica firearms in the world. Today it is a subsidiary of Beretta, its market exponentially expanding – but nevertheless owing its roots to Val Forgett.

Long before there was an A. Uberti Srl, Val and Aldo Uberti started producing 1851 Navy reproductions. The stamping on the barrel lug reads MADE IN ITALY G.U., which stood for Gregorelli & Uberti, the first company to produce an 1851 Navy replica.

Val test firing Reb 1 in 1960. He literally stood behind his products!

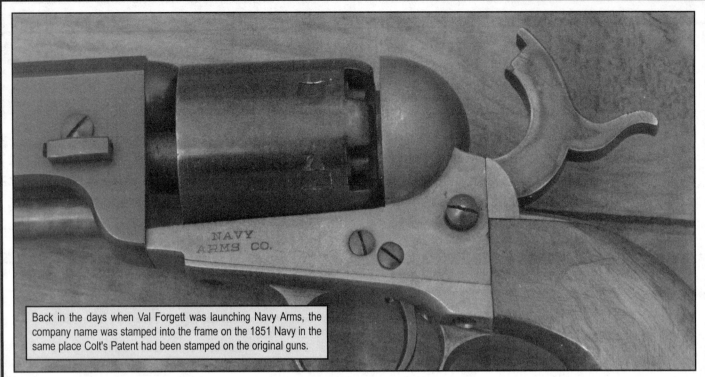

Back in the days when Val Forgett was launching Navy Arms, the company name was stamped into the frame on the 1851 Navy in the same place Colt's Patent had been stamped on the original guns.

In recognition of his unique impact on Italian industry, Val was awarded the title of Cavaliere del Lavaro, a great honor for any Italian, and thus an ever-greater honor for an American.

The product line that Uberti and Navy Arms evolved continues to set the standard for the gunmaking replica industry to the present day. And when Colt's decided to enter the market, it did so under the guidance and signal aid of Val Forgett and Navy Arms Co.

The author remembers meeting Val at Colt's in the late 1960s, while I was serving as a consultant to the management office, and concurrently urging the historic company to follow Val's bold lead. All of the Hartford-based company's blackpowder replica arms owe a large debt of gratitude to the valiant and innovative Val Forgett.

Val's innumerable successes came as the result of his broad expertise on guns and gunmaking, his gift at dealing with people, his strong business acumen, and his innate sense of fair play, which included a willingness to share the profit pie with others.

For an inside look at his impact on the Colt replica line, the reader should consult my introduction and Val's foreword to Dennis Adler's book, *Colt Blackpowder Reproductions & Replicas – A Collector's & Shooter's Guide*, published by Blue Book Publications.

It was Val who spearheaded the creation of the Blackpowder Olympics. His first wife, Heidi, and their daughter Susan, set records in international competitions. They did so with products designed and made by Val.

With his considerable depth of knowledge, a matching vast experience, his keen hunter's and shooter's instincts – and the support of a gun-oriented family (especially son and heir, Valmore III who now presides over Navy Arms), one could expect only a long run of achievement by Val in his distinguished world of gun manufacture, import, export, and sales. I was proud to have Navy Arms market several of my books in the firm's handsome catalog and Ridgefield showrooms.

In recent years Val was plagued by leukemia; but he never lost his joie de vivre. Assisted by family, including wife Eleanor, a gifted artist, he soldiered on. As an officer of the Armor and Arms Club of New York, he was a regular at the historic group's meetings, generally held at the 7th Regiment Armory, New York City. It was also not unusual to see Val at his favorite New York restaurant, Patsy's (236 W. 56th St., 10019), where the owners understand and love the world of fine guns, as did their famous patron. Owners Joseph Scognamillo, and son and chef Sal, also number Rush Limbaugh as a regular patron. Frank Sinatra was yet another of many luminaries known to enjoy their traditional Italian cuisine.

Who could ever forget the grand dinners there, celebrating Val's 70th birthday, or the wedding dinner of

At an arms show in 1960, Val had one of the very first displays of replica black powder arms. He's shown holding the now famous Reb 1, the first Navy Arms model, still in the Forgett family to this day.

Valmore III, and his bride, Diane? Those are the moments we all savor as the years pass on. As Val told the author, "As long as the doctors keep giving me good blood, I'll keep on going." True to his spirit and determination, he never gave up.

Val's old friend and competitor William B. Ruger said it all with his presentation of an Ruger Old Model Army .44 six-shooter, suitably inscribed, To Val Forgett, A Valiant Competitor, from Bill Ruger. Both gentlemen – and nearly all the other giants of the last 50 years of gunmaking – are now gone. Each represents the end of an era. How fortunate the world has been to reap the benefits of the likes of Val Forgett, who has now passed on to his reward, joining the superstars of guns who preceded him in death.

-R.L. Wilson

As an author, historian, and photographer, over the last 30 years I have had the opportunity to befriend some rather remarkable individuals, respected arms makers and collectors such as William B. Ruger, Sr., Lou and Anthony Imperato, Aldo Uberti, Pierangelo Pedersoli, and the entire Pietta family. I also came to know Val Forgett, both as an advisor to my books and as a friend who I could call on for a little historical tidbit about the emergence of the replica black powder industry. Val was knowledgeable of such things because he was there when it began. Moreover, he wasn't just in the business for the money, Val was a dedicated sportsman and enthusiast, a big game hunter who took the African "Big Five" with a black powder rifle, one of the very early civil war reenactors, and a member of the North-South Skirmish Association (N-SSA) since the 1950s. It was his involvement with the N-SSA that inspired him to have the first Colt 1851 Navy replicas designed and manufac-

tured for the Civil War Centennial Celebration, which began in 1961.

Val saw a need for replica Civil War era guns, because up to that time reenactors were using original guns. "As a shooter and budding manufacturer," said Val, "it was wonderful to see such enthusiasm, but as a collector it concerned me to see mint pieces being worn out, literally before my eyes. As an engineer and firearms historian, I was aware of the suspect technologies and manufacturing methods employed by many gunmakers of the 1860s, as well. With these facts in mind Aldo [Uberti] and I set out to build revolvers that would be well made and affordable. Mind you, at the time, the average person made $4,000 to $5,000 a year, and we needed to follow the Henry Ford model in bringing these guns to the masses. We elected to make the 1851 Navy first, followed by the Reb 60 revolver. Aldo and I signed our first contract for 6,000 pistols in 1958." That was the beginning of Navy Arms and the replica firearms industry.

Though it could be said that the rest is history, Val made that history by continuing to innovate and develop new models, new manufacturing techniques, and sales and marketing that catered to the black powder

In the 1950s Val was seriously involved in reenactments and was one of the most skilled mounted reenactors of the era.

enthusiast. The early Navy Arms catalogs were a wealth of information and inspiration to shooters.

Over the last five decades Val Forgett forged an industry founded on the principals of providing quality products at reasonable prices. That tradition continues today through Val Forgett III, who has followed in his father's footsteps and made a few new imprints of his own. Navy Arms is a lasting tribute to the founder of the industry, a gentleman by whom I am proud to have been called a friend.

-Dennis Adler

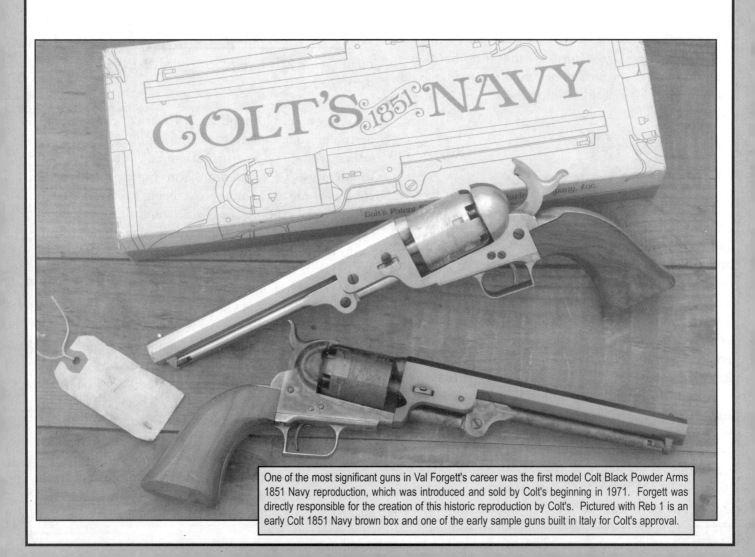

One of the most significant guns in Val Forgett's career was the first model Colt Black Powder Arms 1851 Navy reproduction, which was introduced and sold by Colt's beginning in 1971. Forgett was directly responsible for the creation of this historic reproduction by Colt's. Pictured with Reb 1 is an early Colt 1851 Navy brown box and one of the early sample guns built in Italy for Colt's approval.

The Transition from FLINTLOCK to PERCUSSION IGNITION

by R.L. Wilson

Any firearms collector knows the sequence of firing systems to be a logical progression from the original hand cannon of c. 1350, to the matchlock, the wheel lock, the flintlock, the percussion (cap & ball), and finally to the metallic cartridge breechloader. Despite centuries of research by scholars, the dates of origin for some of these are presently obscure, and likely always will be.

In consideration of the historical transition from flintlock to percussion, for the first time in firearms history, the New World of the Western Hemisphere played a vital role. America – particularly North America – was coming into its own, not only as a place where firearms were a necessary part of life, but as a land of gunmakers.

That hoax book, *Arming America*, by the resoundingly discredited, and indeed disgraced, "historian," former Emory University Professor Michael Bellesiles, tried to diminish America's role in firearms history. His primary claim was that up until the Civil War only about 10% of Americans had firearms, that many of these were broken, and that ours was certainly no "gun culture." He stated that guns did not become common until following the Civil War, when they were dumped on the marketplace by the government and gunmakers, due to excessively high production during that conflict.

Though it took *The New York Times* and the mainstream media about two years to finally acknowledge (begrudgingly) the Bellesiles fraud, arms collectors and researchers spotted his blatant and disgraceful deceit from the beginning.

Returning to the theme of the present article – at the time of the transition from flintlock to percussion, the British gun trade reigned supreme. Such master gunmakers as John and Joseph Manton, James Purdey, and John Rigby produced exquisite flintlocks, and each were also renowned for the quality of their percussion weapons.

A pioneer writer on the history of firearms was yet another British gunmaker, W.W. Greener, whose landmark volume, *The Gun And Its Development*, appeared in numerous editions, beginning in 1881. Reviewing that work, and the more than six centuries of firearms history, it is evident that the hottest market, from the beginning, has been for cutting edge technology, producing the latest and most refined firearms for military and sporting purposes.

When one looks at today's market, what commands the highest prices, and produces the most extraordinary of firearms – without doubt the most superior in the entire history of guns and shooting – are the high-end sporting makers: among them Purdey, Holland & Holland, Westley Richards, Fabbri, Hartmann & Weiss, and America's own Tony Galazan/Connecticut Shotgun Manufacturing Co.

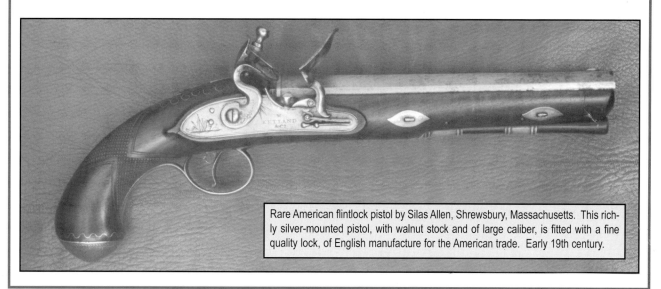

Rare American flintlock pistol by Silas Allen, Shrewsbury, Massachusetts. This richly silver-mounted pistol, with walnut stock and of large caliber, is fitted with a fine quality lock, of English manufacture for the American trade. Early 19th century.

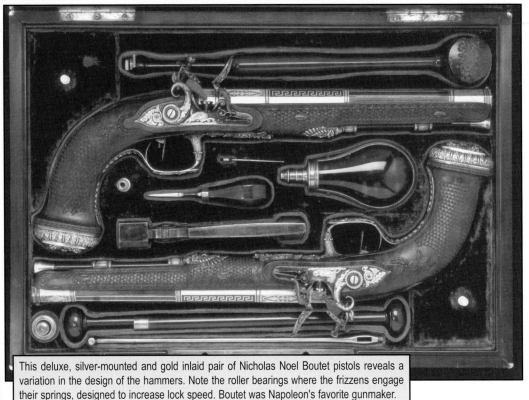

This deluxe, silver-mounted and gold inlaid pair of Nicholas Noel Boutet pistols reveals a variation in the design of the hammers. Note the roller bearings where the frizzens engage their springs, designed to increase lock speed. Boutet was Napoleon's favorite gunmaker.

cap in which was inserted fulminate of mercury, the cap in turn was set on a nipple at the barrel breech, and serving as the anvil to the striker (or hammer), to set off the cap-primer, whose quick shot of flame through a center-hole in the nipple would set off the main charge in the barrel's breech.

The much simplified percussion system was faster than the flintlock – although, ironically, there were die-hards who did not wish to replace their trusted flintlocks with the new cap & ball! Interestingly, there had been many wheellock owners who did not want to accept the new flintlock!

FAULTS OF THE FLINTLOCK

Though the best system of its time, the flintlock was by no means perfect. First and foremost, it was not waterproof. Although inventors like Joseph Manton made what he promoted as a rainproof pan, the fact is, it was not. He even devised a system where a channel would come through the stock vertically, adjacent to the pan, to allow rain to run more quickly away. No matter what was tried, however, the flintlock was never waterproof. Of the Mantons, brother John also built guns with innovations, though Joe was the more creative of the two.

Simply stated, the flintlock system, whose origin is credited to the French in the early 1600s, consisted of a striker or hammer (often known as a cock), with a jaw in which was inserted a carefully chipped piece of flint. With the hammer at "half cock" (a safety system) which has its origins all the way back through the history of gunmaking, to the very beginning), a charge of powder, followed by the lead projectile, were inserted and seated into the barrel breech. The barrel breech was connected by a touch hole to the flash pan (a scooped aperture in which a priming charge was placed), which was covered by an L-shaped piece of steel, termed today as a frizzen. When the hammer was at "full cock" the trigger would be pulled, allowing the flint to spark against the frizzen. As the frizzen flipped forward, the sparks ignited to produce a "flash in the pan." If the system worked as designed to do, the flames from the pan spread into the barrel breech, igniting the main charge, and firing the projectile(s) down the barrel.

How exciting it must have been for the leading gunmakers and inventors of the day, to take the flintlock action, which had reached its zenith in the period of the early 19th century, and create its replacement. That replacement was the simplified system of a percussion

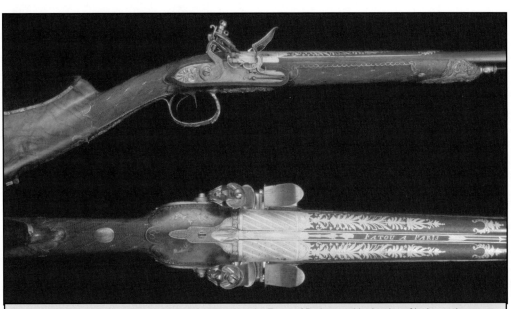

Top and side views of this exquisite flintlock fowling piece by Fatou of Paris reveal intricacies of locks, and an example of a gold inlaid touch hole to resist corrosion. Napoleonic period.

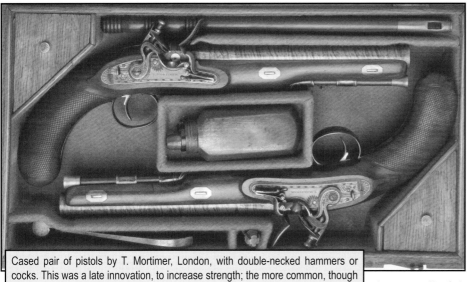

Cased pair of pistols by T. Mortimer, London, with double-necked hammers or cocks. This was a late innovation, to increase strength; the more common, though graceful, goose-necked cocks had a tendency to bend, or break. Platinum inlaid touch holes. Note sliding safety, to engage slot in back side of hammer. c. 1820.

Bird shooters recognized that the flintlock was slow, and thus the gun barrel had to be kept moving, in order to give the proper lead to the bird in flight. The most common mistake of today's bird shooters is stopping the gun as they fire. Imagine how that problem was compounded with the flintlock: from the moment the trigger was pulled, to when the hammer struck the frizzen, to when the powder in the pan was ignited, to the igniting of the main charge!

Yet another weakness of the flintlock was a tendency toward a "flash in the pan," in which the priming powder would ignite, but it would fail to set off the main charge. Badly needed was a system in which the priming charge was "shot" into the breech, not a relatively slow-burning and short trail of ignited powder.

Of further difficulty, the flints were unreliable, and had to be replaced on a regular basis. If the flint wasn't properly secured in the jaws of the cock, it would fail to strike the frizzen in a way that would produce sufficient sparks. A flint might even fall out of the jaws! A weakened mainspring might mean that the flint wouldn't even force the frizzen forward, let alone create the necessary sparks.

Hang fires were yet another problem – assuming the powder in the pan ignited, the main charge might not go off until a few seconds later. The resultant hang fire could cause an accident, since sometimes the shoot-er assumed the charge was not going to fire, with dire consequences. An article in an 1817 issue of *The Sporting Magazine* told of a young sportsman who was killed due to a hang fire, when "the young man . . . stooped, conceiving that the piece had missed fire, arose from his bending position, when, shocking to relate, the contents of the gun were discharged within a few yards of his head, which was so dreadfully shattered as to cause his immediate death."

Yet another weakness of the flintlock was that some of the firing gasses would escape out through the touch hole, and thus not all of the force of the discharge was expended on forcing the ball or pellets out the muzzle. Further, when the flash in the pan was set off, sometimes the shooter was struck in the face with sparks.

STEPS ALONG THE WAY

The percussion cap was not a sudden development, and there were a few attempts at systems which would precede it. The first and best known of these is that of a Scottish preacher, Reverend Alexander John Forsyth, of Belhelvie, Aberdeenshire, who was a keen sportsman, shooter, and amateur chemist. Forsyth was aware of advancements in explosives by such inventors as the French chemist Claude Louis de Berthollet (d. 1822). His experiments, with fulminates of mercury and of silver, and with gunpowder having a potassi-

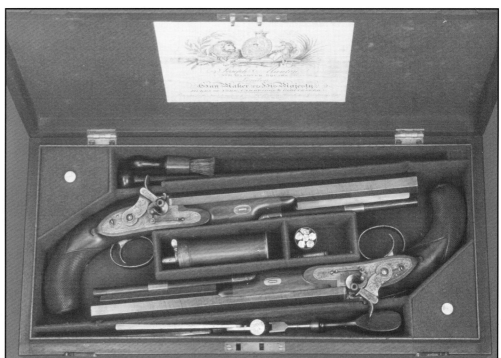

Joseph Manton patent tube lock dueling pistols; note several features shared with flintlock pistols, including especially front action lock. Often flint locks were adapted for the new percussion or tubelock systems.

um chlorate base, rather than potassium nitrate, resulted in explosives which had such power and force they seemed impractical.

But Forsyth, with his firearms experience and insight, foresaw a use for these new developments, and patented a system in April 1807. His gunlock used a carefully regulated amount of powder which was detonating in character, and would explode when struck. This first "percussion lock" marked the doom of the flintlock system.

Forsyth's invention was generally known as the scent-bottle, because of its shape. Built within the years 1808-18, the flintlock's flashpan was replaced by a plug of cylindrical shape. A screw sealed the center of this, and served as the priming magazine. The inner end was secured in the barrel breech by threads, located in the same spot as the touch hole on the barrel of a flintlock gun. The scent bottle magazine pivoted, and each time it was so moved a fresh supply of detonating powder was inserted into position, to be struck by a springfed rod, which in turn was struck by a hammer. Just as with the flintlock, the hammer needed to be drawn back and cocked for firing.

As the hammer struck the rod, the rod hit the detonating powder, creating a flame which was directed into the barrel breech. The Forsyth system would, in a few years, be replaced by the much more simplified percussion cap, of copper, the inside top of which would have a small disk of fulminate of mercury. Once the cap was inserted on top of the nipple, the striking of the outside top of the cap by the hammer would explode the fulminate on the top of the nipple, directing the fire forcefully through the tube of the nipple, directly into the main charge within the barrel breech.

There were shortcomings of the Forsyth system, not the least of which was the possibility that the scent bottle might explode, since it contained a quantity of powder, enough to be used for several primings, by its 180 degree movement each time the shooter wished to fire his gun.

Forsyth quickly offered his invention to the British Ordnance, which was so impressed with the potential that he was invited to establish a workshop within the Tower of London. Master General of Ordnance Lord Moira wanted Forsyth to refine his creation. Taking leave from ministerial duties, the inventor moved to London, and after about a year had brought his creation to what appeared to be a satisfactory conclusion.

J. & J. Miller pill lock revolving rifle, Rochester, New York. The tip of the hammer had a special striker, designed to hit the aperture on the cylinder breech, to detonate the pill. Sometimes that aperture would snap off, making the rifle ineffective.

However, by then Lord Moira was no longer in command, and his successor failed to adopt the Forsyth system. In fact, the inventor was asked to leave the Tower. Forsyth then turned to the quite sophisticated lot of British sportsmen. With patent in place, he established a shop in London, for manufacturing locks and firearms. He was assisted by James Watt (best known as inventor of the steam engine) and by the renowned gunsmith James Purdey. Sportsmen quickly recognized that the Forsyth was a faster system than the flintlock, and were keen to adopt the new guns.

According to authority Robert Held, in his classic work *The Age of Firearms* (p. 174), "By 1815, probably a quarter of all good- and best-quality guns made in England had detonating locks." Approximately a century later a bronze plaque was

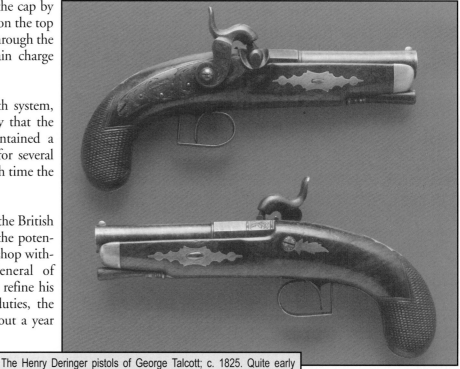

The Henry Deringer pistols of George Talcott; c. 1825. Quite early example of American percussion cap pistols. Greg Martin Collection.

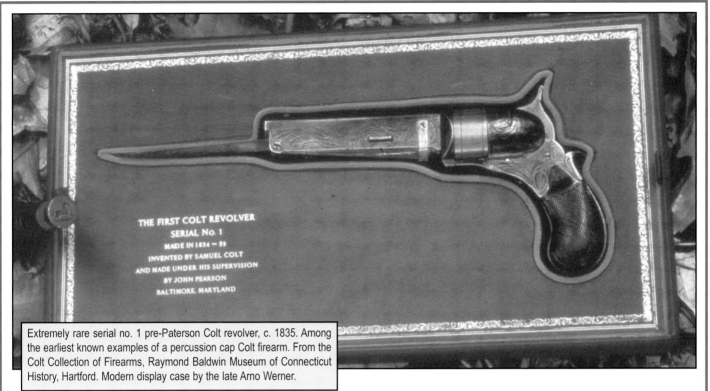

Extremely rare serial no. 1 pre-Paterson Colt revolver, c. 1835. Among the earliest known examples of a percussion cap Colt firearm. From the Colt Collection of Firearms, Raymond Baldwin Museum of Connecticut History, Hartford. Modern display case by the late Arno Werner.

placed in the Tower, paying tribute to Forsyth and his invention. It reads:

> To the Memory of the Reverend
> ALEXANDER JOHN FORSYTH
> M.A., LL.D.
> Minister of Belhelvie
> Aberdeenshire
> In 1805 he conducted experiments
> in the Tower under the Master
> General of Ordnance and in 1807
> invented the percussion system
> which was adopted by the
> British Army in 1839

This Tablet was erected in 1929 by admirers of his Genius.

OTHER SYSTEMS PRECEDING OR CONTEMPORARY WITH THE PERCUSSION CAP

A pill system was invented by Joseph Manton, patented in 1816, in which the exploding pill fitted within the nose of a hollowed out striker or hammer. Manton quickly followed that invention with an improvement, in 1818: a percussion tube lock, in which the tube was inserted into a touch hole, and when struck, would explode, forcing the priming charge into the main charge within the barrel breech. American gunmakers who made rifles using the pill lock system are noted below.

Manton's tube lock system was awkward, and might easily fire in both directions, rather than simply into the barrel breech. It was also rather tiny, and not easy to work with one's fingers.

The simplicity of the percussion cap included the fact that once it was secured on the nipple, it was unlikely to come loose. Caps were made in various sizes, to fit on like-sized nipples. Some of the early nipples even had tiny ridges or other fizzures, making the cap more likely to remain in place. Once the cap was on top of the nipple, it was very close to a seal, and was unlikely to have problems with rain.

As important as anything, the discharge of the gun was much faster than the flintlock – almost instantaneous.

The copper percussion cap dates between the years 1814 and 1820. Credit for its invention is still open to conjecture. The American artist and inventor Joshua Shaw is often mentioned, and though he took out a patent (c. 1822), his was not the first. Shaw authored a book, in which he discussed his invention of the percussion cap, *A Sketch or History of the Copper Cap and Percussion Artillery Primer.* He is believed to have died in September, 1860, in Bordentown, New Jersey.

Another claimant as inventor was the famous Colonel Peter Hawker of England, a renowned writer on shooting. In his classic work, *Instructions to Young Sportsmen*, he laid claim to being the originator of the percussion cap. To quote, "When Joe [Manton] first brought out his detonators [the tubes operating with percussion system] in Davies Street . . . he made the most perfect gun I ever saw; and doubting whether such another could be got, I set my wits to work in order to simplify the invention. At last the plan of a perforated nipple, and the detonating powder in the crown of a small cap, occurred to me. I made a drawing of it, which I took to Joe. After having this explained, he said that he would show me something in a few weeks time; when, lo and behold, there was a rough gun altered precisely on my own plan! His factotum, poor old

Asell, assured me that the whole job was done from my drawing. . . .it proved to answer so well that we now see it in general circulation."

Yet another claimant as inventor was the Frenchman, Prelat, whose career in the firearms field dates from the Napoleonic period, and for a few years after the end of the Napoleonic wars. He took out a patent in 1818, claiming to have invented the percussion cap. Lewis Winants concluded Prelat had claimed what had been the creation of others.

OTHER SYSTEMS WHICH WERE TRIED IN THE TRANSITION

A few alternatives were attempted, and patented, in the transition from the flintlock. In America, we too tried variations on Manton's tubelock, as well as the American punch lock, the patch lock and a system known as the pill lock. An important source of data on all these systems is Lewis Winant's *Early Percussion Firearms – A History of Early Percussion Firearms Ignition – From Forsyth to Winchester .44-40* (1959).

A patch lock is known to have been made by the distinguished London gunmaker Samuel Nock, and is described by Winants as first used "soon after 1807." It was to this gun that Winants credits the first use of the nipple. The patch priming was composed of "flattish cakes of fulminate placed between pieces of paper made waterproof by varnishing. Sometimes the primings were called paper caps, and they resembled our modern paper caps used in toy pistols." The patch was pressed into place on the face of the hammer. As the hammer fell, the patch exploded when it struck the nipple. The result was a priming charge, sent into the barrel breech through the hole through the nipple. All the known specimens of these early guns are of British manufacture. The first nipples were integral with the barrel breech; later they were threaded, and screwed into place. Yet another known maker of patch lock firearms was Cartmell, also of London. A short-coming of this system was that "ready-primed strikers" were needed to attach to the hammers.

The American punch lock was invented by Samuel Guthrie, a medical doctor, and dates from as early as 1830. The system was used primarily on long arms, and seldom on handguns. Guthrie was also known to have been one of three discoverers of chloroform (in 1831), and was one of several versatile innovators who had the ability to excell in several fields of endeavor. Samuel Colt himself fits within that class of creators.

Guthrie's punch lock invention began by his adapting a flintlock gun to the system, which would later be known as a pill lock. Instead of a percussion cap, a small pill, which detonated when struck, was inserted into an aperture which would feed the exploded charge into the barrel breech.

At about the same time as the first punch locks, conversions from flintlock to percussion were becoming popular in both Europe and the United States. Any gunsmith who could effect that conversion, was likewise capable of the same to punch lock. New York gunsmiths began these conversions, and examples are known by Rogers & Heart (Utica), Ephraim Gilbert (Rochester), and William A. Hart (Fredonia).

Very quickly the punch lock came to be known as the pill lock. Among American gunmakers who tried the pill lock system were J. and J. Miller and William Billinghurst, of Rochester, New York, foremost of a school of makers whose revolving rifles were contemporary with Paterson period Colt revolvers (c. 1836-42). A Miller pill lock revolving rifle was in Samuel Colt's own arms collection, acquired to keep tabs on competitors. James Miller's patent, of June 11, 1829, preceded Colt's first U.S. patent of 1836. One reason the pill lock guns proved easily surpassed by the percussion cap was that the pill was awkward to insert, and did not have a good record of remaining where it was placed.

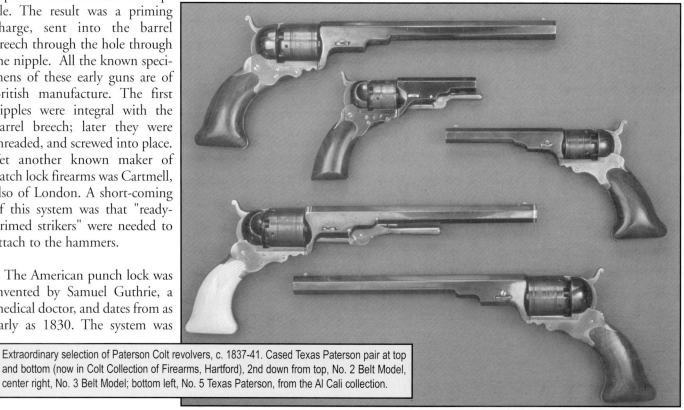

Extraordinary selection of Paterson Colt revolvers, c. 1837-41. Cased Texas Paterson pair at top and bottom (now in Colt Collection of Firearms, Hartford), 2nd down from top, No. 2 Belt Model, center right, No. 3 Belt Model; bottom left, No. 5 Texas Paterson, from the Al Cali collection.

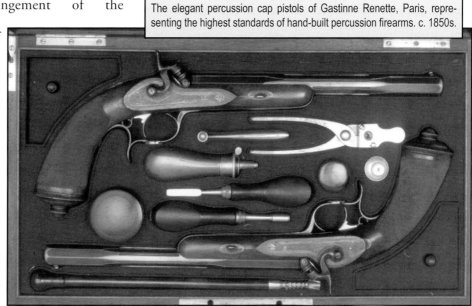

Selection of pepperbox firearms, with early single shot Blunt & Syms (New York) ring trigger pistols; from the 1830s, and into the 1840s, these arms were early examples of the use of the percussion cap, and the pepperboxes were would-be rivals to the Colt revolver.

THE PERCUSSION CAP MAKES THE REVOLVER A PRACTICAL INVENTION

An extremely important factor in the adoption of the percussion cap was that it finally made practical an invention that mechanics and gunsmiths had been experimenting with for centuries: the revolver. The youthful Colt's first experimental repeating pistol was built in 1832; it exploded on firing. A rifle made by Anson Chase and W.H. Rowe (Hartford) in the same year is the earliest Colt firearm to have survived. A cross between a revolving rifle and a Kentucky, the piece is of .37 caliber, of 9 shots, and with a removable 35½ inch octagonal barrel. The nipples are threaded within apertures at the breech of the cylinder, and were (as was common to most other early Colt pre-Paterson experimentals) with covered breeches, as well as covers over the front of the cylinder. Colt soon discovered that the covers made the cylinders into bombs, since the main charge was likely to spread to adjacent chambers.

The extremely rare serial no. 1 pre-Paterson Colt revolver is pictured, which features the breech covers noted above. Of .358 caliber, the six-shot prototype has a 5-inch barrel, fitted with folding bayonet. Overall length is 13¾ inches, with bayonet extended. Each chamber is numbered, from 1 to 6. The revolver shares several features with the initial Colt U.S. revolver patent, of February 25, 1836.

Colt's own collection included examples of the Collier flintlock revolver. These had been used in the Colt vs. Massachusetts Arms Co. trial, in order to prove that his revolver had been the first practical repeating firearm – and that his patent protection should therefore be recognized, and extended. Without the percussion ignition system, Colt would

A pioneer in the adoption of the percussion cap in the United States was Henry Deringer of Philadelphia. Renowned for his Kentucky rifles and his military contract arms, it was Deringer who devised the pocket pistol for which he became famous. Early examples of these pistols, which he first introduced in 1825, were fitted with the percussion ignition system. In a deposition made for part of his case against A.J. Plate of San Francisco, for infringement of the "DERINGER/PHILADELA" trademark, the inventor stated: "the first of these pistols were made for Major Armstrong . . . ." Illustrated is the extremely rare, and quite early, matched pair of Deringers built by the inventor for one-time Chief of U.S. Ordnance, Colonel George Talcott.

Deringer's first attempt at a martial pistol with percussion ignition was the Model 1842 boxlock, of Springfield Armory design. That gun was the first military percussion arm authorized by the United States. Interestingly, as in England, the pioneers in the percussion system were not the military, but civilian shooters and private gunmakers.

The elegant percussion cap pistols of Gastinne Renette, Paris, representing the highest standards of hand-built percussion firearms. c. 1850s.

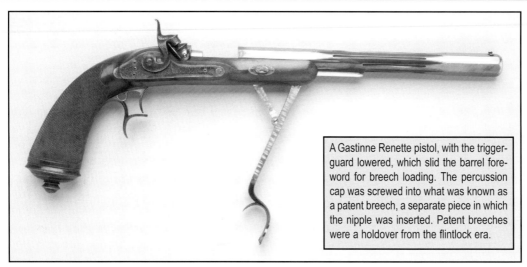

A Gastinne Renette pistol, with the trigger-guard lowered, which slid the barrel fore-word for breech loading. The percussion cap was screwed into what was known as a patent breech, a separate piece in which the nipple was inserted. Patent breeches were a holdover from the flintlock era.

pler than the flintlock, not only had the practicality of firearms been vastly improved, but their ease of manufacture had also reached a new plateau.

The success of the percussion cap, and rapid advancements in manufacturing, were major steps in bringing America into its exalted position as No. 1 in the World. Not only the American firearms industry, but arms collectors, can take great pride in these historic and momentous achievements. Who would have thought that such a tiny device as a percussion cap could symbolize so much. ■

not have been able to create a practical, functioning repeating handgun or longarm.

CONCLUSION

It was more than a coincidence that at the time the percussion system was replacing the flintlock, America's industrial might was rapidly becoming a factor in establishing the United States as a major world power. So innovative, so vital, and so quickly evolving was the American manufacturing powerhouse, that it became the standard by which the production capacity and ability of all nations were measured.

The American System of Manufacture saw what was largely a product of our creative gunmakers – Simeon North, Henry Aston, R. and J.D. Johnson, John H. Hall, Robbins & Lawrence, and the national armories at Springfield and Harpers Ferry. These pioneers were crucial in creating parts interchangeability and mass production, and evolving a mighty industrial base.

Soon percussion firearms were being produced of a very high standard. The basics for doing so, however, had been achieved by such pioneer U.S. contact gunmakers as Simeon North. As early as 1813, North had agreed, in writing, to manufacture pistols in which there was uniformity, "by fitting every part to the same lock." Simeon North was building guns in which he could take the parts from any one, and make it fit to any other – a remarkable achievement in those times. Because the percussion system was sim-

R.L. Wilson, one of the world's leading firearms authorities with dozens of firearms books to his credit, is pictured during the 2003 Orlando NRA Show, holding his deluxe edition of *The Book of Colt Firearms* (published 1993), generally considered the "bible" on Colt firearms.

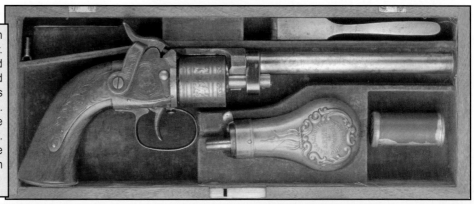

This Massachusetts Arms Co. revolver was an early attempt to compete with the Colt revolver. With percussion cylinder, the lock was standard with a tape primer – an innovation also employed by some other gunmakers, including Sharps, as an alternative to single percussion caps. c. 1851. The tape's advancement to be in line with the hammer was geared to that part's movement. Sharps, as did certain other gunmakers, like Butterfield, employed a tube priming system on some percussion firearms.

Flintlocks by America's Artisan Gunmakers

Written and Photographed by Dennis Adler

"If you want an 18th century rifle, then build one with 18th century tools and techniques."
- Jack Brooks

This magnificent Indian flintlock, handcrafted by Colorado gunmaker Jack Brooks, has a unique hand painted (rather than carved) motif. The Indian warrior painting is by nationally known artist David Wright of Gallatin, Tennessee. The War Club was fashioned by Beaver Bill Keeler of Hamilton, Ohio.

Prior to the development and universal adoption of the metallic cartridge in America by the late 19th century, the flintlock had been the most successful firearm in recorded history.

Developed in the late 16th century as an evolution of the snaphance (c.1540-1545), the flintlock further simplified the operating mechanism, allowing for production on a far grander scale than any previous firearm.

The first known examples of the flintlock are believed to have appeared in France between 1595 and 1620. However, as was pointed out by firearms historian Edward C. Ezell in his essential reference, *Handguns of the World*, "Introduction of a new lock mechanism, of course, did not mean that older forms were immediately abandoned." The wheel lock, snaphance, and flintlock were used concurrently throughout Europe into the early 18th century. By the time of the American Revolution, however, the flintlock had become de rigueur throughout much of Europe, the whole of the British Empire, and particularly in the Colonies, where a uniquely American rendering of the longrifle had emerged in Pennsylvania by the early 1700s.

Once established, the flintlock remained in use for nearly two hundred years, and many were still being shouldered by rough-and-ready companies of Southern militia at the beginning of the American Civil War in 1861.

The flintlock mechanism itself was rugged and not terribly complicated, contributing both to its longevity and continuous use from the early 17th through mid 19th

Author Dennis Adler with a contemporary flintlock fowler manufactured by Pennsylvania gunmaker Gary Rummell. The longrifle, Kentucky-style pistol (holstered) and fowler were essential tools of survival in the American wilderness of the 18th century. Steven and Sue Shroyer handcrafted the late 18th century belt, holster and period accessories. Contemporary Longrifle Association craftsman Phil Cravener built the Kentucky pistol.

centuries. The basic components were the lock plate and pan, the cock (hammer) and jaws (to hold the flint), steel (frizzen) and pan cover, feather spring (for the steel and pan cover), the mainspring, trigger spring, safety catch spring, and the tumbler, combined with the sear, and safety catch bolt (to provide full and half cock positions). It was an easily manufactured device that made the flintlock mechanism suitable to a variety of firearms, from longrifles to pistols, and in varying calibers and sizes ranging from small pocket-sized pistols to hefty 10 gauge fowlers.

Recreating the historic weaponry of the 17th and early 18th centuries is one of the oldest trades in the American firearms industry, predating the reproduction of Civil War era revolvers by decades.

Contemporary Longrifle Association founder Gordon Barlow notes that the earliest reproductions created by American artisan gunmakers date back to the 1940s.

"Most of the original old-time makers have passed away, such as Hacker Martin from Appomattox, Virginia, and William Buckley of Ohio, and others who were studying the old rifles and creating a new art style in the early 1940s and 1950s."

Around 1950, people such as Earl Lanning started to produce what Barlow calls authentic to the period flintlock longrifles and pistols. "They were equal to or better than the originals," says Barlow. "Earl was one of the first to recreate the early Kentucky rifle with a butt two-and-a-half inches thick, a wooden patch box, and the profuse application of brass and silver."

By the early 1960s a great deal of study had been done on what we refer to today as the Kentucky longrifle, and research into the schools of period gunmakers began to emerge in reproductions that were based on original designs from the 1700s.

Pennsylvania was one of the principal regions where the American longrifle was developed in the 18th century and there were various schools of design established in Bedford, Lancaster, and Bucks counties, the Lehigh Valley, York, Lebanon, and Chambersburg. Similar schools of rifle making sprang up in Virginia, North Carolina, Ohio, and along the eastern seaboard states, most of which had rifle makers at some point.

By 1750, the design of the American longrifle had evolved into a new form – a longer barreled, more accurate firearm with graceful, handcrafted stocks elaborately ornamented with brass and silver fittings, hand carving, and symbolic inlays. This was much the same as the handcrafted powder horns and hunting bags of the 18th century, which also bore the style of their makers.

"Back in the 1960s there were around 30 known makers of American longrifles," says Barlow, "today there are well over 400 makers of fine rifles and pistols that surpass in the art form the old Kentucky rifles, though still using similar stylistic ideas."

There are skilled American gunmakers specializing in the specific schools of design of their region, such as Alan Martin in the Allentown area of Pennsylvania, Brian LeMaster and Keith Casteel, who favor the Winchester, Virginia school of design, and Hershel House, in Morgantown, Kentucky, who specializes in the iron mounted rifles traditional of Kentucky and Tennessee.

"There are many schools of design and we are seeing something of a renaissance today of flintlock rifles and pistols reproducing the various regional styles of the 1700s," says Barlow. "The majority of today's artisan gunmakers, however, are combining different designs and adding their own artistic touches to the carving, inlays and engraving, to create some truly remarkable works of art. Take Jud Brennan, for example, who around 16 years ago took his wife and kids and moved to a remote part of Alaska, where he has spent the better part of his career handcrafting Kentucky longrifles and accoutrements. Brennan and his family have built some of the finest and most expensive 18th century longrifles, pipe axes, and powder horns in the world."

There are many well-known artisan gunmakers such as Jack Brooks, Wayne Watson (who built the longrifles used by Daniel Day Lewis in *The Last of the Mohegans*), Frank House, who made the longrifle carried by Mel Gibson in *The Patriot*, and Warren Sellke, who have all become highly sought after for their particular style of rifle or pistol making. This is an art form that demands expertise in many different disciplines, from woodworking, metal forging, and engraving, to the microscopic precision necessary to inlay silver wire often no thicker than a human hair!

"The guys continually push each other," says Barlow, "but it is the most friendly competition I have ever seen in any industry. In the world of contemporary longrifles there is not the competition or rivalry, it's all about teaching and sharing. Many of the top makers write articles for our flintlock magazine to demonstrate how they get a certain finish, or how they do inlays, so that others can learn the techniques. Others participate in training seminars at the university in Bowling Green, Kentucky, where people learn the traditional 18th century gunmaker's skills. The master gunmakers are the teachers. Recreating the American longrifle has almost become a cottage industry."

When we talk about the cost of originals versus reproductions, at least in the world of Colt and Remington revolvers, the original guns are worth 10 fold or more than the reproductions, but this tenet does not apply to the American longrifle. Today's contemporary longrifles, on average, are worth considerably more than most originals without exceptional provenance. Even in the great Butterfield & Butterfield Millennium Sale of 1999, the estimate for a highly embellished French flintlock fowling gun by Bertrand Piraube, manufactured in 1681, was $30,000 to $50,000. The Jud Brennan flintlock is worth more than $80,000. The majority of original American flintlocks seen at auction are in the $3,000 to $5,000 range[1], considerably less then a handcrafted contempo-

rary longrifle by makers such as House, Sellke, Watson, and Brooks, who command prices up to $25,000 for their work.

There is an interesting dichotomy here, however, original flintlock pistols of exceptional design are worth as much as, or more than the best contemporary American reproductions, which average $3,500 to $5,000. The majority of contemporary American longrifles average from $5,000 to $25,000 and demand for these handcrafted flintlocks continues to grow every year.

The Contemporary Longrifle Association (CLA) was founded in 1995 with its first national meeting in Cincinnati, Ohio. The CLA's annual meeting and show is now held at the Lexington, Kentucky convention center, and there are CLA regional shows all across the country.

"The mission of the CLA is to enhance the visibility of the artists that make contemporary longrifles, pistols, and accoutrements such as powder horns, knives, and hunting bags," says Roger Barlow, who was the founder and first president. "The Contemporary Longrifle Association is a non-profit organization and we spend all the money we make trying to perpetuate the art form and the artists. What we have done is develop mini shows, which have sprung up across the country, in Oregon, Washington, Indiana, in Michigan, Pennsylvania, Virginia, West Virginia, Tennessee, and Kentucky. We're expanding every year to raise the public's awareness of this uniquely American art form. The mini shows give people an opportunity to meet the artists, and sit down with them and discuss firsthand the building of a longrifle or pistol, and be involved in the decision making process. It's one thing to buy a flintlock in a store, at auction, or a gun show, quite another to be involved in its design and creation, which could take six or eight months or longer. Owning it is one thing," explains Barlow, "but the trip that you take getting to the ownership is a different thing."

Here then are the results of many trips, and long journeys into the world of contemporary longrifle and pistol making.

[1] Estimates from recent Rock Island, and Greg Martin auctions.

Fashioned after a number of period motifs that Delta Junction, Alaska gunmaker Jud Brennan had wanted to put together on a fine longrifle, the gold and silver for this gun's extraordinary inlays were mined in Alaska by Brennan, who produced the entire piece over a period of three and a half years using 18th century manufacturing techniques. Brennan made 27 pierces in the patch box, sideplates, and finial, which is one piece of sheet silver, before inlaying it into the stock. The wooden patch box, rather than being of traditional sliding style, is hinged like a metal patch box cover, and the inside of the patch box similarly embellished. The carving in the tiger stripe maple stock is Brennan's own style, as are the silver wire inlays, some of which are as fine as a human hair! The lock, sideplate, guard, and tricker were all handmade by Brennan, as well. "The inscription in the buttstock, Liberty & Property, is a great old Virginia saying," notes owner Gordon Barlow of his prized Jud Brennan longrifle. The matching bag and powder horn for the Jud Brennan longrifle were made by Brennan's wife and son, also accomplished artisans in 18th century accoutrements. Julie Brennan sewed the bag and antiqued the leather finish and linen strap. Jessie Brennan, only 17 years old at the time, made the horn to accompany his father's work. They are a very creative family.

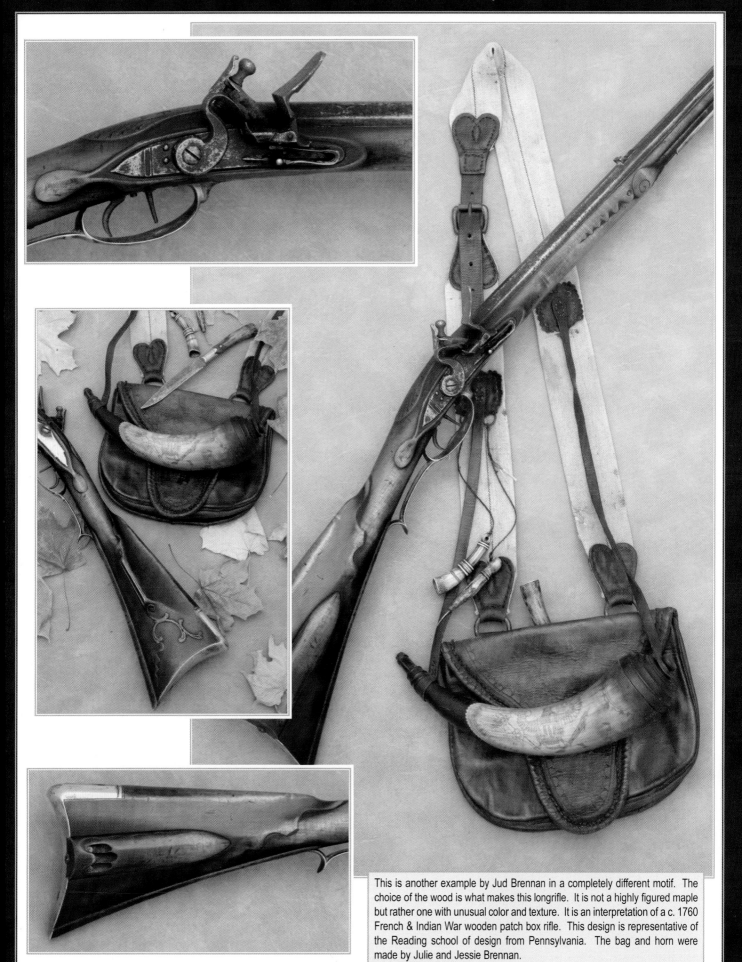

This is another example by Jud Brennan in a completely different motif. The choice of the wood is what makes this longrifle. It is not a highly figured maple but rather one with unusual color and texture. It is an interpretation of a c. 1760 French & Indian War wooden patch box rifle. This design is representative of the Reading school of design from Pennsylvania. The bag and horn were made by Julie and Jessie Brennan.

This is a rifle that Jud Brennan created to capture the style of the Pennsylvania school but with a unique patch box that no one has ever seen before. Though reminiscent of the Pennsylvania school the architecture is Brennan's own. The gun exhibits exceptional carving around the tang and stock, and is perhaps 10 steps above the complexity of the previous example. The powder horn that Brennan fashioned to go with the antique finished rifle is regarded as one of the best contemporary American horns ever produced, with highly detailed scrimshawing and engraved silver. The bag is also one of the finest examples of contemporary design, and was assembled by Brennan's wife, daughter Abby, and Joanna and Rebekah Holbrook.

This exceptional pair is by Dayton, Virginia, gunmaker and engraver Mark Thomas. Thomas also makes hunting bags, accoutrements, and period jewelry. "Mark is an exceptional engraver," says Barlow, and both his carving and architecture are very good." Thomas has developed his own individual style, which is evident in his approach to the patch box, one of the traditional focal points of the American longrifle. "He uses some of the features from the Winchester school but his carving and engraving are unique. There is a considerable amount of engraving in his silver and the rifle really becomes his canvas," says Barlow. Renowned craftsman Steve Lalliof of Cicero, Indiana, made the leather hunting bag, and the powder horn was handmade by David Auker of Laurelton, Pennsylvania. The finger weaved fabric and horn strap, were made by Tom Conde in Mouth of Wilson, Virginia. The finger-weave technique is done entirely by hand. The horn was made by Mark Thomas.

Here is an exceptional longrifle by Englewood, Colorado, gunmaker Jack Brooks, who took an entirely different approach with an American Indian theme that has no carving or inlays at all, but rather meticulously hand-painted embellishment and a lustrous finish. "Jack can make a $25,000 set of pistols, or a highly engraved longrifle," says Barlow, "but here he has chosen to make a unique fowler that is a magnificent piece of art that simply jumps off the page at you." Equally impressive is the hand-beaded bag made by Lally House of Paris, Kentucky, valued at $10,000 and the powder horn made by her husband Frank. They collaborated on the accoutrements for Mel Gibson in *The Patriot* and for Russell Crowe's forthcoming Ridley Scott film *Tripoli*, based on the true story of William Eaton, an American who helped the heir to the throne of Tripoli overthrow a corrupt ruler in the 1800s. The spike Tomahawk was crafted by Rick Guthrie of Saluda, Virginia, and the Otter bag by Gina Connin.

This is a wooden patch box rifle by Gary Brumfield done in the Pennsylvania design. Brumfield is a master gunsmith and part of the Colonial Williamsburg group. He also heads up the school of gun making conducted each year at the university in Kentucky, and is current president of the Contemporary Longrifle Association. "This is a very simple and graceful rifle authentic to the period," says Barlow. The elaborate powder horn and hunting bag were made by Gary Birch of Cincinnati, one of very early pioneers of contemporary horn making, and is now retired. The white hunting shirt is an authentic reproduction researched by Wallace Gusler of Colonial Williamsburg. Gusler has done extensive studies on the American hunting shirt and clothing of the 1700s. This is the most authentic copy of a hunting shirt known to exist. There is also a small tinderbox near the rifle that was recreated by Charlie Miller in Waynesboro, North Carolina. "It just shows the level of craftsmanship and artistry that exists in the Contemporary Longrifle Association today," says Barlow.

This is a rare left-handed American fowler with a handmade lock by Jud Brennan. Barlow notes that it costs around $5,000 to make a lock from scratch! The antiqued fowler looks like it is from the 1700s, as does the antiqued hunting bag by Gary Birch. "He feels the 18th century, he understands the 18th century, and was able to make one of the most remarkable bags ever to exist," says Barlow. "It was made 20 years ago but you'd swear it was made 220 years ago!"

Here is a boy's rifle made by Mel Hankla of Jamestown, Kentucky, and is representative of flintlocks that were occasionally handcrafted for children in the early 19th century. Hankla made it for his son Isaac a decade ago. It is a piece of American history, measuring only 42-inches in overall length yet perfectly scaled to size. Jake Pontfillo of Flushing Queen, New York, made the hunting bag. The backdrop is a pair of child's hunting pants from Gordon Barlow's family dating back to the 18th century, and a 19th century boys shirt.

Frank Bartlett from Castalian Springs, Tennessee, specializes in transitional designs between the German Jaeger, which was popular in America in 1730-40 and the Kentucky longrifle of 1750-60. This is a very heavy sporting rifle with a very large brass guard to provide the additional support necessary to shoulder this firearm. The compass inlay on the left side is in a traditional American style. The unusual hunting bag pictured with the rifle was made by Steve Lalliof.

An unusual mirrored view shows two sides of this unique swivel barrel longrifle built by Jerry Kirklin of Birmingham, Michigan. It is embellished, as would have been swivel breech rifles from the Pennsylvania school of the early 19th century. "Most of these swivel breech designs came from Pennsylvania, and a few from New York," notes Barlow. "Kirklin has created a wonderful representation of this great hunting rifle." Although it is a heavy rifle with dual barrels and locks, it is superbly balanced. David Auker made the powder horn and Stan McLean of Milford, Pennsylvania, crafted the hunting bag. Both are typical designs from the 1820s.

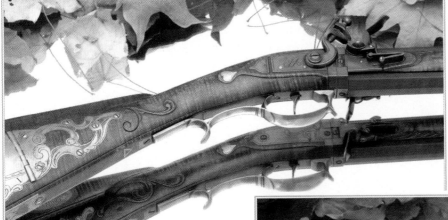

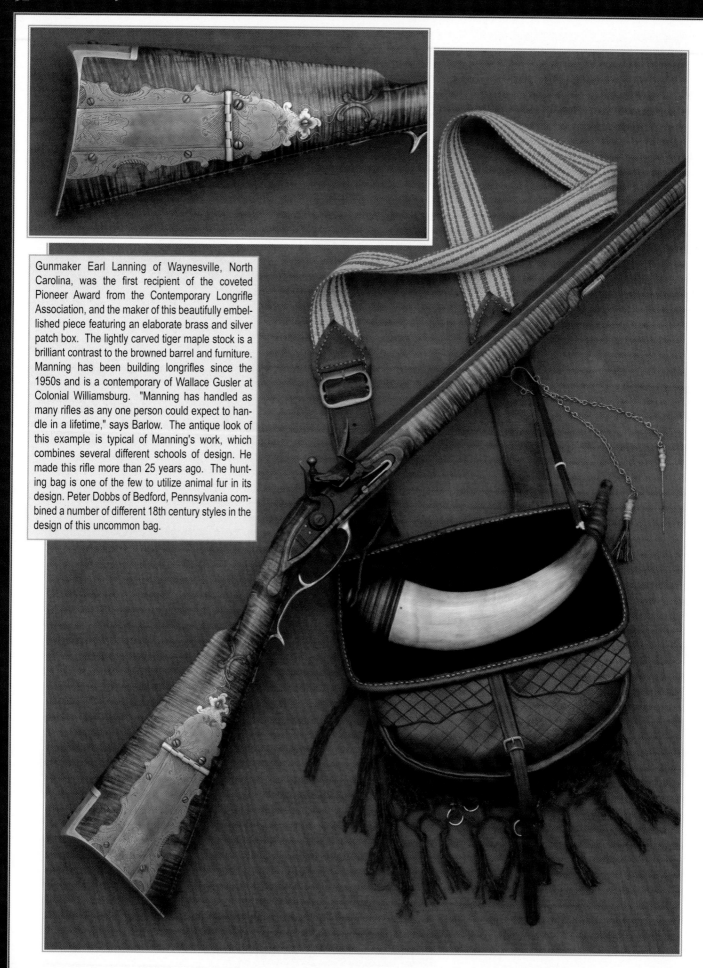

Gunmaker Earl Lanning of Waynesville, North Carolina, was the first recipient of the coveted Pioneer Award from the Contemporary Longrifle Association, and the maker of this beautifully embellished piece featuring an elaborate brass and silver patch box. The lightly carved tiger maple stock is a brilliant contrast to the browned barrel and furniture. Manning has been building longrifles since the 1950s and is a contemporary of Wallace Gusler at Colonial Williamsburg. "Manning has handled as many rifles as any one person could expect to handle in a lifetime," says Barlow. The antique look of this example is typical of Manning's work, which combines several different schools of design. He made this rifle more than 25 years ago. The hunting bag is one of the few to utilize animal fur in its design. Peter Dobbs of Bedford, Pennsylvania combined a number of different 18th century styles in the design of this uncommon bag.

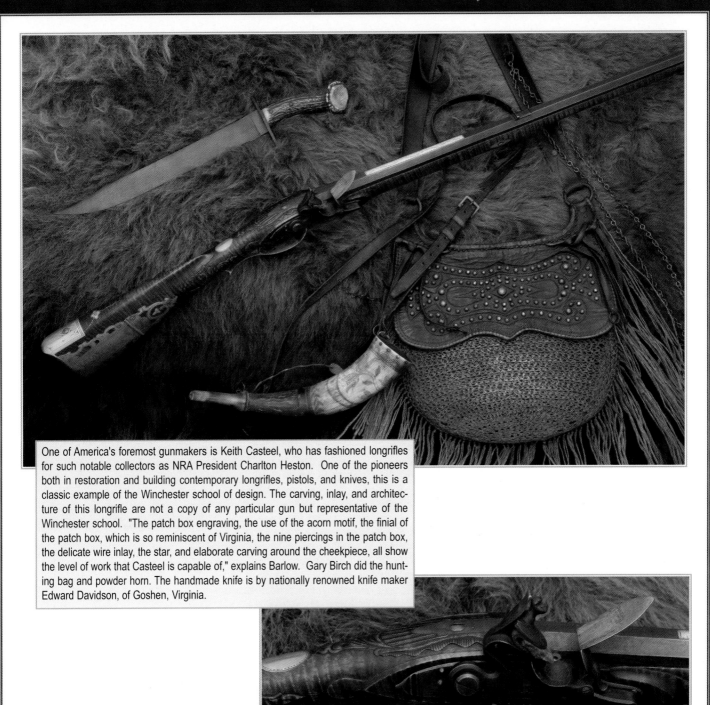

One of America's foremost gunmakers is Keith Casteel, who has fashioned longrifles for such notable collectors as NRA President Charlton Heston. One of the pioneers both in restoration and building contemporary longrifles, pistols, and knives, this is a classic example of the Winchester school of design. The carving, inlay, and architecture of this longrifle are not a copy of any particular gun but representative of the Winchester school. "The patch box engraving, the use of the acorn motif, the finial of the patch box, which is so reminiscent of Virginia, the nine piercings in the patch box, the delicate wire inlay, the star, and elaborate carving around the cheekpiece, all show the level of work that Casteel is capable of," explains Barlow. Gary Birch did the hunting bag and powder horn. The handmade knife is by nationally renowned knife maker Edward Davidson, of Goshen, Virginia.

Herschel House is a pioneer in the contemporary iron mounted Kentucky and Tennessee school of design. "Herschel makes the most spectacular iron mounted rifles, he is the granddaddy of the indus- try," exclaims Barlow. "You would swear this is an original old rifle, and the hardware, the patch box, everything on this rifle except the barrel was forged by House. The iron lock alone on this rifle cost $5,000 to make. If you are lucky enough to be at a show and he walks in and lays something on the table, you'd better buy it now, because 10 minutes later it's gone. Everything Hershel House makes is pre-sold." Of particular note is the shield with eagle set into the cheekpiece. It is House's own design, characteristic of the style seen during the Revolutionary War and the War of 1812. The powder horns and bag are once again a Gary Birch creation. One of the unique features of these particular horns is the heart piercings around the butt plug. The heart was one of the symbols often seen in 18th century America and appears on painted furniture, decorated rifles, and other handmade items of the period.

Another iron-mounted rifle, this one has an unusual figured hickory stock (as opposed to a traditional maple stock), and was built by Mike Schieve of Binghamton, New York. This example features the typical Tennessee patch box style and, while simple in its appearance, is representative of the traditional Tennessee school of design. Jessie Brennan made the bag and horn.

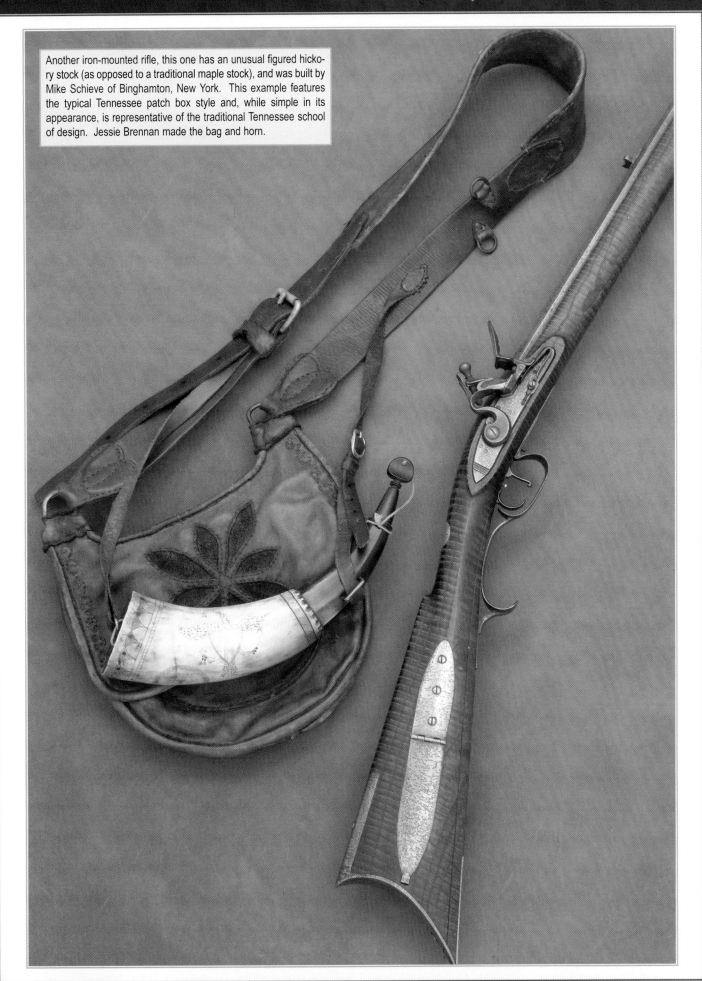

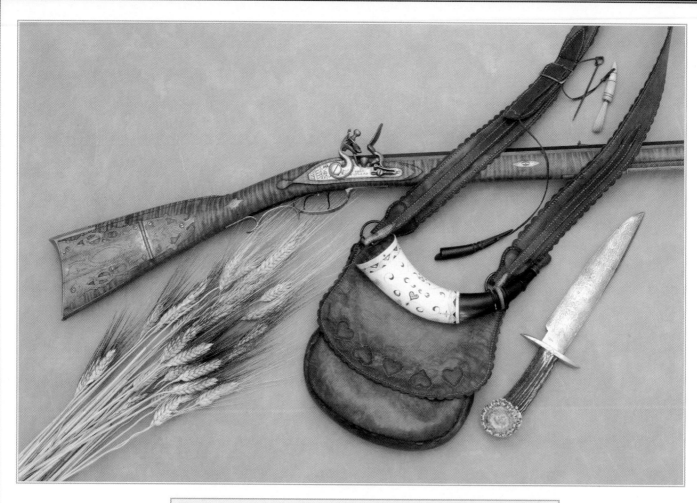

This is a Virginia style rifle built by Louis Smith in Tennessee. It has exceptional engraving and inlay work and a very distinctive lightly finished stock. Not following any specific design, this example incorporates traits from all of the Virginia schools of the 1700s. Jerry Fisher in Friendship, Indiana, made the horn and hand tooled hunting bag. The knife pictured is by Keith Casteel using a damascus blade hammered out by Ed Small.

This is a most unusual rifle in that all of the pieces that would tra-ditionally be metal (except for the lock, stock, and barrel) are made of carved horn. Not surprisingly, the maker, Roland Cadle of Bedford, Pennsylvania, is a horn maker by trade. The trigger guard, patch box, side plate, muzzle piece, butt piece, thimbles, and inlays are all horn! Richard Duvellius of Ohio, crafted the hunt-ing bag, the powder horn is by John Proud of Cortland, New York.

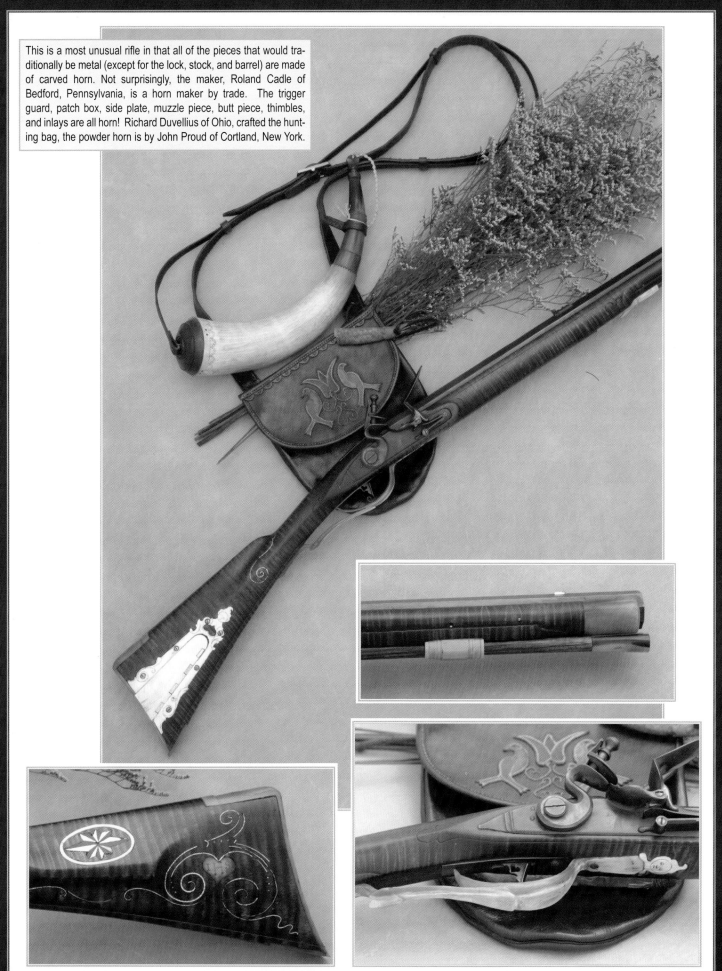

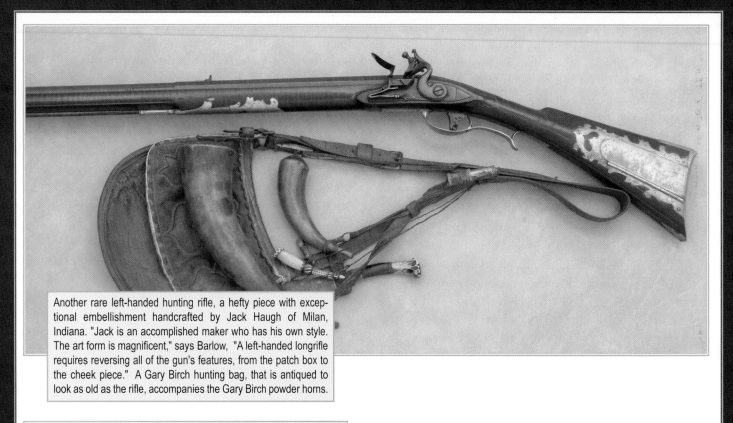

Another rare left-handed hunting rifle, a hefty piece with exceptional embellishment handcrafted by Jack Haugh of Milan, Indiana. "Jack is an accomplished maker who has his own style. The art form is magnificent," says Barlow, "A left-handed longrifle requires reversing all of the gun's features, from the patch box to the cheek piece." A Gary Birch hunting bag, that is antiqued to look as old as the rifle, accompanies the Gary Birch powder horns.

Brian LaMaster of Winchester, Virginia, studied with Wayne Watson and Keith Casteel, and has become an accomplished maker of 18th and 19th century firearms and accoutrements. This beautiful example of his work is from the Winchester school of design and features the traditional acorn and star motif. LaMaster's carving and inlay work are of exceptional quality. The hand-sewn bag is by Jan Riser in Atlanta, and the horn is by Bruce Horne of Bloomington, Illinois, one of the leading horn makers in the world. The canteen is an original from the 17th century.

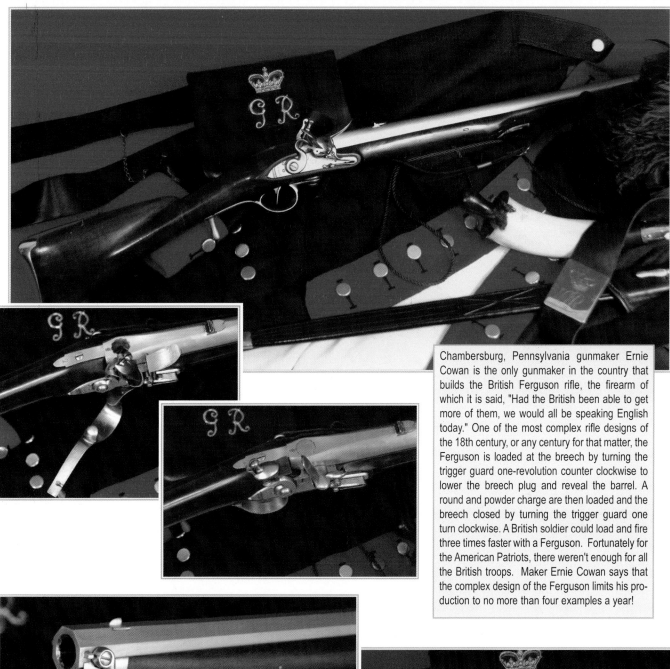

Chambersburg, Pennsylvania gunmaker Ernie Cowan is the only gunmaker in the country that builds the British Ferguson rifle, the firearm of which it is said, "Had the British been able to get more of them, we would all be speaking English today." One of the most complex rifle designs of the 18th century, or any century for that matter, the Ferguson is loaded at the breech by turning the trigger guard one-revolution counter clockwise to lower the breech plug and reveal the barrel. A round and powder charge are then loaded and the breech closed by turning the trigger guard one turn clockwise. A British soldier could load and fire three times faster with a Ferguson. Fortunately for the American Patriots, there weren't enough for all the British troops. Maker Ernie Cowan says that the complex design of the Ferguson limits his production to no more than four examples a year!

Ernie Cowan also builds another rare British fusil, the Pattern 1776 Rifle, which was based on the German Pattern rifle built in Hanover. This example has a swamped octagonal barrel and the innovative swivel ramrod, which made loading more efficient by simply pulling the steel rod from the thimbles, swiveling it over the barrel, tamping down the load and swiveling it back into place. Cowan makes around four to six of the Pattern 1776 rifles yearly in both British and Hanoverian versions.

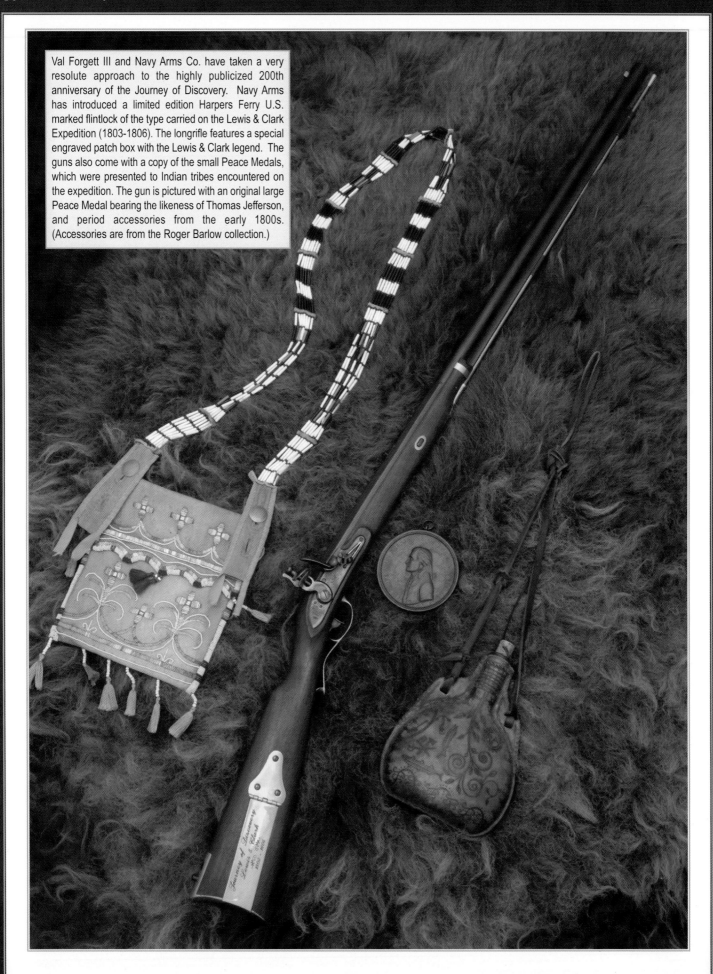

Val Forgett III and Navy Arms Co. have taken a very resolute approach to the highly publicized 200th anniversary of the Journey of Discovery. Navy Arms has introduced a limited edition Harpers Ferry U.S. marked flintlock of the type carried on the Lewis & Clark Expedition (1803-1806). The longrifle features a special engraved patch box with the Lewis & Clark legend. The guns also come with a copy of the small Peace Medals, which were presented to Indian tribes encountered on the expedition. The gun is pictured with an original large Peace Medal bearing the likeness of Thomas Jefferson, and period accessories from the early 1800s. (Accessories are from the Roger Barlow collection.)

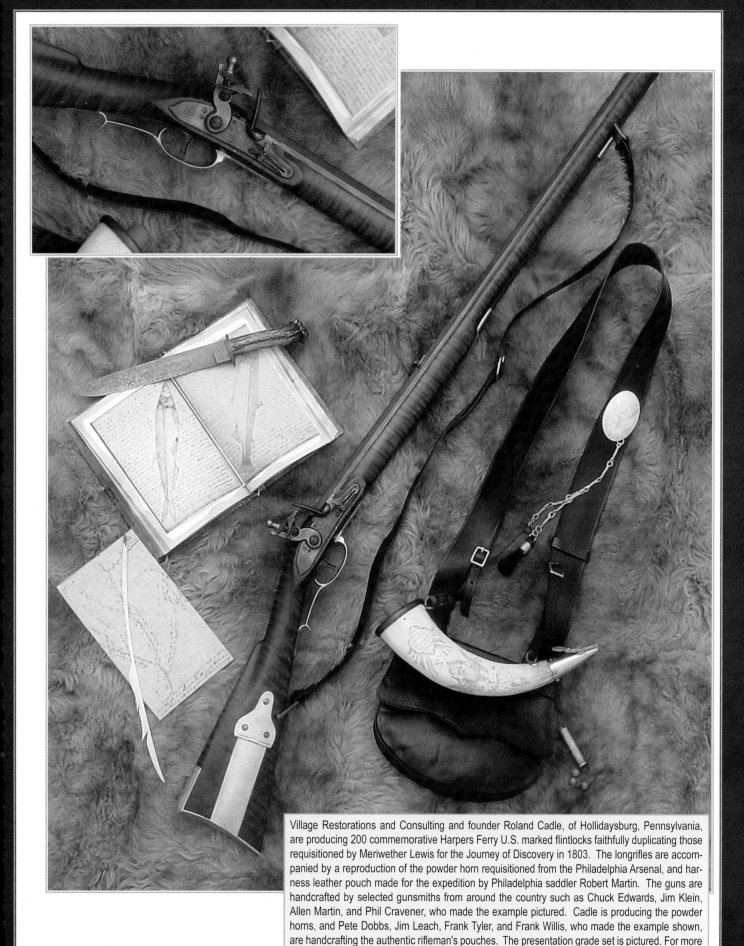

Village Restorations and Consulting and founder Roland Cadle, of Hollidaysburg, Pennsylvania, are producing 200 commemorative Harpers Ferry U.S. marked flintlocks faithfully duplicating those requisitioned by Meriwether Lewis for the Journey of Discovery in 1803. The longrifles are accompanied by a reproduction of the powder horn requisitioned from the Philadelphia Arsenal, and harness leather pouch made for the expedition by Philadelphia saddler Robert Martin. The guns are handcrafted by selected gunsmiths from around the country such as Chuck Edwards, Jim Klein, Allen Martin, and Phil Cravener, who made the example pictured. Cadle is producing the powder horns, and Pete Dobbs, Jim Leach, Frank Tyler, and Frank Willis, who made the example shown, are handcrafting the authentic rifleman's pouches. The presentation grade set is pictured. For more information contact Village Restorations at 814-239-8200 or email villagerestoration@yahoo.com.

Latrobe, Pennsylvania gunmaker Phil Cravener has been building longrifles and pistols longer than most of his contemporaries. Now in his mid sixties, he is focusing his work on Pennsylvania school longrifles and scrimshawed powder horns. Pictured are three examples depicting different schools of design. The top rifle is an early York County design inspired by George Eister, a golden age rifle maker. In the middle is an early Lancaster County rifle with a simple two-piece patch box characteristic of the pre-Revolutionary War period. Bottom is a post 18th century style rifle inspired by George Kettering with some influence by John Fleeger. "During this period there were more gunmakers than customers," says Cravener with a laugh. "The gunmakers gradually increased the engraved brass and silver inlay work and carved decoration to attract the market's attention."

Cravener notes, "Decoration on this post 1800-style rifle demonstrates the extent later smiths went to capture market. Even the carving at the rear ramrod thimble was replaced by elaborate engraved nickel silver inlay. The ramrod was stained in a spiral pattern purely for decoration." The work is exemplary of Cravener's gunmaking style.

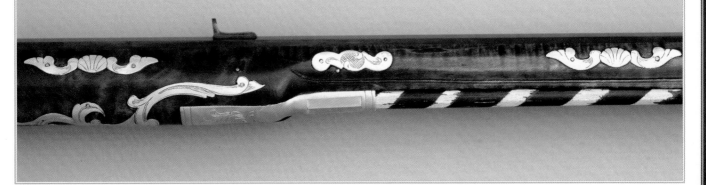

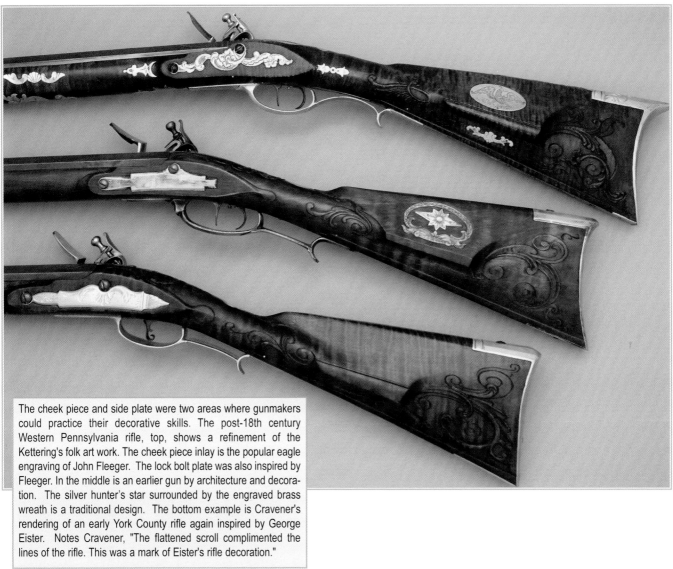

The cheek piece and side plate were two areas where gunmakers could practice their decorative skills. The post-18th century Western Pennsylvania rifle, top, shows a refinement of the Kettering's folk art work. The cheek piece inlay is the popular eagle engraving of John Fleeger. The lock bolt plate was also inspired by Fleeger. In the middle is an earlier gun by architecture and decoration. The silver hunter's star surrounded by the engraved brass wreath is a traditional design. The bottom example is Cravener's rendering of an early York County rifle again inspired by George Eister. Notes Cravener, "The flattened scroll complimented the lines of the rifle. This was a mark of Eister's rifle decoration."

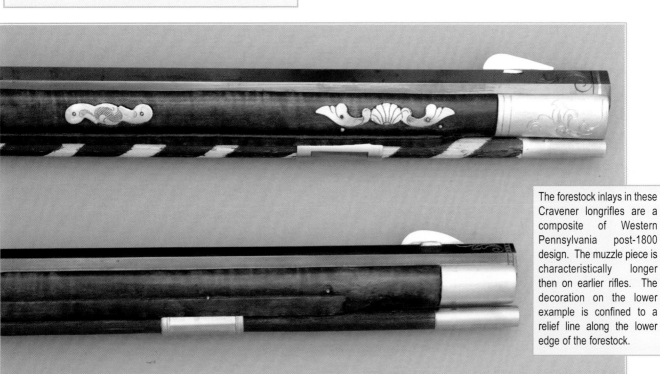

The forestock inlays in these Cravener longrifles are a composite of Western Pennsylvania post-1800 design. The muzzle piece is characteristically longer then on earlier rifles. The decoration on the lower example is confined to a relief line along the lower edge of the forestock.

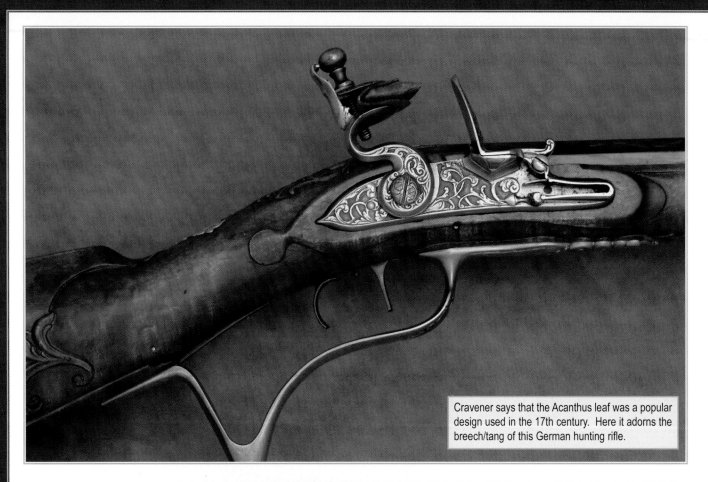

Cravener says that the Acanthus leaf was a popular design used in the 17th century. Here it adorns the breech/tang of this German hunting rifle.

Cravener's rendering of a German hunting rifle of the early 18th century sports a sliding wood patch box cover, relief carving and a chiseled and engraved lock. Notes Cravener, "The carving quality of this period reflected the best of the European Guild system. Many artisans spent their lives doing little else other than carving stocks." The design of the trigger guard, typical of this style of German hunting rifle aided in the support and balance of this hefty flintlock. The contoured, engraved and scrimshawed horn, also made by Cravener, was inspired by the Fort Pitt horn in Jim Dresslar's book *The Engraved Powder Horn*.

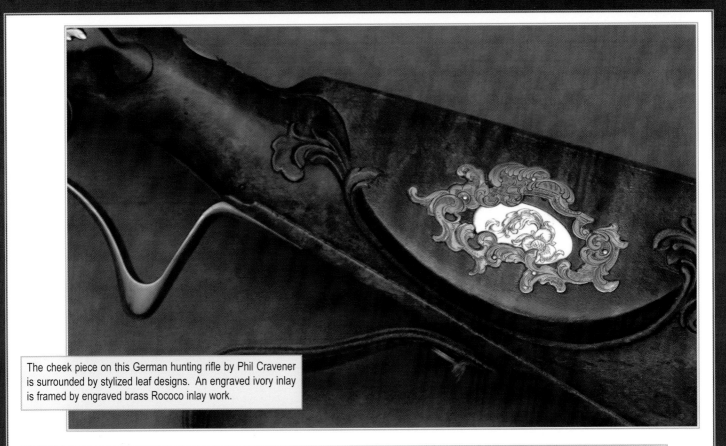

The cheek piece on this German hunting rifle by Phil Cravener is surrounded by stylized leaf designs. An engraved ivory inlay is framed by engraved brass Rococo inlay work.

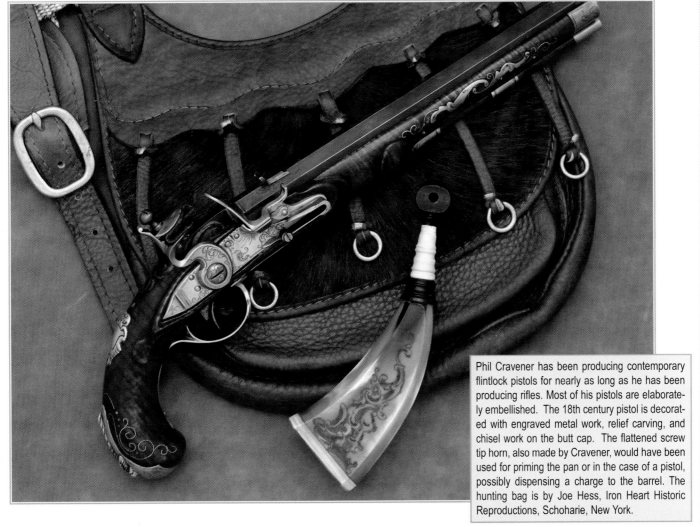

Phil Cravener has been producing contemporary flintlock pistols for nearly as long as he has been producing rifles. Most of his pistols are elaborately embellished. The 18th century pistol is decorated with engraved metal work, relief carving, and chisel work on the butt cap. The flattened screw tip horn, also made by Cravener, would have been used for priming the pan or in the case of a pistol, possibly dispensing a charge to the barrel. The hunting bag is by Joe Hess, Iron Heart Historic Reproductions, Schoharie, New York.

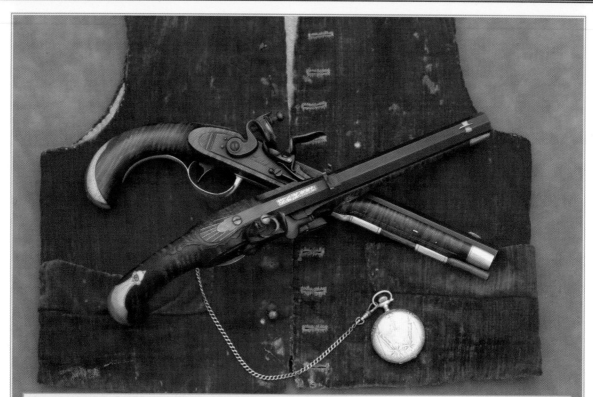

Flintlock pistols by Keith Casteel duplicate the Winchester, Virginia school of design and work by Simon Lauck, who was the master maker at the Winchester School c. 1800. These pistols feature traditional embellishments such as the petal star for the silver escutcheons, the acorn finials on the trigger guards, line engraving on the pistols, silver wire inlay, octagonal faceted thimbles and engraving of the nose cap. Casteel's name is engraved in the barrel and lock.

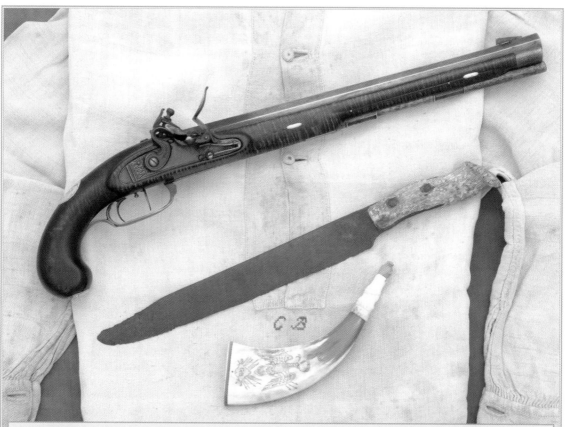

The long barreled Kentucky pistol was a uniquely American design and the great Herschel House of Morgantown, Kentucky built this antique finish contemporary flintlock with iron lock, trigger guard, muzzle piece and thimbles. Roland Cadle, of Hollidaysburg, Pennsylvania, made the flattened powder horn.

Mel Hankla received a grant early in life and went to Morgantown, Kentucky, and spent almost two years studying under Herschel House and learning how to make pistols. A true apprentice of House, Hankla is an accomplished horn maker. This pistol is very similar to the types that were made in Kentucky in the 1700s. Lally House made the quilted knife sheath pictured, and Mark Thomas did the pistol powder flask.

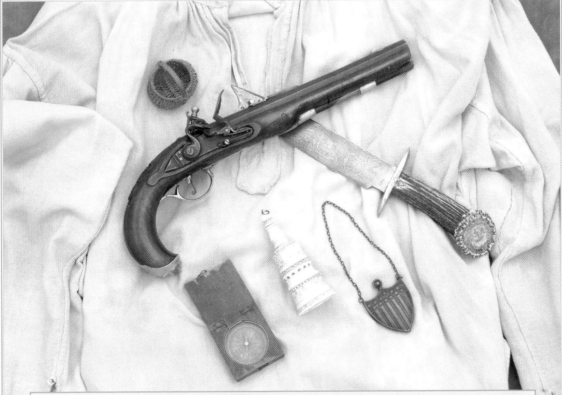

Harrisburg, Pennsylvania gunmaker Wayne Heckert, current president of the Contemporary Longrifle Association, made this traditional Pennsylvania-style pistol of the early 1800s. Gary Birch created the elaborate horn and ivory pistol flask, and Keith Casteel made the knife. Both the compass and flint box are original early 19th century pieces.

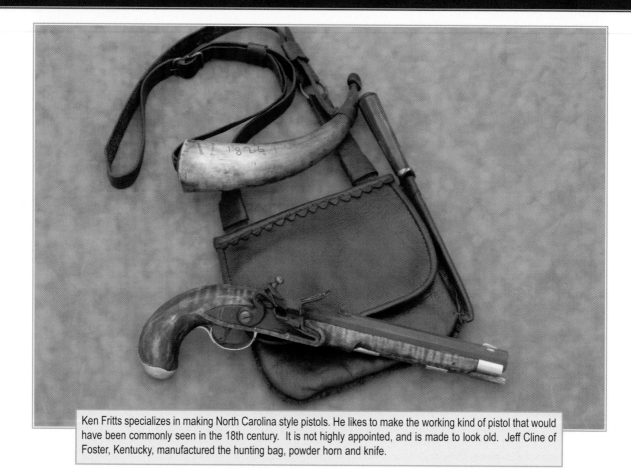

Ken Fritts specializes in making North Carolina style pistols. He likes to make the working kind of pistol that would have been commonly seen in the 18th century. It is not highly appointed, and is made to look old. Jeff Cline of Foster, Kentucky, manufactured the hunting bag, powder horn and knife.

This is a remarkable gun in that the lock is originally from a late 17th century English pistol. Well-known Pennsylvania gunmaker William Kennedy took the lock and fashioned a new and period correct pistol around it. The gun features exceptional baroque woodcarving and a barrel that goes from eight-sided octagon, to 16-sided octagon, to 32-sided octagon, to round. The antiques finish and furniture make it look like a 320-year old gun. An original sword and accessories from the pre-Revolutionary War period, c. 1750, surround it. Kennedy has been making guns for almost 30 years and has built at least 200 custom flintlocks over that period.

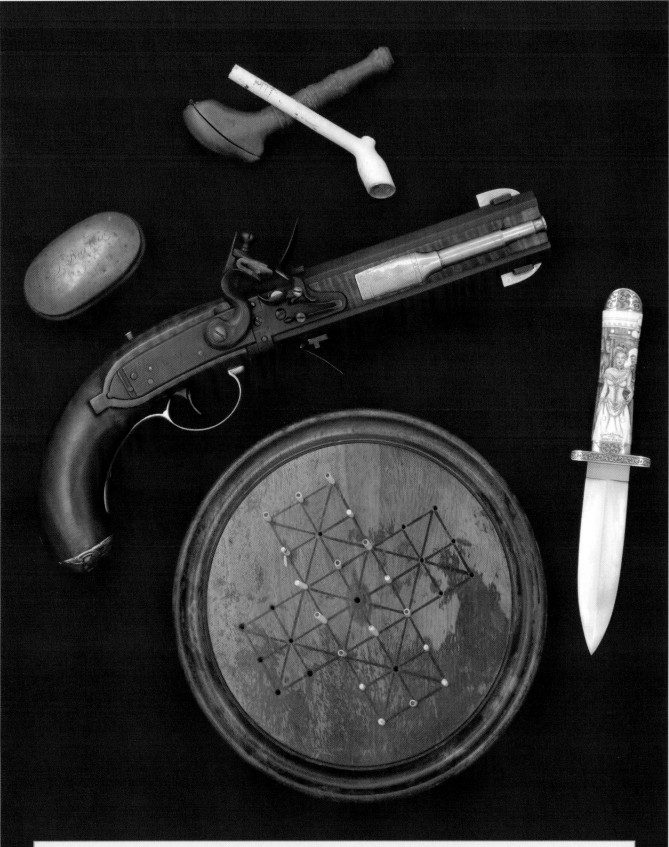

The swivel barrel rifle and pistol were designed to allow a quick second shot and were amongst the earliest multiple shot designs of the 18th century. Leonard Day of Westhampton, Massachusetts, created this example more than 20 years ago. "It is hard to show the brilliance of this design," says Barlow, "it is as American as it gets with the beautiful full length wood and brass ramrod." Day has made some of the finest contemporary longrifles and pistols of the last half-century, and though he considers himself "semi-retired," he continues to accept private commissions. (To learn more about Leonard Day see the Second Edition *Blue Book of Modern Black Powder Values*, pages 34, 35 and 36).

No matter how much changed over the centuries, from the matchlock, to the wheel lock to flintlock, they all needed powder, and the powder flask and powder horn were the vessels of choice for more than 400 years. During the late 16th century and throughout the 17th, 18th, and early 19th centuries, the horn was a requisite accoutrement. Pictured are 17th century style horns (from top to bottom) by Mark Thomas, Jud Brennan, and Bruce Horne, all members of the Honorable Company of Horners. "The powder horn is essentially a document of its time, depicting maps, battles, and travel. They each tell their own story," explains Barlow.

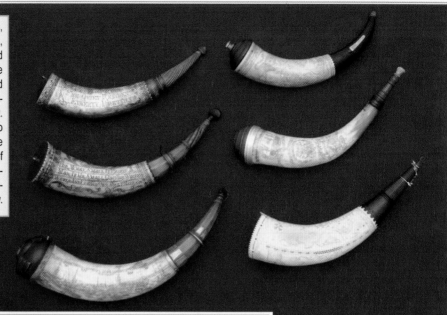

Most of the horns pictured represent the period from the 1750s to the 1820s. Some are of the folk art design, other from the French & Indian War period. Pictured left top to bottom decorative and map horns by Phil Cravener, Ron Ehlert, and Joe Scott. Right top to bottom, horns by Lee Larkin, John Barrett, and Kathy and Scott Sibley.

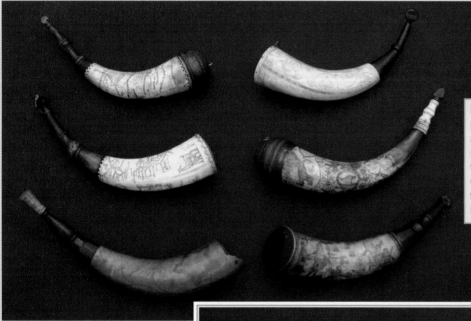

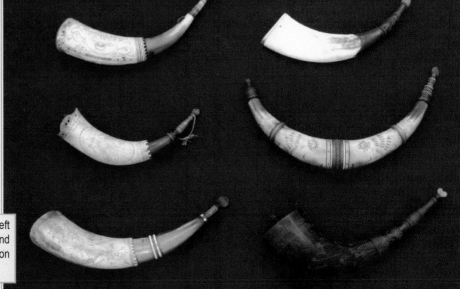

A variety of powder horn styles pictured from left top to bottom by Mark Odel, Gary Birch, and Dave Price, and right top to bottom by Gordon Barlow, Tom White, and Willy Frankfort.

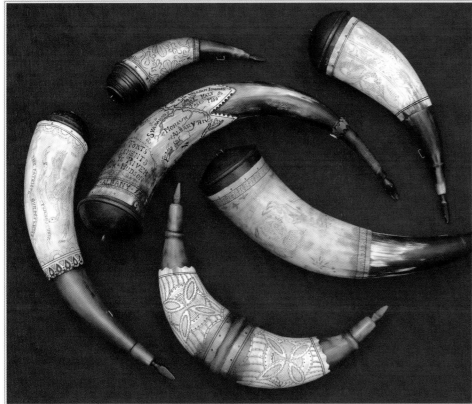

One of the leading horn, knife, and Tomahawk makers in Pennsylvania is Steven Shroyer of Bedford. Shroyer has been producing exceptional work for close to 30 years. Pictured are six of his traditional period designs. Pictured clockwise from the top, the smallest horn is a very common German folk art style with a relief carved tip. The largest horn (top center) gives a good view of the butt plug, which in the U.S. was usually made of cherry or walnut, "but cherry was the most preferred," says Shroyer. This large powder horn is a map horn showing the counties of Albany, New York, and all of waterways and settlements. The scrimshawed map leads to a "fish mouth" and the tapered curve of the horn. Measuring over 19 inches, Shroyer says that this is a typical size. The horn at the top right is a Pennsylvania folk art style. The next horn down is another of the largest sizes and is elaborately scrimshawed with maps, military figures, inscriptions, and a coat of arms. This is a British military style horn that might have been carried by an officer. The unusual double horn is adhered together with a wooden band that lets powder pass through from one side to the other. The horn has two stem plugs and the scrimshawing one side is exactly duplicated on the opposite. The last example is a Revolutionary War style horn. It features an eagle clutching the *E. Pluribus Unum* banner in its talons, and below, the legend, *The Patriots, Our Defenders*. The horn is stained with dyes to create the colors.

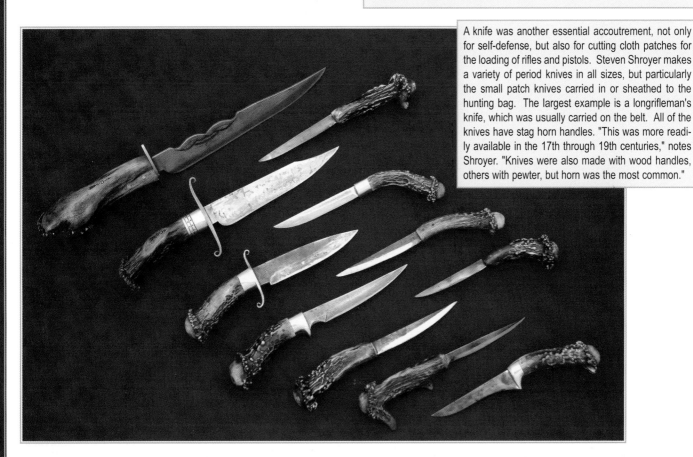

A knife was another essential accoutrement, not only for self-defense, but also for cutting cloth patches for the loading of rifles and pistols. Steven Shroyer makes a variety of period knives in all sizes, but particularly the small patch knives carried in or sheathed to the hunting bag. The largest example is a longrifleman's knife, which was usually carried on the belt. All of the knives have stag horn handles. "This was more readily available in the 17th through 19th centuries," notes Shroyer. "Knives were also made with wood handles, others with pewter, but horn was the most common."

Anatomy of a Flintlock

By Wallace B. Gusler

Photography by Dennis Adler

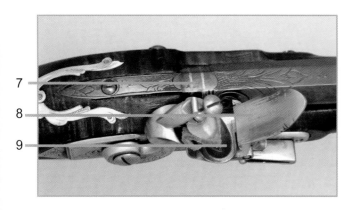

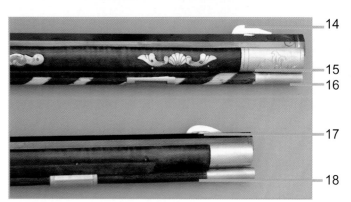

There are various terminologies for the individual components which make up a flintlock. Over time, some of the names have been changed but the original nomenclatures, penned in the early 18th century, are the most descriptive and colorful.

A longrifle was customarily called "she," indicating the feminine, but the parts which make up the Longrifle are either masculine or feminine in name depending upon their purpose, and this was not by coincidence. The terminologies and explanations which follow have been used for more than three centuries.

1. Hindsight. The rearmost sight on the longrifle.
2. Box. The patch box and patch box cover. (All original terms.)
3. Tricker. The trigger.
4. Guard. The trigger guard.
5. Cock. Also known as the hammer in modern terminology.
6. Lock. Containing cock, pan, and frizzen. The plate on the opposite side of the stock is called the side plate.
7. Breech.
8. Steel. Also known as the hammer or frizzen.
9. Pan. The touch hole is located in the side of the barrel and allows the spark from the pan to ignite the powder charge in the barrel.
10. Heel. Top of the butt piece.
11. Butt Piece.
12. Toe. Bottom of the butt piece.
13. The stock, from the breech back to the butt piece can also be called the breech and carved stocks have been noted as being "flourished in the breech." Contemporary nomenclature refers to this part as the butt stock and cheek piece.
14. Barrel. Octagonal barrels were known as square barrels. Rifling was originally known as lands and furrows, an agricultural term.
15. Muzzle Piece.
16. Rammer. Also ramrod.
17. Foresight.
18. Thimble. The rearmost Thimble on the longrifle was known as the tail piece in the 18th and 19th century.

A SECTION

Federal, state, and local regulations regarding black powder muzzleloaders may vary from state to state. Please contact a local gun dealer or law enforcement agency for information on regulations in your area.

All price add-ons for special orders and options are based on the manufacturer's suggested list prices without potential dealer discounting. Engraving prices on less than 100% condition reproductions and replicas should be discounted by a minimum of 50%.

ALLEN FIREARMS

Previous importer located in Santa Fe, NM, importing Aldo Uberti & Co. reproductions and replicas until early in 1987.

After Allen Firearms closed, Old-West Gun Co., now Cimarron F.A. located in Fredericksburg, TX, purchased the remaining inventory. Since all guns sold by Allen Firearms were manufactured by Uberti (they even used the same catalog), please refer to Uberti in the U section of this text.

For more information and current pricing on Allen Firearms line of firearms, please refer to the 24th Ed. *Blue Book of Gun Values* by S.P. Fjestad (now online also).

AMERICA REMEMBERS

Current organization located in Ashland, VA, that privately commissions historical, limited/ special editions in conjunction with various manufacturers. Previously located in Mechanicsville, VA, until 1999. Consumer direct sales.

America Remembers is a private non-governmental organization dedicated to the remembrance of notable Americans and important historical American events. Along with its affiliates, the Armed Forces Commemorative Society®, American Heroes and Legends®, and the United States Society of Arms and Armour™, the company produces special issue limited edition firearms. America Remembers purchased the antique arms division of the U.S. Historical Society on April 1, 1994. Older U.S.H.S. reproductions and replicas can be located in the U section of this text.

Please refer to *Colt Blackpowder Reproductions & Replicas—A Collector's & Shooter's Guide* for color pictures of the America Remembers pistols described below. America Remembers Colt commemoratives can be found on pages 90, 99, 100, 102, 105, 110, and 111.

For more information and current pricing on America Remembers firearms, please refer to the 24th Ed. *Blue Book of Gun Values* by S.P. Fjestad (now online also).

LIMITED/SPECIAL EDITIONS

Values listed below reflect America Remembers official issue prices, listed as Last issue price. These do not necessarily represent secondary marketplace prices. No other values are listed since America Remembers limited/special editions do not appear that frequently in the secondary marketplace. This is because America Remembers typically sells to consumers directly, without involving normal gun dealers and distributors. Because of this consumer direct sales program, many gun dealers do not have a working knowledge about what America Remembers models are currently selling for. The publisher suggests that those people owning America Remembers limited/special editions contact America Remembers (see Trademark Index) for current information, including secondary marketplace liquidity.

REVOLVERS: PERCUSSION

While not specifically mentioned, the revolvers listed below all have various degrees of ornamentation and other embellishments (including some inscriptions).

AMERICAN EAGLE 1860 ARMY - .44 cal. perc., engraved cylinder, American Eagle highlighting the barrel, color case hardened frame, hammer and loading lever, 24Kt. gold plated backstrap, front sight, and trigger guard, silver plated trigger. Edition limited to 500. Mfg. by Uberti.

Last issue price was $1,795.

CALIFORNIA SESQUICENTENNIAL TRIBUTE WALKER REVOLVER - .44 cal. perc. Edition limited to 150 beginning 2000. Mfg. by Colt Blackpowder Arms Co.

Last issue price was $1,895.

C.S.S. H.L. HUNLEY 1851 NAVY REVOLVER - .36 cal. perc. Edition limited to 750. Mfg. by Uberti.

Last issue price was $1,795.

JOHNNY CASH TEXAS PATERSON - .36 cal. perc. Edition limited to 1000. Mfg. by Uberti.

Last issue price was $1,500.

GETTYSBURG 1863 REVOLVER - .44 cal. perc., 1860 Army commemorating the July 1863 battle. This model features a 24Kt. gold battle scene surrounding the rebated cylinder. The left side of the barrel bears the legend "GETTYSBURG PENNSYLVANIA JULY 1863". On the right side is an inscription from Lincoln's Gettysburg Address, "We here highly resolve that these dead shall not have died in vain." The backstrap, trigger guard and front sight blade are 24Kt. gold plated. A French fit solid walnut display case contains the revolver and both Union and Confederate belt buckles in solid brass, and a parchment paper replica of the Gettysburg Address. Edition limited to 1,863. Mfg. by Uberti.

Last issue price was $1,395.

HISTORIC U.S. NAVY TRIBUTE 1851 NAVY - .36 cal. perc., cylinder engraved with naval battle scene in gold and nickel silver, decorated barrel lug, recoil shield, frame, and barrel, 24Kt. gold plated hammer, trigger guard, and backstrap. Edition limited to 500. Mfg. by Uberti.

Last issue price was $1,595.

LONE STAR TRIBUTE WALKER .44 - .44 cal. perc., deep black finish and 24Kt. gold embellishment with portraits of Houston, Austin, and Seguin on the left barrel lug, "Victory or Death" and the Alamo on the left frame, Bowie, Travis, and Crockett on the right barrel lug. Texas longhorns on the right frame, medallions on the cylinder and the legend "Come and Take it" on the backstrap. The top of the barrel lug has "Texas" written over it, bordered by "The Lone Star State" and "1845 The 28th State." Edition limited to 150. Mfg. by Uberti.

Last issue price was $1,795.

TEXAS RANGER DRAGOON - .44 cal. perc., Whitneyville Hartford Dragoon embellished with the portrait of Col. Jack Hayes on the left barrel lug, the barrel bears the legend "TEXAS RANGERS HALL OF FAME AND MUSEUM", silver plated cylinder, backstrap, trigger guard, and medallion inset on the left grip inscribed "Free as the breeze, Swift as a Mustang, Tough as a cactus." Cased with a gold plated 3rd Generation Colt Signature Series powder flask, blue bullet mold, combination tool and Eley Bros. cap tin. Edition limited to 1000. Mfg. by Uberti.

Last issue price was $1,795.

WALKER SESQUICENTENNIAL TRIBUTE REVOLVER - .44 cal. perc., deep black finish, embellished with 24Kt. Gold portraits of Sam Colt, Capt. Sam Walker, Eli Whitney, Jr., medallions on the cylinder, banner along barrel, 24Kt. gold plated backstrap, hammer, trigger guard, ebony grips. Edition limited to 300. Mfg. by Uberti.

Last issue price was $1,695.

WHITNEYVILLE HARTFORD SESQUICENTENNIAL DRAGOON - .44 cal. perc., Colt blue finish, nickel silver embellishment with portraits of Sam Colt and Eli Whitney, Jr. on the barrel lugs, Sesquicentennial banner along barrel, action figures on cylinder finished in nickel silver against blue background, Hartford Conn. medallion inset into both grips, vine scroll engraving and eagle's head on backstrap, serial number XXX of 100 engraved on the bottom of the trigger guard. Color case hardened frame, hammer, and loading lever, silver backstrap and trigger guard. Designed by Dennis Adler and America Remembers, and cased in a two-drawer cabinet French fit for the gun, with a pull out drawer containing a signed leather bound and numbered edition of Dennis Adler's book, *Colt Blackpowder Reproductions & Replicas—A Collector's & Shooter's Guide.* Edition limited to 100. Mfg. by Colt Blackpowder Arms Co.

Last issue price was $1,895.

TEXAS RANGER WALKER COLT REVOLVER - .44 cal. perc., deep black finish 3RD Generation Colt Blackpowder Arms Walker embellished with gold-plated barrel, backstrap and trigger guard, etched 24-kt gold portraits of legendary Texas Rangers Samuel Walker and John Coffee Hays flank a group photograph dating from the late 1800s on the left barrel lug, portraits of Bill McDonald and William A. Wallace on the right barrel lug, and gold plated figures on the roll engraved cylinder. The gun is further embellished with Texas Rangers etched along the the length of the barrel and the Texas Ranger Hall of Fame and Museum logo on the backstrap along with classic 19th century scroll engraving. Edition limited to 300. New 2000. Mfg. by Uberti.

Last issue price was $1,895.

PATERSON BELT MODEL REVOLVER - .36 cal. perc., antique blue finish, antique gray finish, or charcoal blue finish, Belt Model based on the Ehlers Fifth or New Model No. 2 revolver. The first in America Remembers' new Heritage Series, offering never before reproduced Colt models, the Paterson features the unique Ehlers-type backstrap and grip design, short 3.5 in. octagonal barrel and early Paterson-style loading lever. Designed by Dennis Adler, handcrafted by R.L. Millington from Uberti Paterson components. Hand finished and cased with accessories in a period style French fit, solid walnut presentation box built by Pennsylvania furniture maker Duncan Everhart, each Paterson revolver has the appearance of an aged original pistol. Edition limited to 100. New 2001.

Last issue price was $1,695.

Add $125 for antique gray or charcoal blue finish.

RIFLES: PERCUSSION

THOMPSON CENTER HISTORIC WHITETAIL MUZZLELOADER - .50 cal. perc. Edition limited to 300. Mfg. by Thompson Center Arms, Co.

Last issue price was $1,495.

MODEL 1853 CONFEDERATE ENFIELD - .58 cal. perc. Edition limited to 500. Mfg. by Armi Sport.

Last issue price was $1,900.

AMERICAN ARMS, INC.

Previous importer and manufacturer located in N. Kansas City, MO, until 2000.

American Arms also imported a line of black powder revolvers manufactured by Pietta, and a line of lever action rifles by Uberti. Please refer to the individual manufacturer's listings for pricing.

For more information and current pricing on American Arms, Inc. firearms, please refer to the 24th Ed. *Blue Book of Gun Values* by S.P. Fjestad (now online also).

GRADING	100%	98%	95%	90%	80%	70%	60%

RIFLES: IN-LINE IGNITION

HAWKEYE - .50 or .54 cal. perc., 22 in. round blue or stainless steel barrel, dual safety contemporary styled design, stock has rubber recoil pad. Disc. 1993.

$265	**$220**	**$175**

Last MSR was $275.

Add $120 for stainless steel.

AMERICAN FRONTIER FIREARMS MFG., INC.

Previous manufacturer located in Aguanga, CA.

Although these were cartridge firing revolvers, they were converted Colt and Remington black powder pistols. The guns were hand-assembled and finished from parts specially cast in Italy for American Frontier Firearms. Last produced in 2000. Only available on secondary market.

Since these are cartridge firing revolvers converted from black powder reproduction pistols, and require a FFL to transfer, these listings will be moved to the 25th Edition *Blue Book of Gun Values* by S.P. Fjestad after this edition.

REVOLVERS: CARTRIDGE CONVERSIONS & OPEN TOP

1851 NAVY RICHARDS CONVERSION - .38 Special, .38 Long Colt, .44 Russian, or .44 Colt cal., 4.75, 5.5, or 7.5 in. octagon barrel, (roll) engraved cylinder, blue steel finish, varnished walnut grips. No ejector rod.

$715	**$550**	**$425**

Last MSR was $795.

1851 NAVY RICHARDS & MASON CONVERSION - .38 Special, .38 Long Colt, .44 Russian, or .44 Colt cal., 4.75, 5.5, or 7.5 in. octagon barrel with Mason ejector assembly, (roll) engraved cylinder, blue steel finish, varnished walnut grips.

$715	**$550**	**$425**

Last MSR was $795.

GRADING	100%	98%	95%	90%	80%	70%	60%

1860 ARMY RICHARDS CONVERSION - .38 Special, .38 Long Colt, or .44 Colt cal., 4.75, 5.5, or 7.5 in. round barrel, with or without ejector assembly, engraved (roll) cylinder, blue steel finish, silver plated trigger guard, varnished walnut grips.

	$715	$550	$425

Last MSR was $795.

1861 NAVY RICHARDS CONVERSION - .38 Special, or .38 Long Colt cal., 4.5 or 7.5 in. round barrel with ejector assembly, blue steel finish, silver plated backstrap and trigger guard, varnished walnut grips.

	$715	$550	$425

Last MSR was $795.

1871-72 OPEN TOP FRONTIER MODEL - .38 Special, .38 Long Colt, or .44 Colt cal., 4.75, 5.5, or 7.5 in. round barrel with ejector assembly, blue steel finish, varnished walnut grips.

	$715	$550	$425

Last MSR was $795.

POCKET NAVY RICHARDS & MASON CONVERSION - .32 cal., 4.5 in. octagon barrel with ejector assembly, blue steel finish, silver plated backstrap and trigger guard, color case hardened trigger and hammer, varnished walnut grips.

	$445	$375	$275

Last MSR was $495.

1858 REMINGTON NEW ARMY CAVALRY MODEL - .38 Special, .44 Colt or .45 Long Colt cal., 7.5 in. barrel with ejector assembly, blue steel finish, color case hardened hammer, varnished walnut grips.

	$715	$550	$425

Last MSR was $795.

1858 REMINGTON NEW ARMY ARTILLERY MODEL - .38 Special, .44 Colt and .45 Long Colt cal., 5.5 in. barrel with ejector assembly, blue steel finish, color case hardened hammer, varnished walnut grips.

	$715	$550	$425

Last MSR was $795.

1858 REMINGTON ORIGINAL FACTORY-TYPE CONVERSION - .38 Special, .44 Colt, or .45 Long Colt cal., 5.5 or 7.5 in. barrels, original loading lever and no gate or ejector assembly, blue steel finish, color case hardened hammer, varnished walnut grips.

	$715	$550	$425

Last MSR was $795.

POCKET REMINGTON - .22, .32, or .38 Special cal., 3.5 barrel with or without ejector rod or gate, blue steel finish, color case hardened hammer, varnished walnut grips.

	$445	$375	$275

Last MSR was $495.

AMERICAN HISTORICAL FOUNDATION, THE

Current private organization which privately commissions historical commemoratives in conjunction with leading manufacturers and craftsmen around the world. The Foundation is located in Richmond, VA. Consumer direct sales only, via phone, correspondence, or personal visit.

The Foundation's limited edition models are not all manufactured at one time. Rather, guns are fabricated as demand dictates to always keep availability below demand.

Please refer to *Colt Blackpowder Reproductions & Replicas—A Collector's & Shooter's Guide* for color pictures of the American Historical Foundation pistols described below.

For more information on The American Historical Foundation firearms, please refer to the 24th Ed. *Blue Book of Gun Values* by S.P. Fjestad (now online also).

LIMITED/SPECIAL EDITIONS

Values listed below reflect the Foundation's original or most recent issue prices. These do not necessarily represent secondary marketplace prices. No other values are listed since the Foundation's limited/special editions do not appear that frequently in the secondary marketplace. This is because the Foundation has always sold to consumers directly, without involving normal gun dealers and distributors. Foundation collectors include museums, veterans, and other interested parties who normally keep these items for a considerable time period. Because of this consumer direct sales program, many gun dealers do not have a working knowledge about what AHF models are currently selling for. The publisher suggests that those people owning the Foundation's Commemorative Issue models contact the Foundation (see Trademark Index) for current information, including secondary marketplace liquidity.

REVOLVERS: PERCUSSION

While not specifically mentioned, the revolvers listed below all have various degrees of ornamentation and other embellishments (including some inscriptions). Values listed below do not include original display cases (typically priced between $179 and $395).

TEXAS PATERSON - .36 cal. perc., 9 in. barrel, frame and barrel lug hand engraved in Gustav Young style, entire gun 24Kt. gold plated. In presentation case with spare cylinder, powder charger, circular capper, combination tool and cleaning rod. Edition limited to 950. Mfg. by Pedersoli.

Last issue price was $2,195.

1848 WALKER - .44 cal. perc., barrel, frame, and barrel lug, loading lever, hammer, trigger guard and backstrap hand engraved in Gustav Young style, entire gun 24Kt. gold plated. In presentation case with spare cylinder, powder flask, bullet mold, and combination tool. Edition limited to 950. Mfg. by Uberti.

Last issue price was $2,195.

THE BLUE AND THE GRAY DRAGOONS - .44 cal. perc., individually cased set offered as "The Blue" and "The Gray". "The Blue" is hand-engraved in the vine scroll motif with a gold inlaid US on the barrel lug, and "E PLURIBUS UNUM" engraved in the barrel. The backstrap and trigger guard are 24Kt. gold plated. Cased with powder flask, combination tool, and bullet mold. The Confederate counterpart, "The Gray" has an antique gray finish with duplicate engraving, except for a Confederate emblem on the barrel lug, and the words "DEO VINDICE" on the barrel. Both models were manufactured by Colt and priced separately.

Last issue price was $2,495.

A second series was also produced with a 24Kt. gold plated Union 3rd Model Dragoon fully engraved, and a silver plated Confederate 2nd Model Dragoon. This pair was done to commemorate the 125th Anniversary of the Civil War. Priced separately.

Last issue price was $2,495.

1849 WELLS FARGO - .31 cal. perc., barrel, lug, frame, hammer, backstrap and trigger guard fully engraved in vine scroll motif and plated in 24Kt. gold. Excellent relief of the roll engraved cylinder scene. Edition limited to 950. Mfg. by Uberti.

Last issue price was $1,995.

JEFFERSON DAVIS 1851 NAVY WITH SHOULDER STOCK - .36 cal. perc., barrel, frame, barrel lug, loading lever, hammer, trigger guard, backstrap and all metal surfaces of shoulder stock superbly hand engraved in Gustav Young style. Copied from an original 1851 Navy presented to Jefferson Davis by Samuel Colt, when Davis was U.S. Secretary of War in 1858. Available with a full-length gray velvet lined presentation case allowing the gun to be displayed with the shoulder stock attached. The case also provides for a powder flask, bullet mold, combination tool, and two covered compartments for accessories. This is the most sought after and difficult to find model ever produced by The American Historical Foundation. Edition limited to 250. Display case was an additional $395. Mfg. by Uberti.

Last issue price was $2,995.

GEN. ROBERT E. LEE MODEL 1851 NAVY - .36 cal. perc., engraved tribute model commemorating the great Confederate military commander. Edition limited to 1000. Mfg. by Uberti.

Last issue price was $2,195.

WILD BILL HICKOK MODEL 1851 NAVY - .36 cal. perc., hand engraved scrollwork on barrel lug, loading lever, frame, backstrap and trigger guard, silver plated and fitted with engraved ivory stocks; a tribute to the "Prince of Pistoleers." The 1851 Navy was also sold as a pair (Hickok always carried two) displayed in a French fit, glass-top case, with the "Deadman's Hand" (Aces and Eights), and two simulated badges from Hickok's career as a frontier lawman. Edition limited to 500. Guns were priced separately, as was the display case. Mfg. by Uberti.

Last issue price was $1,195.

COLT GOLDEN TRIBUTE MODEL 1860 ARMY - .44 cal. perc., barrel, lug, frame, loading lever, hammer, backstrap and trigger guard engraved in vine scroll motif and plated in 24Kt. gold. Banner along the barrel inscribed "COLONEL SAMUEL COLT." Edition limited to 950. Mfg. by Colt.

Last issue price was $1,195.

COL. J. S. MOSBY MODEL 1860 ARMY - .44 cal. perc., barrel, lug, frame, loading lever, hammer, backstrap and trigger guard fully engraved in vine scroll motif, with Confederate flag engraved above the wedge, Colonel John Singleton Mosby engraved in script along the barrel, 24Kt. gold plated cylinder, hammer, and trigger. Remainder of gun finished in sterling silver. A striking commemorative pistol in a French fit case. Edition limited to 150. Mfg. by Colt.

Last issue price was $2,495.

JOHNNY REB BILLY YANK UNION AND CONFEDERATE SET - .36 cal. perc. (Navy) or .44 cal. perc. (Army), barrels, cylinders, and frames engraved in Union and Confederate themes and vine scroll motifs. Confederate model plated in sterling silver, Union model in 24Kt. gold. Edition limited to 250 of each.

COLT GOLDEN TRIBUTE 1862 POCKET POLICE - .36 cal. perc., barrel, lug, frame, hammer, backstrap and trigger guard engraved in vine scroll motif and plated in 24Kt. gold. Cased with gold plated bullet mold, powder flask, and combination tool. Edition limited to 950.

Last issue price was $1,895.

J.E.B. STUART LEMAT - .44 cal. perc. and grapeshot barrels, cylinder, barrels and frame etched in 24Kt. gold with Confederate emblems, scrollwork, crossed sabers, and GEN. J.E.B. STUART on the grapeshot barrel. Loading lever, trigger, grip screw, and lanyard ring plated in 24Kt. gold. Edition limited to 500. Mfg. by Navy Arms.

Last issue price was $2,895.

GEN. THOMAS J. "STONEWALL" JACKSON LEMAT - .44 cal. perc. and grapeshot barrels, cylinder, barrels and frame etched in 24Kt. gold with Confederate emblems, scrollwork, crossed sabers, and "GEN. STONEWALL JACKSON" engraved on the grapeshot barrel. Edition limited to 500.

Last issue price was $2,895.

AMERICAN WESTERN ARMS, INC.

Current trademark and importer located in Del Ray Beach, FL, previously located in El Paso, Texas. Manufacturing is located in Gardone, Italy, beginning 2000.

American Western Arms, Co., purchased Armi San Marco and formed American Western Arms Italia, to manufacture authentic Colt SAA models, and Richards-Mason-type cartridge conversions of the Colt 1851 Navy, 1860 Army, 1861 Navy, and 1872 Open Top. After a short production run, the cartridge conversion models were discontinued in order to increase production of the 1873 Colt Single Action Army.

Since these are cartridge firing revolvers converted from black powder reproduction pistols, and require a FFL to transfer, these listings will be moved to the 25th Edition *Blue Book of Gun Values* by S.P. Fjestad after this edition.

For more information and current pricing on American Western Arms, Co. firearms, please refer to the 24th Ed. *Blue Book of Gun Values* by S.P. Fjestad (now online also).

GRADING	100%	98%	95%	90%	80%	70%	60%

REVOLVERS: CARTRIDGE CONVERSIONS & OPEN TOP

1851 NAVY RICHARDS-TYPE CARTRIDGE CONVERSION - .38 Special, .38 Colt, or .44 Colt, 5.5 or 7.5 in. octagon barrel, color case hardened frame and hammer. Disc. 2000.

$640 $540 $435

Last MSR was $750.

1860 ARMY RICHARDS-TYPE CARTRIDGE CONVERSION - .38 Special, .38 Colt, or .44 Colt, 5.5 or 8 in. round barrel, color case hardened frame and hammer. Disc. 2000.

$640 $540 $435

Last MSR was $750.

1861 NAVY RICHARDS-TYPE CARTRIDGE CONVERSION - .38 Special, .38 Colt, or .44 Colt, 5.5 or 7.5 in. round barrel, color case hardened frame and hammer. Disc. 2000.

$640 $540 $435

Last MSR was $750.

1872 OPEN TOP - .38 Special, .38 Colt, or .44 Colt, 5.5 or 7.5 in. round barrel, color case hardened frame and hammer. Disc. 2000.

$640 $540 $435

Last MSR was $750.

ARM SPORT LLC

Current customizer located in Eastlake, CO.

Gunsmith R.L. Millington specializes in authentic, hand-built conversions of Colt and Remington black powder pistols to metallic cartridge, custom engraving, refinishing, and antique refinishing. All prices listed are for conversion work only. Colt, Pietta, and Uberti Colt, and Remington models for conversion are in addition to the prices listed. See the appropriate sections for the retail prices of these models. Customers may also supply their own guns for conversion. Antiquing and period-style engraving are additional.

Since these are cartridge firing revolvers converted from black powder reproduction pistols, and require a FFL to transfer, these listings will be moved to the 25th Edition *Blue Book of Gun Values* by S.P. Fjestad after this edition.

REVOLVERS: CARTRIDGE CONVERSIONS

1839 TEXAS PATERSON - .38 Smith & Wesson or .38 Colt, Richards Type II conversion, 5-shot cylinder, spring-loaded ejector, loading gate. Cut down barrel lengths offered.

MSR $875

This firearm must be purchased through an FFL dealer.

1847 WALKER AND DRAGOON MODELS - .44 Colt or .45 Long Colt, Richards conversion.

MSR $895

This firearm must be purchased through an FFL dealer.

COLT POCKET DRAGOON, WELLS FARGO MODEL - .38 Colt, Richards conversion, with loading gate and ejector.

MSR $875

Subtract $250 without loading gate and ejector.

This firearm must be purchased through an FFL dealer.

1851 NAVY, 1861 NAVY - .38 Colt, .38 Smith & Wesson, or .38 Special, Richards-Mason conversion.

MSR $875

This firearm must be purchased through an FFL dealer.

GRADING	100%	98%	95%	90%	80%	70%	60%

1860 ARMY - .44 Colt, Richards Type I (firing pin in breech ring) or Richards Type II (firing pin in hammer) conversion.

   MSR   **$895**

This firearm must be purchased through an FFL dealer.

1862 POCKET NAVY, 1862 POCKET POLICE - .38 Colt, Richards-Mason conversion, firing pin in hammer, loading gate and ejector.

   MSR   **$875**

Subtract $250 without loading gate and ejector.
This firearm must be purchased through an FFL dealer.

1858 REMINGTON ARMY - .44 Colt or .45 Long Colt, original 5-shot cylinder design, no loading gate, no ejector, firing pin in hammer.

   MSR   **$565**

Add $200 for original 1869 style ejector.
This firearm must be purchased through an FFL dealer.

REMINGTON NAVY - .38 Colt, or .38 Special, with ejector and loading gate, firing pin in hammer.

   MSR   **$785**

Subtract $300 without loading gate and ejector.
This firearm must be purchased through an FFL dealer.

REMINGTON POCKET PISTOL - .32 Smith & Wesson Short, 5-shot, firing pin in hammer.

   MSR   **$365**

This firearm must be purchased through an FFL dealer.

DELUXE EHLERS FIFTH MODEL PATERSON REVOLVER - .36 cal. perc., nickel plated and period engraved frame and barrel, 24Kt. gold plated loading lever, hammer, cylinder, and trigger, Belt Model based on the Ehlers Fifth or New Model No. 2 revolver, features the Ehlers-type backstrap and grip design, 3.5 in. octagonal barrel and early Paterson-style loading lever, designed by Dennis Adler, handcrafted by R.L. Millington from Uberti components, cased with accessories in a period style French fit, solid walnut presentation box built by Pennsylvania furniture maker Duncan Everhart. Edition limited to 25. New 2002.

   MSR   **$3,500**

This firearm must be purchased through an FFL dealer.

ARMI SAN MARCO

Previous manufacturer located in Gardone, Italy, acquired by American Western Arms Co. in 2000 and reorganized as American Western Arms, Italia. See American Western Arms Co. listing. Previously imported by E.M.F., located in Santa Ana, CA. and sold through E.M.F., Traditions, Cabela's, and retail gun stores.

All Armi San Marco black powder cap and ball and cartridge conversion models were discontinued in 2000.

In 1993, the Hartford line was introduced by E.M.F. These models have steel frames with German silver plated backstrap and trigger guard, inspector's cartouche on grip, and trade for approximately $20-$40 higher than standard Armi San Marco versions.

PISTOLS: FLINTLOCK & PERCUSSION

1777 CHARLEVILLE PISTOL - .69 cal. flintlock, 7.5 in. white steel smooth bore barrel, brass furniture, belt hook, walnut stock, 2.75 lbs.

          $175   **$155**   **$105**

GRADING	100%	98%	95%	90%	80%	70%	60%

SINGLE SHOT PERCUSSION DERRINGER - .31 cal. perc., Colt-style, single shot, 2 in. round brass plated barrel, blue frame, walnut grips. Disc. 2000.

MSR	$95	$75	$60	$45

Add $35 for presentation case.

REVOLVERS: PERCUSSION

1847 WALKER MODEL - .44 cal. perc., 9 in. barrel, color case hardened frame, loading lever and hammer, brass trigger guard and steel backstrap, 4.5 lbs. Disc. 2000.

$225 $205 $140

Last MSR was $320.

1ST MODEL DRAGOON - .44 cal. perc., 8 in. barrel, color case hardened frame, loading lever and hammer, silver plated backstrap and trigger guard. Disc.

$240 $210 $165

2ND MODEL DRAGOON - similar to 1st Model Dragoon, except 7.5 in. barrel. Disc. 2000.

$240 $210 $165

Last MSR was $304.

3RD MODEL DRAGOON - .44 cal. perc., 7.5 in. barrel, Western Model has silver plated brass backstrap, Military Model has steel backstrap – cut for stock, Texas Model has brass backstrap. Disc. 2000.

$245 $220 $170

Last MSR was $312.

Add $15 for Western Model.

1849 WELLS FARGO - .31 cal. perc., 3 in., 4 in., 5 in. octagon barrel, 5 shot, color case hardened frame and hammer, no loading lever, brass trim, 1.5 lbs. Disc.

$200 $180 $140

1851 NAVY - .36 or .44 cal. perc., 7.5 in. octagon barrel, (roll) engraved cylinder, color case hardened frame and loading lever, silver plated brass backstrap and square back trigger guard. Sheriff's Model has 5 in. barrel, brass trigger guard and backstrap. Disc. 2000.

$135 $120 $100

Last MSR was $192.

Subtract $20 for brass back strap and trigger guard.
Subtract $25 for brass frame.
Add $80 for engraved steel frame.
Add $100 for shoulder stock.

1860 ARMY - .44 cal. perc., 8 in. round barrel, color case hardened frame, hammer and loading lever, Sheriff's Model has 5 in. barrel, 2.75 lbs. Disc. 2000.

$170 $150 $120

Last MSR was $216.

Add $5 for Sheriff's Model.
Add $45 for fluted cylinder model.
Add $100 for engraved steel.
Add $135 for stock.
Subtract $35 for brass frame.

1861 NAVY - .36 cal. perc., 7.5 in. round barrel, color case hardened frame, hammer and loading lever, silver-plated brass backstrap and trigger guard (very similar to 1860 Army, except cal. and shorter Navy grips). Disc. 2000.

$180 $165 $120

Last MSR was $248.

GRADING	100%	98%	95%	90%	80%	70%	60%

1862 POLICE POCKET - .36 cal. perc., 4.5, 5.5, or 6.5 in. barrel, color case hardened steel frame, hammer and loading lever or brass frame, cylinder semi-fluted or engraved, 1.6 lbs. Disc. 2000.

	$180	$165	$120				

Last MSR was $248.

Subtract $64 for brass frame model.

1858 REMINGTON ARMY - .44 cal. perc., 6 shot, 8 in. octagon barrel, brass frame, trigger guard and back-strap, walnut grips, 2.38 lbs. Disc. 2000.

	$135	$115	$100				

Last MSR was $176.

Add $140 for stainless steel target model.
Add $104 for engraving on brass frame.
Add $40 for steel frame.
Add $106 for 12 in. barrel Buffalo Target Model.

RIFLES: PERCUSSION

HAWKEN RIFLE - .45, .50, .54, or .58 cal. perc., color case hardened hammer and lock, brass patch box. Disc. 2000.

	$230	$200	$160				

Last MSR was $325.

ST. LOUIS HAWKEN - .50, .54, or .58 cal. perc., color case hardened hammer and lock, 28 in. octagon barrel, brass trim, 7 lbs. 15 oz.

	$260	$230	$175				

Add $65 for curly maple stock.

ROCKY MOUNTAIN SHORT RIFLE - .50 cal. perc., 24 in. octagon barrel, brass furniture.

	$225	$200	$140				

ARMI SAN PAOLO S.r.l.

Previous trademark previously named Armi San Paolo beginning 1971 and originaly located in San Paolo, Italy. Armi San Paolo S.r.l. currently located in Concesio, Italy changed its name to Euroarms Italia S.r.l. in January 2002. Euroarms Italia S.r.l. (formerly Armi San Paolo) also owns Euroarms of America and is currently imported by Cabela's, located in Sydney, NE, Euroarms of America located in Winchester, VA, Dixie Gun Works, Inc. located in Union City, IN, and Navy Arms Co. located in Union City NJ. Previously imported by Kendall International located in Paris, KY and Muzzle Loaders, Inc. located in Burke, VA. Available through dealers and catalog houses. See the Euroarms Italia S.r.l. section for current model pricing.

The origin of Armi San Paolo can be traced back to 1957 when two young Americans asked Luciano Amadi to reproduce the original 1851 Colt Navy revolver. Val Forgett, Sr., a businessman in the firearms field, and William B. Edwards, the technical editor of *Guns* magazine, were in Europe as part of an American gun tour, and in search of a manufacturer for black powder reproductions and replicas.

At that time, Luciano Amadi was employed at Beretta, and assisted a group of Indonesian military officers who resided in Gardone V.T. for three years to follow up a commitment of 55,000 M1 Garands for their government. He was also one of the few people at the plant who could speak English at the time. During dinner with Forgett and Edwards while in Gardone, plans were made to go ahead with the project.

It took Mr. Amadi many months to import an original Colt 1851 Navy, and even more time to find an Italian manufacturer willing to accept this new manufacturing proposal.

Vittorio Gregorelli, who owned a parts supply company making components for Beretta firearms in Brescia, was not licensed to manufacture guns at the time, and finally believed in the project when Mr. Amadi presented him with an initial order for 250 Colt 1851 Navy revolvers. A $500 check started the tooling process!

During this same time period, Aldo Uberti, also a previous Beretta employee, began manufacturing

GRADING	100%	98%	95%	90%	80%	70%	60%

black powder reproductions in Gardone, next to Brescia. Uberti records indicates that the first Uberti model was returned from the Italian proof house on Oct. 14th, 1959.

By 1959, the black powder reproduction and replica industry was already off to a good start in Italy, and Gregorelli was followed by Davide Pedersoli, who started producing muzzle loading replicas in 1960–1961, when Amadi presented him with a Kentucky pistol to replicate.

In the early 1960s Giacomo Grassi, Giuseppe Doninelli, along with a person named Gazzola were involved in a company manufacturing small caliber semi-auto pistols called Gradoga. In 1971 when Gradoga closed, Giacomo Grassi and Giuseppe Doninelli joined Luciano Amadi (who already had a small gun trading company) to form Armi San Paolo in a small town 25 Km south of Brescia called San Paolo the core of its name.

Armi San Paolo grew to employ approx. 60 people, and Euroarms of America Inc. was formed in Winchester, VA to distribute all Armi San Paolo products. In 1987, the replica market shrank, and Armi San Paolo started the move from San Paolo, Italy to Concesio, Italy with the move being completed during 1990.

ARMSPORT, INC.

Current importer located in Miami, FL. Available through dealers and distributors.

CANNONS

BORDA MODEL - .50 cal., wick ignition, nickel plated. Disc. 1994.

> $200 $170 $135

Last MSR was $195.

Add $80 for gold plating.

NAPOLEON MODEL - .45, .50, .69, or .75 cal., wick ignition, nickel plated. Disc. 1994.

> $450 $390 $310

Last MSR was $525.

Add $100 for gold plating.
Add $150 for .75 cal.
Add $120 for .69 cal.

YORKTOWN MODEL - .50 cal., wick ignition, nickel plated. Disc. 1994.

> $200 $170 $135

Last MSR was $195.

Add $100 for gold plating.

PISTOLS: FLINTLOCK & PERCUSSION

CORSAIR MODEL - .44 cal. perc. double barrel, blue finish, color case hardened hammer and lock, brass trim.

> $265 $210 $135

DUELING MODEL - .45 cal. perc., blue finish, color case hardened hammer and lock, brass trim.

> $200 $150 $110

KENTUCKY MODEL - .45 or .50 cal. perc. & flintlock, blue finish, color case hardened hammer and lock, brass trim.

> $175 $140 $110

Add $10 for flintlock.

REVOLVERS: PERCUSSION

1847 WALKER - .44 cal. perc., color case hardened frame, hammer, and loading lever, brass trigger guard, steel backstrap, 6 shot, 4.5 lbs.

> $255 $225 $170

Last MSR was $305.

GRADING	100%	98%	95%	90%	80%	70%	60%

1851 NAVY - .36 or .44 cal. perc., brass or color case hardened frame, brass trigger guard and backstrap, 6 shot.

	$110	$95	$75				

Last MSR was $160.

Add $40 for color case hardened steel with engraved cylinders.
Add $100 for engraved gold and nickel.

1860 ARMY - .44 cal. perc., brass frame, trigger guard, and backstrap, color case hardened hammer and loading lever, 6 shot.

	$145	$115	$85				

Last MSR was $165.

Add $35 for color case hardened steel.
Add $160 for stainless steel.
Add $115 for engraved gold and silver.
Add $30 for steel Sheriff Model.

1858 REMINGTON ARMY - .44 cal. perc., blue frame, brass trigger guard, steel backstrap, 6 shot.

	$160	$140	$125				

Last MSR was $230.

Add $115 for stainless steel.
Add $90 for engraved gold and silver.
Add $25 for Target Model.
Subtract $25 for brass frame.
Subtract $30 for nickel plated brass.

REMINGTON BUFFALO TARGET - .44 cal. perc., 12 in. octagon barrel, brass frame and trigger guard, adj. sights, based on 1858 Navy frame, 38 oz.

	$210	$180	$135				

Last MSR was $220.

Add $10 for nickel plated brass.

REMINGTON POCKET - .31 cal. perc., 5 shot, 4 in. octagon barrel, brass frame, 15 oz. Disc. 1994.

	$130	$105	$85				

Last MSR was $160.

RIFLES: FLINTLOCK & PERCUSSION

BRISTOL KID RIFLE - .32 or .36 cal. perc. Disc. 1984.

	$220	$190	$140				

Add $15 for standard version, $25 for deluxe.

HAWKEN RIFLE - .45, .50, .54, or .58 cal. perc. or flintlock, color case hardened hammer and lock, percussion cap holder in stock, chrome lined barrels.

	$425	$375	$285				

Add $25 for flintlock.

HAWKENTUCKY RIFLE - .36 or .50 cal. perc. or flintlock, color case hardened hammer and lock, percussion cap holder in stock, chrome lined barrels.

	$360	$290	$200				

Add $10 for flintlock.

KENTUCKY RIFLE - .36, .45, or .50, cal. perc. or flintlock, color case hardened hammer and lock, percussion cap holder in stock, chrome lined barrels, brass trim.

	$345	$300	$225				

Add $10 for flintlock.
Add $55 for deluxe with engraved white steel hammer and lock.

GRADING	100%	98%	95%	90%	80%	70%	60%

SHARPS RIFLE/CARBINE - .45 or .54 cal. perc., 22 (carbine) or 28 in. barrel. Mfg. by Industria Armi Bresciane. New 1992.

MSR	$750	$575	$500	$400

Add $25 for 28 in. octagon barrel.

TRYON TRAILBLAZER - .50 or .54 cal. perc., color case hardened hammer and lock, cap holder in stock.

	$450	$390	$300

Add $45 for deluxe engraved.

TRYON BACK ACTION RIFLE - .50 or .54 cal. perc., 28 and 30 in. barrel. Mfg. 1992-94.

	$600	$550	$420

Last MSR was $825.

Add $55 for silver finish.

SHOTGUNS: PERCUSSION

KENTUCKY RIFLE/SHOTGUN COMBO - .45 or .50 cal. perc., 20 ga., similar to Kentucky Rifle.

	$470	$400	$200

SxS SHOTGUN - 12 or 10 ga. perc., blue finish, color case hardened hammer and lock.

	$420	$380	$300

Add $20 for 10 ga.

ASSOCIATION FOR THE PRESERVATION OF WESTERN ANTIQUITY

Previously distributed by William Benjamin Ltd. located in Ashville, NC.

REVOLVERS: PERCUSSION

1862 COLT NAVY - .36 cal. perc., standard construction, roll engraved cylinder with 24Kt. gold inlay, only 100 revolvers made, sold in custom cameo art presentation case depicting a miner panning for gold. Some sets also contained a seated Liberty silver dollar and a $20 Double Eagle gold piece. Disc. 1994.

	$825	$710	$570

Last MSR was $995.

The coin's values should be based on current numismatic pricing - current value for entire set (including coins) is approx. $2,395.

AUSTIN & HALLECK GUN CRAFTERS

Current manufacturer currently located in Provo, UT. Previously located in Weston, MO, until 2002. Dealer sales only.

RIFLES: FLINTLOCKS & PERCUSSION

MOUNTAIN RIFLE FLINTLOCK - .50 cal. flintlock, 32 in. octagon barrel, double throw adj. set triggers, curly maple stock, slow rust brown furniture and barrel finish, fixed buck horn rear and silver blade w/brass base front sights, 1:66 in. twist for round ball or 1:28 in. twist for bullets, 7.5 lbs.

MSR	$639	$550	$475	$400

Add $130 for Select grade stock.

MOUNTAIN RIFLE PERCUSSION - .50 cal. perc., 32 in. octagon barrel, double throw adj. set triggers, curly maple stock, slow rust brown furniture and barrel finish, fixed buck horn rear and silver blade w/brass base front sights, 1:66 in. twist for round ball or 1:28 in. twist for bullets, 7.5 lbs.

MSR	$589	$525	$450	$360

Add $130 for Select grade stock.

GRADING	100%	98%	95%	90%	80%	70%	60%

RIFLES: IN-LINE IGNITION

MODEL 320 LR BLU - .50 cal. perc., 26 in. octagon to tapered round barrel, high polish blue finish, adj. rear and fixed front Tru-Glo fiber optic sights, drilled and tapped for scope mounting, fully adj. match grade trigger w/trigger block safety, black synthetic checkered, Realtree-Hardwoods High Definition, or Mossy Oak Breakup stock, black 1 in. recoil pad, 7.88 lbs.

MSR	$399	$360	$300	$245

Add $40 for Realtree-Hardwood High Definition or Mossy Oak Breakup stock (new 2003.)

MODEL 320 LR S/N - .50 cal. perc., similar to Model 320 LR BLU, except electroless nickel-plated finish, 7.88 lbs.

MSR	$429	$385	$330	$275

Add $40 for Realtree-Hardwood High Definition or Mossy Oak Breakup stock (new 2003.)

MODEL 420 LR CLASSIC BLU - .50 cal. perc., 26 in. octagon to tapered round barrel, adj. rear and fixed front Tru-Glo fiber optic sights, drilled and tapped for scope mounting, fully adj. match grade trigger w/trigger block safety, checkered fancy grade maple flat comb stock, 1 in. recoil pad, 7.88 lbs.

MSR	$509	$465	$395	$345

Add $200 for Hand Select grade wood.
Add $450 for Exhibition grade wood.

MODEL 420 LR CLASSIC S/N - .50 cal. perc., similar to Model 420 LR Classic, except electroless nickel-plated finish, 7.88 lbs.

MSR	$539	$495	$425	$375

Add $200 for Hand Select grade wood.
Add $450 for Exhibition grade wood.

MODEL 420 LR MONTE CARLO - .50 cal. perc., 26 in. octagon to tapered round barrel, adj. rear and fixed front Tru-Glo fiber optic sights, drilled and tapped for scope mounting, fully adj. match grade trigger w/trigger block safety, checkered fancy grade maple Monte Carlo stock, 1 in. recoil pad 7.88 lbs.

MSR	$509	$465	$395	$345

Add $200 for Hand Select grade wood.
Add $450 for Exhibition grade wood.

MODEL 420 LR MONTE CARLO S/N - .50 cal. perc.,similar to Model 420 LR Monty Carlo, except electroless nickel-plated finish, 7.88 lbs.

MSR	$539	$495	$425	$375

Add $200 for Hand Select grade wood.
Add $450 for Exhibition grade wood.

B SECTION

BENSON FIREARMS, LTD.

Previous importer/distributor of A. Uberti reproductions and replicas 1987-1989, located in Seattle, WA. All reproductions and replicas were manufactured in Gardone, Italy.

Benson Firearms imported A. Uberti models that were marked "Benson Firearms Seattle, WA." In 1989 Benson Firearms, Ltd. combined with Uberti USA, Inc. located in New Milford, CT.

All reproductions and replicas were manufactured to the same exact specifications as the original models. Crafted with an unmistakable fire blue finish. See similar models from A. Uberti for current Benson pricing.

BERETTA

Current manufacturer located in Brescia, Italy 1526-present. Currently imported exclusively by Beretta U.S.A. Corp. located in Accokeek, MD since 1980.

Beretta purchased Aldo Uberti & Co. in 2000.

For more information and current pricing on both new and used Browning firearms, please refer to the 24th Ed. *Blue Book of Gun Values* by S.P. Fjestad (now online also).

GRADING	100%	98%	95%	90%	80%	70%	60%

SHOTGUNS: PERCUSSION, O/U

COMMEMORATIVE MODEL M1000 - 12 ga. perc., 30 in. barrel, limited production. Disc. 1994.

$650 $545 $430

Last MSR was $840.

BONDINI

Previous manufacturer located in Italy. Previously imported by Helmut Hofman, Inc. located in Placitas, NH, House Of Muskets located in Pagosa Lakes, CO, and Austin-Sheridan, USA, located in Middlefield, CT.

PISTOLS: FLINTLOCK & PERCUSSION

ASHABELLA COOK UNDERHAMMER - .45 cal. perc., unique underhammer design uses trigger guard as mainspring.

$220 $185 $140

WM. PARKER PISTOL - .45 cal. flintlock or perc., 11 in. octagon brown barrel, silver plated furniture, double set triggers.

$280 $245 $200

Add $10 for flintlock.

F. ROCHATTE - .45 cal. perc., round barrel, single set trigger, hand checkered stock.

$250 $210 $160

RIFLES: PERCUSSION

SANFTL SCHUETZEN RIFLE - .45 cal. perc., 31 in. octagon barrel, unique backward lock, both aperture and open iron sights, Schuetzen style buttplate and trigger guard, brass furniture.

$850 $750 $650

SHOTGUNS: PERCUSSION

GALLYON SHOTGUN - 12 ga., perc., blue barrel, single shot.

$330 $290 $230

Add $150 for extra 12 ga. barrel.

GRADING	100%	98%	95%	90%	80%	70%	60%

BROWNING

Current manufacturer/importer with headquarters located in Morgan, UT. Browning guns originally were manufactured in Ogden, UT, circa 1880. Browning firearms are manufactured by Fabrique Nationale in Herstal and Liege, Belgium. Since 1976, Browning has also contracted Miroku of Japan and A.T.I. in Salt Lake City, UT to manufacture both long arms and handguns. In 1992, Browning (including F.N.) was acquired by GIAT of France. During late 1997, the French government received $82 million for the sale of F.N. Herstal from the Walloon business region surrounding Fabrique Nationale in Belgium.

For more information and current pricing on both new and used Browning firearms, please refer to the 24th Ed. *Blue Book of Gun Values* by S.P. Fjestad (now online also).

RIFLES: PERCUSSION

JONATHAN BROWNING MOUNTAIN RIFLE - .50 cal. perc., 30 in. octagon barrel, single set trigger, engraved lock plate, select walnut stock, cased with medallion and powder horn. 1,000 mfg. in 1978.

$750 $595 $400

Last MSR was $650.

MOUNTAIN RIFLE - .45 or .54 cal. perc., similar to Jonathan Browning Mountain Rifle, without Centennial embellishments, not cased.

$595 $525 $475

C SECTION

CABELA'S INC.

Current sporting goods retailer with catalog sales, headquarters located in Sydney, NE. Consumer direct (store or mail order) sales only.

Cabela's should be contacted directly (see Trademark Index) to receive a catalog on their extensive black powder model lineup. Cabela's continues to be a primary U.S. retailer for Pietta black powder pistols and Pedersoli black powder rifles and shotguns.

CHATTAHOOCHEE BPA

Current manufacturer located in Cumming, GA. Chattahoochee BPA manufactures an authentic reproduction of the Colt 1861 Special Rifle-Musket by Amoskeag and LG&Y. Consumer direct sales.

Chattahoochee reproduction rifles are approved by the North-South Skirmish Association.

GRADING	100%	98%	95%	90%	80%	70%	60%

RIFLES: PERCUSSION

COLT 1861 SPECIAL RIFLE/MUSKET - .58 cal. perc., 31.5 in. 2 band or 40 in. 3 band Infantry and Artillery barrel lengths, Armory bright polished steel finish with authentic markings, hand finished walnut stock, Artillery, 8 lbs. 4 oz., Infantry, 9 lbs. 3 oz., all models come with "match grade" internal lock parts.

MSR	$695	$640	$560	$465

CHENEY RIFLE WORKS

Cheney Rifle Works has changed its name to Wilderness Rifle Works, but is still located in Waldron, IN.

All Cheney manufactured rifles are priced similar to comparable models in the Wilderness Rifle Works section.

CIMARRON F.A. CO.

Current importer/distributor located in Fredericksburg, TX. Cimarron currently imports A. Uberti, F.lli Pietta, and other Italian manufactured reproductions and replicas of both cartridge and black powder models. Consumer direct or dealer sales.

Cimarron F.A. Co. was previously named Old-West Gun Company.

Cimarron sells authentic western reproductions of Colt and Remington black powder pistols. Packaged for Cimarron, the majority of reproductions sold are manufactured by Uberti. In 1999, Cimarron began marketing cartridge conversion models of Colt black powder pistols, including the 1851 Navy, 1860 Army, in addition to the 1872 Open Top. Cimarron also offers engraved versions of most Colt and Remington models. 1851 Navy and 1860 Army were disc. 2000.

For more information and current pricing on both new and used Cimarron F.A. Co. firearms, please refer to the 24th Ed. *Blue Book of Gun Values* by S.P. Fjestad (now online also).

Add the following amounts for engraving:

Add $650 for "A" style engraving (30% coverage).

Add $750 for "B" style engraving (50% coverage).

Add $1,100 for "C" style engraving (100% coverage).

Add $1,475 for "Full" coverage engraving.

Add $1,475 for "Texas Cattlebrands" engraving.

Add $250 for old style case hardened frame.

GRADING	100%	98%	95%	90%	80%	70%	60%

Add the following amounts for custom finishes:

Add $150 for custom nickel finish.

Add $150 for premium nickel finish (highly polished).

Add $350 for silver plating.

Add $295 for custom Armory Old Style bone meal color case hardening (done in the USA).

REVOLVERS: CARTRIDGE, SA

Since these are cartridge firing revolvers converted from black powder reproduction pistols, and require a FFL to transfer, these listings will be moved to the 25th Edition *Blue Book of Gun Values* by S.P. Fjestad after this edition.

1871-72 OPEN TOP - .38 Colt, .38 S&W Spl., .44 Colt, .44 Russian, or .45 S&W Schofield cal., 5.5 or 7.5 in. round barrel, color case hardened frame and hammer, Navy style brass backstrap and trigger guard, or Army style steel backstrap and trigger guard. Available in standard blue finish, charcoal blue, nickel, or antique Original finish. Manufactured to Cimarron's specifications by Uberti. New 2000.

MSR	$529	$435	$315	$265

Add $30 for charcoal blue finish.

Add $70 for original finish.

1851 RICHARDS-MASON CARTRIDGE CONVERSION - .38 Special cal., 5.5 or 7.5 in. octagonal barrel, color case hardened frame and hammer, brass backstrap and trigger guard. Available in standard blue finish, charcoal blue, antique Original finish. Manufactured by Uberti. New 2002.

MSR	$469	$380	$335	$285

Add $30 for charcoal blue finish.

Add $40 for original finish.

Add $25 for silver plated backstrap and trigger guard.

1860 RICHARDS-MASON CARTRIDGE CONVERSION - .44 Colt, .44 Russian, 45 Schofield cal., 5.5, 7.5 or 8 in. round barrel, color case hardened frame and hammer, steel backstrap and trigger guard. Available in standard blue finish, charcoal blue, antique Original finish. Manufactured by Uberti. New 2002.

MSR	$469	$380	$335	$285

Add $30 for charcoal blue finish.

Add $40 for original finish.

REVOLVERS: PERCUSSION

TEXAS PATERSON - .36 cal. perc., 7.5 in. octagon barrel, standard hidden trigger design, blue steel hardware, loading lever, 2.5 lbs.

MSR	$429	$350	$305	$265

Add $30 for blue charcoal or white finish.

Add $50 for original finish.

Subtract $10 without loading lever.

1847 WALKER - .44 cal. perc., charcoal finish, color case hardened frame, hammer, and loading lever, brass trim, engraved cylinder, 4.4 lbs.

MSR	$399	$325	$280	$230

Add $30 for blue charcoal or white finish.

Add $50 for original finish.

1848 BABY DRAGOON - .31 cal. perc., 4 in. barrel, 5 shot, color case hardened frame, hammer, no loading lever, engraved cylinder, 1.4 lbs.

MSR	$309	$250	$220	$185

Add $25 for silver plated backstrap and trigger guard.

Add $30 for charcoal or white finish.

GRADING	100%	98%	95%	90%	80%	70%	60%

DRAGOON (WHITNEYVILLE-HARTFORD, 1ST, 2ND, OR 3RD MODEL) - .44 cal. perc., 6 shot, brass grip strap, color case hardened frame, hammer, and loading lever, brass trim, 3.9 lbs.

MSR	$389	$315	$275	$235

Add $10 for Whitneyville Model.
Add $25 for silver plated backstrap, or cut for stock (3rd Model Dragoon).
Add $180 for shoulder stock.
Add $30 for blue charcoal or white finish.
Add $50 for antique original finish.

1849 WELLS FARGO - .31 cal. perc., 4 in. octagon barrel, 5 shot, color case hardened frame, hammer, no loading lever, brass trim, 1.5 lbs.

MSR	$309	$250	$220	$185

Add $25 for silver plated backstrap and trigger guard.
Add $30 for blue charcoal or white finish.
Add $50 for antique original finish.

1849 POCKET - .31 cal. perc., with loading lever, 4 in. barrel, 5 shot, color case hardened frame, hammer, and loading lever, brass trim, 1.5 lbs.

MSR	$309	$250	$220	$185

Add $25 for silver plated backstrap and trigger guard.
Add $30 for charcoal or white finish.
Add $50 for antique original finish.

1851 NAVY/1851 NAVY LONDON MODEL - .36 cal. perc., 7.5 in. octagon barrel, 6 shot, roll engraved cylinder, brass or steel (Navy London Model) grip frame, round or square trigger guard, 2.8 lbs.

MSR	$329	$265	$235	$200

Add $25 for silver plated backstrap and trigger guard.
Add $10 for Navy London Model.
Add $30 for blue charcoal or white finish.
Add $50 for original finish.

1860 ARMY CIVILIAN MODEL - .44 cal. perc. 8 in. barrel, 6 shot, loading lever, color case hardened frame, hammer, and loading lever, rebated cylinder, brass or steel backstrap and bass trigger guard, 2.6 lbs.

MSR	$339	$275	$240	$205

Add $25 for silver plated backstrap and trigger guard.
Add $30 for charcoal or white finish.
Add $50 for original finish.

1860 ARMY MILITARY MODEL - .44 cal. perc., 8 in. barrel, 6 shot, loading lever, color case hardened frame, hammer, and loading lever, fluted or rebated cylinder, steel backstrap and trigger guard, cut for stock, 2.6 lbs.

MSR	$339	$275	$240	$205

Add $10 for fluted cylinder.
Add $25 for silver plated backstrap and trigger guard.
Add $30 for charcoal or white finish.
Add $50 for original finish.

1861 NAVY CIVILIAN/MILITARY - .36 cal. perc., 7.5 in. round barrel, fluted or rebated cylinder, brass (Civilian) or steel backstrap and trigger guard, color case hardened frame, hammer, and loading lever, cut for stock, 2.5 lbs.

MSR	$339	$275	$240	$205

Add $25 for silver plated backstrap and trigger guard.

GRADING	100%	98%	95%	90%	80%	70%	60%

Add $30 for charcoal or white finish.
Add $50 for antique original finish.

1862 POCKET POLICE - .36 cal. perc., 5.5 or 6.5 in. barrel, color case hardened frame, hammer, and loading lever, cylinder, semi-fluted cylinder, 1.6 lbs.

| MSR | $329 | $265 | $230 | $200 |

Add $25 for silver plated backstrap and trigger guard.
Add $30 for charcoal or white finish.
Add $50 for antique original finish.

1862 POCKET NAVY - .36 cal. perc., 5.5, or 6.5 in. barrel, color case hardened frame, hammer, and loading lever, rebated cylinder, 1.6 lbs.

| MSR | $329 | $265 | $230 | $200 |

Add $25 for silver plated backstrap and trigger guard.
Add $30 for charcoal or white finish.
Add $50 for antique original finish.

1858 REMINGTON ARMY - .44 cal. perc., 7.5 in. barrel, 2.6 lbs.

| MSR | $329 | $265 | $230 | $200 |

Add $30 for charcoal finish.
Add $50 for antique original finish.

1858 REMINGTON NAVY - .36 cal. perc., 7.5 in. barrel, 2.5 lbs. Disc.

$150 $180 $145

Last MSR was $249.

AUGUSTA CONFEDERATE - .36 cal. perc., 7.5 in. octagon barrel, color case hardened hammer and trigger, all brass frame, engraved cylinder, 2.5-2.75 lbs.

$210 $180 $135

Last MSR was $210.

GRISWOLD AND GUNNISON CONFEDERATE - .36 or .44 cal. perc., similar to Augusta Confederate Model, except has round barrel forward of lug, and plain, non-engraved cylinder. Disc. 1994.

$210 $180 $135

Last MSR was $150.

LEECH AND RIGDON CONFEDERATE - .36 cal. perc., 7.5 in. octagon barrel, color case hardened frame, hammer and trigger, engraved cylinder, brass backstrap and trigger guard, 2.75 lbs.

| MSR | $339 | $275 | $240 | $205 |

Add $50 for antique original finish.

TEXAS CONFEDERATE DRAGOON - .44 cal. perc., 7.5 in. round barrel, color case hardened frame, hammer, and loading lever, brass trim, "Tucker, Sherrard, and Co.", 4 lbs. Disc. 1994.

$265 $235 $180

Last MSR was $210.

1858 REMINGTON - .44 cal. perc., 7.5 in. barrel, 6 shot, blue steel, brass trigger guard, 2.6 lbs.

$230 $200 $160

Last MSR was $260.

Add $40 for adj. sights.

GRADING	100%	98%	95%	90%	80%	70%	60%

1858 REMINGTON STAINLESS - similar to 1858 Remington, has brass strap and trigger guard. Disc. 1994.

$315 $275 $220

Last MSR was $260.

Add $40 for adj. sights.

1858 REMINGTON NEW NAVY - .36 cal. perc., 6.5 in. octagon barrel, 6 shot, blue frame, 2.5 lbs. Disc. 1994.

$225 $195 $145

Last MSR was $185.

Add $40 for adj. sights.

RIFLES: FLINTLOCK & PERCUSSION

1866 REVOLVING CARBINE - .44 cal. perc., 18 in. barrel, 6 shot, blue steel, brass trigger guard, walnut stock, 4.6 lbs. Disc. 1994.

$345 $300 $240

Last MSR was $320.

HAWKEN SANTA FE - .54 cal. perc., single shot, 32 in. oct. barrel, damascened finish, double set triggers, walnut stock, 9.5 lbs. Disc. 1994.

$385 $330 $265

Last MSR was $350.

JEREDIAH SMITH SANTA FE HAWKENS - .50 or .54 cal. flintlock or perc., similar to above.

$385 $330 $265

Last MSR was $445.

Add $35 for Flintlock.

LEMAN TRADE RIFLE - .45, .50, .54, or .58 cal. perc. Disc. 1994.

$250 $220 $160

Last MSR was $250.

Add $15 for .54 or .58 cal.

ST. LOUIS RIFLE - .45, .50, .54, or .58 cal. flintlock or perc., color case hardened hammer lock and trigger guard, octagon barrel. Disc. 1994.

$345 $280 $210

Last MSR was $280.

Add $15 for .54 or .58 cal. percussion.
Add $15 for flintlock.

COLT'S MANUFACTURING COMPANY, INC.

Current firearms manufacturer with headquarters located in West Hartford, CT.

Colt's Manufacturing Company, Inc. is the previous manufacturer of 2nd Generation Colt percussion revolvers located in Hartford, CT. Colt used subcontractors to supply rough castings for the manufacture of these black powder pistols. Throughout the production years 1971-1982, these rough castings were produced in Italy and the reproductions were completed in the United States. Initially, Val Forgett and Navy Arms provided these parts/components during 1971-73. Lou Imperato supplied these parts from 1974-76. In both instances, these revolvers were assembled and finished in Colt's facilities in Connecticut. Finally, from 1978-1982, Colt subcontracted both parts procurement and final production to Lou Imperato and Iver Johnson Arms in Middlesex, NJ. Colt percussion revolvers produced by Iver Johnson had frames, center pins, nipples, and screws manufactured in the United States. In all instances, these revolvers were manufactured in accordance with Colt's strict specifications and quality control. Additionally, Colt's performed final inspection for all models. All percussion models manufactured from 1971 through 1982, either by Colt or its subcontractor, are regarded as authentic Colt pistols and not Italian replicas.

The Colt Custom Shop also produced a limited number of special editions through the early 1990s from 2nd Generation production inventory. (Colt 2nd Generation models in the white are still known to exist.)

Please refer to *Colt Blackpowder Reproductions & Replicas—A Collector's & Shooter's Guide* for additional color pictures of the 2nd Generation Colt Percussion Revolver makes and models listed below. Second Generation Colts can be found on pages 12 through 22, and pages 78, 82, and 83.

For more information and current pricing on both new and used Colt firearms, please refer to the 24th Ed. *Blue Book of Gun Values* by S.P. Fjestad (now online also).

GRADING	NIB	98%	95%

REVOLVERS: PERCUSSION, 2ND GENERATION

Colt 2nd Generation Percussion models are listed in Series order as produced by Colt Firearms.

Special note regarding all prices listed for NIB (New in Box) specimens.

> **Subtract approx. $100 for revolvers under $2,000 if without original box or with damaged packaging.**
> **Subtract approx. $200-$250 for revolvers over $2,000 if without original box or with damaged packaging.**
> **On cased revolvers listed below, subtract 20% or more for missing or damaged accessories and/or damaged presentation case.**

"C" Series Revolvers

These Colt percussion revolvers were reintroduced in 1971 (1851 Navy) and 1974 (3rd Model Dragoon). Both models were discontinued in late 1976 (no reference is made to them in either the 1977 Colt Catalog or Colt Price List). The 1851 Navy and Third Model Dragoon were the only models to be produced in both the "C" Series and "F" Series configurations. While the fit and finish of both series is of the highest quality, the difference is unmistakable. The "C" Series has a beautiful bright "Royal Blue" finish while the "F" Series has a more durable dark "Colt Blue" finish. Another distinguishing feature is the serial number range (4201 to 25099 for the "C" Series 1851 Navy and 20901 to 25099 for the "C" Series Third Model Dragoon).

1851 NAVY "C" SERIES (SILVER BACKSTRAP & SQUARE BACK TRIGGER GUARD) - .36
cal. perc., 7.5 in. octagon barrel, hinged loading lever and six shot cylinder with roll engraved naval battle scene, "C" Series Royal Blue barrel and cylinder, color case hardened frame, loading lever, plunger, and hammer, silver plated brass backstrap and square back trigger guard, one-piece walnut stocks, 42 oz. This is the first series of second generation 1851 Navy revolvers produced. Serial number range 4201-25099. Mfg. 1971-78.

$600	$400	$325

Last MSR was $200.

Note: The prices quoted above are for "C" Series 1851 Navy revolvers with wood grain cardboard box and styrofoam insert. "C" Series 1851 Navys with the early SAA style black flip top box in excellent condition command a $100.00 premium (serial number range 4201 to 5199). "C" Series 1851 Navys with the tan and brown flip top box in excellent condition command a $50.00 premium (serial number range 5200 to 12999).

1851 NAVY/3RD MODEL DRAGOON BERMAN CASED SET 1 OF 50 SPECIAL EDITION -
.36 (Navy) and .44 (Dragoon) cals. perc., this set includes two revolvers a Colt Model 1851 Navy percussion revolver with 7.5 in. octagon barrel, hinged loading lever, six shot cylinder with roll engraved naval battle scene, silver plated brass backstrap and square back trigger guard, and a Colt Third Model Dragoon percussion revolver with 7.5 in. round barrel, hinged loading lever, six shot cylinder with rectangular bolt cuts and roll engraved Texas Ranger and Indian scene, and polished brass round trigger guard and backstrap. Both revolvers feature a "C" Series "Royal Blue" barrel and cylinder with a case hardened frame, loading lever, plunger and hammer, each revolver is class "C" engraved, has gold inlaid frame border and barrel bands, and

GRADING	NIB	98%	95%

two piece ivory grips with gold Colt medallions. This set includes an English fit presentation case with red velvet lined interior that is designed to accommodate two revolvers, an 1851 Navy accessory set and a Third Model Dragoon accessory set. Produced in 1978-79 for Jerry Berman & Sons in a series of 50 sets.

	$8,500	$6,200	$4,600

Last MSR was $10,500.

1851 NAVY CONQUISTADORES DEL CIELO SPECIAL EDITION

1851 NAVY CONQUISTADORES DEL CIELO SPECIAL EDITION - .36 cal. perc., 7.5 in. octagon barrel, hinged loading lever, six shot cylinder with roll engraved naval battle scene, "C" Series Royal Blue barrel and cylinder, color case hardened frame, loading lever, plunger, and hammer, nickel plated brass backstrap and square back trigger guard, one-piece walnut stocks. This set includes a custom walnut presentation case with French fit gold velvet lining and glass top. The case is designed to accommodate a single revolver, bag type powder flask, "L" shaped nipple wrench/screw driver, two cavity brass bullet mold, cap tin, and a 1976 edition of the Conquistadores Del Cielo newsletter rolled into a scroll. The 1851 Navy revolver is engraved with the original owner's name on the backstrap as well as special Conquistador roll markings on the barrel and barrel lug. 174 mfg.

	$3,000	$2,100	$1,600

1851 NAVY KLAY-COLT

1851 NAVY KLAY-COLT - .36 cal. perc., 7.5 in. octagon barrel, hinged loading lever, six shot cylinder with roll engraved naval battle scene, "C" Series Royal Blue barrel and cylinder, fire blued screws, color case hardened frame, loading lever, plunger, and hammer, silver plated brass backstrap and round (early 3rd model style) trigger guard, one-piece burl walnut stocks. Colt supplied these revolvers "in-the-white" to Frank Klay & Associates for completion. 25 mfg.

	$1,950	$1,400	$1,100

Last MSR was $1,350.

Add $450-$900 for cased w/accessories, including English fit mahogany presentation case, powder flask, two cavity brass bullet mold, "L" shaped nipple wrench and Eley cap container.

Last MSR was $1,650.

✳ *1851 Navy Klay–Colt Engraved* - similar to the 1851 Navy Klay-Colt, except deluxe Gustav Young style engraving. 125 mfg.

	$3,100	$2,175	$1,625

Last MSR was $2,800.

Add $550-$900 for cased w/accessories, including English fit mahogany presentation case, powder flask, two cavity brass bullet mold, "L" shaped nipple wrench and Eley cap container.

Last MSR was $2,800.

1851 NAVY "C" SERIES (BRASS BACKSTRAP & SQUARE BACK TRIGGER GUARD)

1851 NAVY "C" SERIES (BRASS BACKSTRAP & SQUARE BACK TRIGGER GUARD) - .36 cal. perc., 7.5 in. octagon barrel, hinged loading lever and six shot cylinder with roll engraved naval battle scene, "C" Series Royal Blue barrel and cylinder, color case hardened frame, loading lever, plunger, and hammer, brass backstrap and square back trigger guard, one-piece walnut stocks, 42 oz. 500 mfg. 1978 only.

	$650	$425	$325

Last MSR was $200.

This revolver is also known as "The Shooter."

1851 NAVY "C" SERIES (ROUND TRIGGER GUARD)

1851 NAVY "C" SERIES (ROUND TRIGGER GUARD) - .36 cal. perc., 7.5 in. octagon barrel, hinged loading lever and six shot cylinder with roll engraved naval battle scene, "C" Series Royal Blue barrel and cylinder, color case hardened frame, loading lever, plunger, and hammer, silver plated or solid brass backstrap and round trigger guard, one-piece walnut stocks. Round trigger guard revolvers were produced in very small quantities in several serial number ranges within the primary "C" Series 1851 Navy range (4201–25099). 100± mfg.

	$1,200	$750	$575

Last MSR was $200.

GRADING	NIB	98%	95%

1851 NAVY/3RD DRAGOON WITH GOLD BARREL BAND AND "B" ENGRAVING

Both revolvers feature a gold barrel band at the muzzle, gold rampant colt flush inlaid on the left barrel lug and class "B" engraving. A. A. White Engravers executed the embellishments found on many of these revolvers. These revolvers were sold in a variety of configurations as follows:

* *Revolver #1:* - 1851 Navy .36 cal. percussion with 7.5 in. octagon barrel, hinged loading lever, six shot cylinder with roll engraved naval battle scene, "C" Series Royal Blue barrel and cylinder, case hardened frame, loading lever, plunger and hammer, brass backstrap and square back trigger guard, one-piece walnut stocks. 42 oz. 50 Mfg.

* *Revolver #2:* - 3rd Model Dragoon .44 cal. percussion with 7.5 in. round barrel, hinged loading lever, six shot cylinder with rectangular bolt cuts and roll engraved Texas Ranger and Indian scene, "C" Series Royal Blue barrel and cylinder, case hardened frame, loading lever, plunger and hammer, brass backstrap and round trigger guard, one-piece walnut stocks. 66 oz. 50 mfg.

* *1851 Navy Single Revolver (Gold Barrel Band and "B" Engraving)* - with enhancements as described above. Single 1851 Navy only (no presentation case or accessories). Issued from the same production quantity for the model listed above.

$1,600	**$1,125**	**$850**

Last MSR was $1,350.

* *1851 Navy Cased Pair (Gold Barrel Band and "B" Engraving)* - with enhancements as described above. Includes two 1851 Navy revolvers, two Colt 1851 Navy accessory sets and a two drawer dark walnut chest. Each drawer has an English fit dark blue velvet interior that is designed to house one revolver and a complete set of accessories. Issued from the same production quantity for the model listed above.

$3,900	**$2,775**	**$2,000**

Last MSR was $4,895.

* *3rd Model Dragoon Single Revolver (Gold Barrel Band and "B" Engraving)* - with enhancements as described above. Single 3rd Model Dragoon only (no presentation case or accessories). Issued from the same production quantity for the model listed above.

$1,600	**$1,125**	**$850**

Last MSR was $1,350.

* *3rd Model Dragoon Cased Pair (Gold Barrel Band and "B" Engraving)* - with enhancements as described above. Includes two 3rd Model Dragoon revolvers, two Colt 3rd Model Dragoon accessory sets and a two drawer dark walnut chest. Each drawer has an English fit dark blue velvet interior that is designed to house one revolver and a complete set of accessories. Issued from the same production quantity for the model listed above.

$3,900	**$2,775**	**$2,000**

Last MSR was $4,895.

* *1851 Navy & 3rd Model Dragoon Cased Pair (Gold Barrel Band and "B" Engraving)* - with enhancements as described above. Includes an 1851 Navy revolver with Colt 1851 Navy accessories, a 3rd Model Dragoon revolver with Colt 3rd Model Dragoon accessories, and a two drawer walnut chest similar to the one provided with the 1851 Navy Cased Pair and 3rd Model Dragoon Cased Pair listed above. These revolvers were issued from the same production quantities for the models listed above.

$3,900	**$2,775**	**$2,000**

Last MSR was $4,895.

* *1851 Navy & 3rd Model Dragoon Cased Pair (Gold Barrel Band, "B" Engraving and Ivory Grip)* - Includes one 1851 Navy revolver and one 3rd Model Dragoon revolver with the following exceptions to the enhancements as described above: The backstraps and trigger guards of each revolver are silver plated rather than plain brass. The grip is one-piece smooth ivory rather than one-piece walnut. This set also includes a Colt Custom Shop walnut presentation case with a French fit Tyrol red velvet interior. This case is designed to house the two revolvers only (no accessories). These revolvers were issued from the same production

GRADING	NIB	98%	95%

quantities for the models listed above. However, it is estimated that less than 10 sets of this type were produced.

	$4,250	**$3,000**	**$2,250**

1851 NAVY ROBERT E. LEE COMMEMORATIVE - .36 cal. perc., 7.5 in. octagon barrel, hinged loading lever, six shot cylinder with roll engraved naval battle scene, "C" Series Royal Blue barrel and cylinder, case hardened frame, loading lever, plunger, and hammer, silver plated brass backstrap and round trigger guard, one-piece walnut stocks, "ROBERT E. LEE COMMEMORATIVE NINETEEN SEVENTY-ONE" engraved along the left side of the barrel. Includes an English fit walnut presentation case with gray velvet lining, "stand of flags" style powder flask, "L" shaped nipple wrench, two cavity brass bullet mold, and cap tin. 4,750 mfg. 1971 only.

	$675	**$475**	**$375**

Last MSR was $250.

1851 NAVY ULYSSES S. GRANT COMMEMORATIVE - .36 cal. perc., 7.5 in. octagon barrel, hinged loading lever, six shot cylinder with roll engraved naval battle scene, "C" Series Royal Blue barrel and cylinder, case hardened frame, loading lever, plunger, and hammer, silver plated brass backstrap and square back trigger guard, one-piece walnut stocks, "ULYSSES S. GRANT COMMEMORATIVE NINETEEN SEVENTY-ONE" engraved along the left side of the barrel. Includes an English fit walnut presentation case with navy blue velvet lining, bag style powder flask, "L" shaped nipple wrench, two cavity brass bullet mold, and cap tin. 4,750 mfg. 1971 only.

	$675	**$475**	**$400**

Last MSR was $250.

1851 NAVY U. S. GRANT – ROBERT E. LEE CASED SET COMMEMORATIVE - Two gun cased set, including the Robert E. Lee and Ulysses S. Grant revolvers as described above. In addition, this set was supplied with an English fit two gun walnut presentation case with maroon velvet lined interior designed to house a "stand of flags" powder flask, "L" shaped nipple wrench, two cavity brass bullet mold, and cap tin. 250 mfg. in 1971.

	$1,900	**$1,300**	**$950**

Last MSR was $500.

3RD MODEL DRAGOON "C" SERIES - .44 cal. perc., 7.5 in. round barrel, hinged loading lever, six shot cylinder with rectangular bolt cuts and roll engraved Texas Ranger and Indian scene, "C" Series Royal Blue barrel and cylinder, case hardened frame, loading lever, plunger and hammer, brass backstrap and round trigger guard, one-piece walnut stocks, 66 oz. This is the first series of second generation 3rd Model Dragoons produced. Serial number range 20901–25099. 3,899 mfg. 1974-78.

	$700	**$475**	**$350**

Last MSR was $259.

✳ ***3rd Model Dragoon "C" Series Prototype*** - serial number range 20801-20825. 25 mfg.

	$1,250	**$775**	**$575**

3RD MODEL DRAGOON BICENTENNIAL COMMEMORATIVE - .44 cal. perc., 7.5 in. round barrel, hinged loading lever, six shot cylinder with rectangular bolt cuts and roll engraved Texas Ranger and Indian scene, high polish blue barrel and cylinder, case hardened frame, loading lever, plunger, and hammer, silver plated brass backstrap and round trigger guard, one-piece walnut stocks with eagle medallion inlaid in left side. This revolver was originally part of a three gun set that also included Bicentennial versions of the Colt Single Action Army and Colt Python. Over the years, many of these sets have been broken up. Prices are for the Third Model Dragoon model alone. 1,776 mfg. 1976.

	$750	**$475**	**$375**

GRADING	NIB	98%	95%

3RD MODEL DRAGOON 150TH ANNIVERSARY ENGRAVING SAMPLER

- .44 cal. perc., 7.5 in. round barrel, hinged loading lever, six shot cylinder with rectangular bolt cuts and roll engraved Texas Ranger and Indian scene, high polish blue barrel and cylinder, brass backstrap and round trigger guard, color case hardened frame, loading lever, plunger, and hammer, one-piece ivory stocks, scrimshawed on the left side in script with: R. Henshaw 1831, L. Nimschke 1850 - 1900, C. Helfricht 1871 -1921, & Contemporary. Models were "B" engraved with samples of each engraving style. 50 mfg., 25 in high polish blue, and 25 in bright nickel.

* *High Polish Blue Finish*

$2,500	$1,800	$1,350

Last MSR was $1,560.

* *Full Bright Nickel Finish*

$2,700	$1,950	$1,450

Last MSR was $1,764.

3RD MODEL DRAGOON (MN SERIES)

- .44 cal. perc., 7.5 in. round barrel, hinged loading lever, six shot cylinder with rectangular bolt cuts and roll engraved Texas Ranger and Indian scene, brass backstrap and round trigger guard, high polish blue barrel and cylinder, color case hardened frame, loading lever, plunger, and hammer, one-piece walnut stocks, 66 oz. Only 100 mfg., 75 as described above, 5 as described above but with one-piece ivory stocks, 20 with full bright nickel finish and one-piece ivory stocks.

* *High Polish Blue/Walnut*

$975	$700	$525

* *High Polish Blue/Ivory*

$1,350	$950	$700

* *Full Bright Nickel/Ivory*

$1,950	$1,375	$1,000

3RD MODEL DRAGOON L. D. NIMSCHKE 1 OF 50 SPECIAL EDITION

- .44 cal. perc., 7.5 in. round barrel, hinged loading lever, six shot cylinder with rectangular bolt cuts and roll engraved Texas Ranger and Comanche Indian scene, silver plated barrel, frame, trigger guard, and backstrap, gold plated hammer, cylinder, wedge, trigger, and loading lever, high polish blue screws, one-piece ivory stocks with high relief American eagle hand carved on both sides. Includes an Arlo Werner hand-made presentation case that is covered in blue leather and tooled in gold. The French fit purple velvet lined interior is designed to hold a single revolver without accessories. American Master Engravers produced these revolvers exclusively for The Heritage Guild from "in-the-white" Third Model Dragoons supplied by Colt.

$4,950	$3,550	$2,650

Last MSR was $3,790.

3RD MODEL DRAGOON STATEHOOD EDITION

- .44 cal. perc., 7.5 in. round barrel, hinged loading lever, six shot cylinder with rectangular bolt cuts and roll engraved Texas Ranger and Indian scene, high polish blue barrel and cylinder, case hardened frame, loading lever, plunger, and hammer, gold plated brass backstrap and round trigger guard, two piece ivory stocks. These revolvers were gold-inlaid and engraved, honoring the 50 states, Washington, D.C., and the U.S.A. The serial numbers were the name of each state. Includes a special custom walnut presentation case with a French fit green velvet lined drawer designed to accommodate the Statehood Dragoon as well as a complete set of Colt Third Model Dragoon accessories that are numbered to the gun. 52 mfg.

$8,250	$6,000	$4,500

Last MSR was $12,500.

GRADING	NIB	98%	95%

"F" Series Revolvers: Percussion

Production of these revolvers began in November 1978 with the 1860 Army and continued with the release of the various models described below until all production ceased in November 1982. Special Edition and Limited Edition models continued to be issued from the Colt Custom Shop inventory through the mid 1990s. Rumors persist, even at this late date, that a few in-the-white specimens are still hidden away at Colt's. "F" Series revolvers were produced with a durable dark "Colt Blue" finish while the "C" Series finish is a more lustrous "Royal Blue."

1851 NAVY "F" SERIES - .36 cal. perc., 7.5 in. octagon barrel, hinged loading lever, six shot cylinder with roll engraved naval battle scene, "F" Series Colt Blue barrel and cylinder, color case hardened frame, loading lever, plunger, and hammer, silver plated backstrap and square back trigger guard, one-piece walnut stocks, 42 oz. This is the second series of second generation 1851 Navy revolvers produced. 3,950 mfg. 1980-81.

	$575	$375	$300

Last MSR was $420.

1851 NAVY BLANK CYLINDER - .36 cal. perc., 7.5 in. octagon barrel, hinged loading lever, six shot cylinder provided without engraving (Blank Cylinder), "F" Series Colt Blue barrel and cylinder, case hardened frame, loading lever, plunger, and hammer, silver plated brass backstrap and square back trigger guard, one-piece walnut stocks, 42 oz. 300 mfg 1981 only.

	$775	$525	$400

Last MSR was $420.

1851 NAVY STAINLESS STEEL - .36 cal. perc., 7.5 in. octagon barrel, hinged loading lever, six shot cylinder roll engraved with naval battle scene, stainless steel barrel, cylinder, frame, loading lever, plunger, hammer, backstrap, and square back trigger guard, one-piece walnut stocks, 42 oz. 490 mfg. 1982 only.

	$1,100	$775	$600

Last MSR was $473.

1860 ARMY - .44 cal. perc., 8 in. round barrel, creeping loading lever, six shot cylinder roll engraved with naval battle scene, "F" Series Colt Blue barrel, cylinder and backstrap, case hardened frame, loading lever, plunger, and hammer, brass trigger guard, one-piece walnut stocks. 42 oz. 6,300 mfg. 1978-1982.

	$700	$500	$375

Last MSR was $431.

1860 ARMY BRIGHT NICKEL (MN SERIES) - .44 cal. perc., 8 in. round barrel, creeping loading lever, six shot cylinder roll engraved with naval battle scene, full bright nickel finish and one-piece ivory stocks, 42 oz. 12 mfg.

	$2,250	$1,575	$1,175

Last MSR was $580.

1860 ARMY INTERSTATE COMMEMORATIVE EDITION CASED SET - .44 cal. perc., 8 in. two revolver set with creeping loading levers, six shot cylinders roll engraved with naval battle scene and one-piece walnut stocks. Revolver #1 has a full antique gold finish. Revolver #2 has a full antique silver finish. This set includes an English fit walnut presentation case with Tyrol red interior. The case accommodates the two revolvers and a complete set of Colt 1860 Army accessories–"Stand of Flags" powder flask, two cavity blue steel bullet mold, "L" shaped nipple wrench, and Eley cap tin. Limited Edition of approx. 20 sets.

	$3,600	$2,500	$1,900

Last MSR was $1,495.

1860 ARMY 150TH ANNIVERSARY ENGRAVING SAMPLER - .44 cal. perc., 8 in. round barrel, creeping loading lever, six shot cylinder roll engraved with naval battle scene, high polish blue barrel, cylinder, and backstrap, case hardened frame, loading lever, plunger, and hammer, brass trigger guard, one-piece

GRADING	NIB	98%	95%

ivory stocks. Four different engraving styles are executed in class "B" coverage. The left grip is scrimshawed as follows: R. Henshaw 1831, L. Nimschke 1850–1900, C. Helfricht 1871–1921, Contemporary. Only 20 mfg., 10 in high polish blue, 10 in full bright nickel.

* ***High Polish Blue Finish***

	$2,700	$1,900	$1,425

Last MSR was $1,290.

* ***Full Bright Nickel Finish***

	$2,950	$2,100	$1,575

Last MSR was $1,484.

1860 ARMY ELECTROLESS NICKEL - .44 cal. perc., 8 in. round barrel, creeping loading lever, six shot cylinder roll engraved with naval battle scene, full electroless nickel finish and one-piece walnut stocks. Approx. 50 mfg. 1982 only.

	$1,600	$1,100	$800

Last MSR was $465.

1860 ARMY ELECTROLESS NICKEL CASED WITH SHOULDER STOCK - .44 cal. perc., 8 in. round barrel, creeping loading lever, six shot cylinder roll engraved with naval battle scene, electroless nickel finish on all steel parts, brass trigger guard, one-piece walnut stocks. Includes a walnut presentation case with French fit green velvet interior, complete set of Colt 1860 Army accessories, 3rd model shoulder stock with brass yoke and buttplate and electroless nickel finish on latch, thumbscrew, swivel, ring, and screws. This set also includes a Colt two-tone 2nd ed. belt buckle. Approx. 10-20 sets were produced.

	$2,500	$1,700	$1,250

1860 ARMY BUTTERFIELD OVERLAND DESPATCH SPECIAL EDITION - .44 cal. perc., 5.5 in. round barrel, creeping loading lever, six shot cylinder engraved with Butterfield Stagecoach scene, spare cylinder with engraved portrait of Col. David Butterfield, Conestoga wagon, and longhorn steer, barrel engraved with "BUTTERFIELD OVERLAND DESPATCH," surrounded by vine scroll detail on left side, "SPECIAL EDITION 1 of 500" on the right side, "F" Series Colt Blue barrel, cylinders and backstrap with cut for shoulder stock, case hardened frame, loading lever, plunger, and hammer, brass trigger guard, one-piece walnut stocks. Includes French fit book-style presentation case. 500 mfg. 1979 only.

	$1,100	$750	$550

Last MSR was $995.

1860 ARMY 1 OF 500 CASED LIMITED EDITION - .44 cal. perc., 8 in. round barrel, creeping loading lever, six shot cylinder roll engraved with naval battle scene, "F" Series Colt Blue barrel, cylinder and backstrap, case hardened frame, loading lever, plunger, and hammer, brass trigger guard, one-piece walnut stocks. This set includes a black painted walnut French fit presentation case with gold velvet lining, gold plated 2nd edition belt buckle, complete accessory set including "stand of flags" powder flask, two cavity blue steel bullet mold, "L" shaped nipple wrench, and cap tin. 500 mfg. 1979 only.

	$1,025	$700	$525

1860 FLUTED ARMY - .44 cal. perc., 8 in. round barrel, creeping loading lever, six shot full fluted cylinder without engraving, "F" Series Colt Blue barrel, cylinder, and backstrap, case hardened frame, loading lever, plunger, and hammer, brass trigger guard, one-piece walnut stocks. 2,670 mfg.

	$725	$500	$375

Last MSR was $456.

* ***1860 Fluted Army Special XFC Series*** - .44 cal. perc., similar to 1860 Fluted Army, except full bright nickel finish, and XFC serial number prefix. They were among the last 2nd gen. percussion revolvers produced by Colt. Serial number range XFC1-XFC10.

GRADING	NIB	98%	95%

>One-piece smooth ivory stocks.

| | $2,500 | $1,750 | $1,325 |

>One-piece ebony stocks, and class "C" engraving coverage.

| | $3,200 | $2,250 | $1,700 |

>One-piece smooth ivory stocks, and class "C" engraving coverage.

| | $3,500 | $2,475 | $1,850 |

1860 ARMY STAINLESS STEEL
- .44 cal. perc., 8 in. round barrel, creeping loading lever, six shot cylinder roll engraved with naval battle scene, stainless steel barrel, cylinder, frame, loading lever, plunger, hammer, backstrap, and trigger guard, one-piece walnut stocks, 42 oz. 1,596 mfg. 1982 only.

| | $825 | $575 | $425 |

Last MSR was $485.

1860 ARMY U.S. CAVALRY COMMEMORATIVE CASED PAIR
- .44 cal. perc., includes two Colt Model 1860 Army percussion revolvers with 8 in. round barrel, creeping loading lever, six shot cylinder roll engraved with naval battle scene, blue barrel marked "UNITED STATES CAVALRY COMMEMORATIVE" on left side, cylinder, and backstrap, case hardened frame, loading lever, plunger, and hammer, brass trigger guard, one-piece walnut stocks, and English fit walnut presentation case with blue velvet lining. The case accommodates two revolvers and a "stand of flags" powder flask, blue two cavity bullet mold, "L" shaped nipple wrench, cap tin, and a detachable 3rd model shoulder stock. 2,945 cased sets mfg. 1977-1980.

| | $1,250 | $825 | $625 |

Last MSR was $995.

* **1860 Army U.S. Cavalry Commemorative Cased Pair "C" Suffix** - similar to 1860 Army U.S. Cavalry Commemorative Cased Pair, except these sets have a "C" stamped beneath the serial number on the frame. These sets have duplicate serial numbers therefore, the "C" was assigned to these revolvers in order for each revolver to have a unique serial number. 40 sets mfg. with "C" suffix serial no.

| | $1,350 | $900 | $675 |

Last MSR was $995.

* **1860 Army U.S. Cavalry Commemorative w/Stock "C" Suffix** - similar to 1860 Army U.S. Cavalry Commemorative Cased Pair, except single gun cased set with a matching 3rd model shoulder stock, a complete set of accessories, and with "C" stamped beneath the ser. no. Issued from the same production quantity as the model above. 40 mfg.

| | $1,150 | $800 | $600 |

* **1860 Army U.S. Cavalry Commemorative Custom Gold Inlaid** - similar to 1860 Army U.S. Cavalry Commemorative Cased Pair, except, gold inlaid barrel band at the muzzle, gold star flush inlaid between each chamber at the rear of the cylinder, and inscription "XX of 40" engraved on the left side of each frame. 17 pair mfg.

| | $3,000 | $2,100 | $1,575 |

* **1860 Army U.S. Cavalry Commemorative Custom Engraved and Gold Inlaid** - similar 1860 Army U.S. Cavalry Commemorative Custom Gold Inlaid, except class "A" vine style scroll engraving on the barrels, class "B" engraving on the frames and stock mount, with wolf's head engraving on the hammers. Vine style engraving embellishes all accessories except the cap tin. 23 pair mfg.

| | $6,500 | $4,700 | $3,500 |

Last MSR was $4,500.

GRADING	NIB	98%	95%

1861 NAVY - .36 cal. perc., 7.5 in. round barrel, creeping loading lever, six shot cylinder roll engraved with naval battle scene, "F" Series Colt Blue barrel and cylinder, case hardened frame, loading lever, plunger, and hammer, silver plated brass backstrap and trigger guard, one-piece walnut stocks, 42 oz. 3,166 mfg. 1980-81.

	$675	$475	$350

Last MSR was $420.

1861 NAVY STAINLESS STEEL - .36 cal. perc., 7.5 in. round barrel, creeping loading lever, six shot cylinder roll engraved with naval battle scene, stainless steel barrel, cylinder, frame, loading lever, plunger, hammer, backstrap, and trigger guard, one-piece walnut stocks. 8 mfg. 1982 only.

	$6,750	$4,875	$3,650

Last MSR was $473.

1862 POCKET NAVY - .36 cal. perc., 5.5 in. octagon barrel, hinged loading lever, five shot cylinder with roll engraved stagecoach scene, "F" Series Colt Blue barrel and cylinder, case hardened frame, loading lever, plunger, and hammer, silver plated brass backstrap and trigger guard, one-piece walnut stocks, 27 oz. 5,306 mfg. 1979-1981.

	$500	$350	$250

Last MSR was $394.

1862 POCKET NAVY 1 OF 500 LIMITED EDITION - .36 cal. perc., 5.5 in. octagon barrel, hinged loading lever, five shot cylinder with roll engraved stagecoach scene, "F" Series Colt Blue barrel and cylinder, case hardened frame, loading lever, plunger, and hammer, silver plated brass backstrap and trigger guard, one-piece walnut stocks. This set includes a black painted walnut French fit presentation case with gold velvet lining, special Colt 1st edition gold plated belt buckle with black anodized background, and a complete Colt accessory set (eagle style powder flask, two cavity blued steel bullet mold, "L" shaped nipple wrench, and cap tin). 500 mfg. 1979-80.

	$825	$550	$400

1862 POCKET NAVY BRIGHT NICKEL (MN SERIES) - .36 cal. perc., 5.5 in. octagon barrel, hinged loading lever, five shot cylinder with roll engraved stagecoach scene, full bright nickel finish and one-piece ivory stocks. 25 Mfg. 1984 only.

	$1,650	$1,175	$875

Last MSR was $450.

1862 POCKET NAVY 150TH ANNIVERSARY ENGRAVING SAMPLER - .36 cal. perc., 5.5 in. octagon barrel, hinged loading lever, five shot cylinder with roll engraved stagecoach scene, high polish blue barrel and cylinder, case hardened frame, loading lever, plunger, and hammer, brass backstrap and trigger guard, one-piece ivory stocks. Four different engraving styles are executed in class "B" coverage. The scrimshawed left grip reads as follows: R. Henshaw 1831, L. Nimschke 1850–1900, C. Helfricht 1871–1921, contemporary. 20 mfg., 10 in high polish blue, 10 in bright nickel.

* *High Polish Blue Finish*

	$2,050	$1,475	$1,100

Last MSR was $960.

* *Full Bright Nickel Finish*

	$2,250	$1,600	$1,200

Last MSR was $1,155.

GRADING	NIB	98%	95%

1862 POCKET POLICE - .36 cal. perc., 5.5 in. round barrel, creeping loading lever, five shot half fluted cylinder, "F" Series Colt Blue barrel and cylinder, case hardened frame, loading lever, plunger, and hammer, silver plated brass backstrap and trigger guard, one-piece walnut stocks. 3,756 mfg. 1980-81.

	$550	$375	$275

Last MSR was $394.

1862 POCKET POLICE 1 OF 500 LIMITED EDITION - .36 cal. perc., 5.5 in. round barrel, creeping loading lever, five shot half fluted cylinder, "F" Series Colt Blue barrel and cylinder, case hardened frame, loading lever, plunger, and hammer, silver plated brass backstrap and trigger guard, one-piece walnut stocks. This set includes a black painted walnut French fit presentation case with gold velvet lining, special Colt 1st edition edition gold plated belt buckle with a black anodized background, and a complete Colt accessory set (eagle style powder flask, two cavity blued steel bullet mold, "L" shaped nipple wrench, and cap tin). 500 mfg. 1979-80.

	$875	$575	$450

1862 POCKET POLICE BRIGHT NICKEL (MN SERIES) - .36 cal. perc., 5.5 in. round barrel, creeping loading lever, five shot half fluted cylinder, full bright nickel finish with one-piece ivory stocks. 25 Mfg. 1984 only.

	$1,800	$1,275	$975

Last MSR was $450.

1862 POCKET POLICE 150TH ANNIVERSARY ENGRAVING SAMPLER - .36 cal. perc., 5.5 in. round barrel, creeping loading lever, five shot half fluted cylinder, high polish blue barrel and cylinder, case hardened frame, loading lever, plunger, and hammer, brass backstrap and trigger guard, one-piece ivory grip. Class "B" engraving coverage is executed in four different styles. The scrimshawed left grip reads, R. Henshaw 1831, L. Nimschke 1850–1900, C. Helfricht 1871–1921, Contemporary. 4 examples were produced. Another 16 were manufactured as described above but with a full bright nickel finish.

* *High Polish Blue Finish*

	$2,900	$2,100	$1,575

Last MSR was $960.

* *Full Bright Nickel Finish*

	$2,200	$1,575	$1,175

Last MSR was $1,155.

1847 WALKER - .44 cal. perc., 9 in. round barrel, hinged loading lever, six shot cylinder with roll engraved Texas Ranger and Indian scene, "F" Series Colt Blue barrel, cylinder and backstrap, case hardened frame, loading lever, plunger, and hammer, brass trigger guard, one-piece walnut stocks, 73 oz., 4 digit ser. no. 2,920 mfg. 1980-82.

	$975	$700	$525

Last MSR was $562.

* *1847 Walker Variation with Five Digit Serial Number* - Same features as the 1847 Walker listed above. This was a factory error where Dragoon range serial numbers were mistakenly applied to these revolvers. Serial number range 32256–32500. 244 mfg. 1981 only.

	$1,100	$750	$575

Last MSR was $562.

WALKER COLT HERITAGE MODEL - .44 cal. perc., 9 in. round barrel, hinged loading lever, six shot cylinder, blue barrel, cylinder, and backstrap, case hardened frame, loading lever, plunger, and hammer, brass trigger guard, one-piece walnut stocks. This model is embellished with gold etched portraits of Samuel Colt and Samuel Walker on the barrel lugs and a floral pattern banner gold etched on the barrel. Includes a French

GRADING	NIB	98%	95%

fit walnut presentation case with green velvet lining, walnut book rack, and a signed, leather bound edition of R.L. Wilson's book *The Colt Heritage* numbered to the gun. 1,853 mfg. 1980-81.

	$1,100	$750	$600

Last MSR was $1,475.

1ST MODEL DRAGOON - .44 cal. perc., 7.5 in. round barrel, hinged loading lever, six shot cylinder with oval bolt cuts and roll engraved Texas Ranger and Indian scene, "F" Series Colt Blue barrel and cylinder, color case hardened frame, loading lever, plunger, and hammer, brass backstrap and square back trigger guard, one-piece walnut stocks, 66 oz. 3,700 mfg. 1980-82.

	$600	$400	$300

Last MSR was $448.

1ST MODEL DRAGOON YORKTOWN VICTORY LIMITED EDITION - .44 cal. perc., 7.5 in. round barrel, hinged loading lever, six shot cylinder with oval bolt cuts and roll engraved Texas Ranger and Indian scene, "F" Series Colt Blue barrel and cylinder, color case hardened frame, loading lever, plunger, and hammer, brass backstrap and square back trigger guard, one-piece walnut stocks. Includes a French fit, walnut presentation case with Tyrol red velvet interior built to house a single revolver without accessories. A brass plaque is affixed to the lid, which reads as follows: "America's Victory Celebration, Yorktown Virginia, October 19, 1981, One of One Hundred, 1781–1981, S-N." 100 mfg. 1981 only.

	$1,000	$675	$500

2ND MODEL DRAGOON - .44 cal. perc., 7.5 in. round barrel, hinged loading lever, six shot cylinder with rectangular bolt cuts and roll engraved Texas Ranger and Indian scene, "F" Series Colt Blue barrel and cylinder, color case hardened frame, loading lever, plunger, and hammer, brass backstrap and square back trigger guard, one-piece walnut stocks, 66 oz. 2,700 mfg. 1980-82.

	$650	$450	$350

Last MSR was $448.

3RD MODEL DRAGOON "F" SERIES - .44 cal. perc., 7.5 in. round barrel, hinged loading lever, six shot cylinder with rectangular bolt cuts and roll engraved Texas Ranger and Indian scene, "F" Series Colt Blue barrel and cylinder, color case hardened frame, loading lever, plunger, and hammer, brass backstrap and round trigger guard, one-piece walnut stocks, 66 oz. This is the second series of second generation 3rd Model Dragoons produced. Ser. no. range 25100–34500. 2,900 mfg. 1980-82.

	$625	$425	$325

Last MSR was $448.

3RD MODEL DRAGOON GIUSEPPE GARIBALDI LIMITED EDITION - .44 cal. perc., 7.5 in. round barrel, hinged loading lever, six shot cylinder with rectangular bolt cuts, "F" Series Colt Blue barrel and cylinder, case hardened frame, loading lever, plunger, and hammer, brass backstrap and round trigger guard, one-piece walnut stocks. This model is embellished with gold etched portraits of Samuel Colt and Giuseppe Garibaldi on the cylinder and gold etched panels on the barrel. This set includes a French fit, walnut presentation case with a swiveling etched glass lid. The Tyrol red velvet lined interior is designed to accommodate a single Colt 3rd Model Dragoon without accessories. 106 mfg.

	$1,000	$675	$500

Last MSR was $950.

* **3rd Model "Freak" Dragoon** - this model was produced from a small quantity of unfinished Garibaldi Models and is within the same unique serial number range. The barrel and blank cylinder remain "in-the-white" and without any of the gold etching. Case hardened frame, loading lever, plunger, and hammer, brass backstrap and round trigger guard, one-piece walnut stocks. Also, no presentation case was furnished. 94 mfg.

	$700	$450	$350

Last MSR was $395.

GRADING	NIB	98%	95%

BABY DRAGOON - .31 cal. perc., 4 in. octagon barrel without loading lever, five shot cylinder roll engraved with Texas Ranger and Indian scene, "F" Series Colt Blue barrel and cylinder, case hardened frame and hammer, silver plated brass backstrap and trigger guard, one-piece walnut stocks. 1,352 mfg. 1981-82.

	$600	$400	$300

Last MSR was $405.

BABY DRAGOON 1 OF 500 LIMITED EDITION - .31 cal. perc., 4 in. octagon barrel without loading lever, five shot cylinder roll engraved with Texas Ranger and Indian scene, "F" Series Colt Blue barrel and cylinder, case hardened frame and hammer, silver plated brass backstrap and trigger guard, one-piece walnut stocks. This set includes a black painted walnut French fit presentation case with gold velvet lining, and a complete Colt accessory set (eagle style powder flask, brass two cavity bullet mold, "L" shaped nipple wrench, and cap tin) 500 mfg. 1979-80.

	$975	$650	$500

COLT BLACKPOWDER ARMS CO.

Previous manufacturer and retailer of 3rd Generation Colt Black Powder pistols and muskets located in Brooklyn, NY 1994-2002.

All 3rd Generation Colt blackpowder models are also referred to as Signature Series Models.

A reprise of the original Colt Blackpowder line, along with historic models not offered in the 2nd Generation, and a new series of Commemoratives, each model (with the exception of the Heirloom Tiffany 1860 Army and 1842 Texas Paterson) bears the Sam Colt signature on the backstrap. These 3rd Generation models are manufactured under an authorized licensing agreement with Colt Firearms by Colt Blackpowder Arms Company – the same company (and many of the same craftsmen) responsible for the 2nd Generation Colt revolvers. Although parts for the Signature Series are cast in Italy, they are fully assembled and hand finished in the United States using the proprietary Colt formulas for bluing and color case hardening.

Colt Blackpowder Arms Company Signature Series revolvers are regarded as authentic Colt pistols. The 3rd Generation models have original Colt markings, including the barrel address and serial number stampings. There are no foreign proof marks on these authentic Colt models.

Please refer to *Colt Blackpowder Reproductions & Replicas—A Collector's & Shooter's Guide* for color pictures of the 3rd Generation Colt Blackpowder makes and models listed below. Third Generation Colts can be found on pages 23 through 37, and pages 77, 84, 85, 86, and 94.

GRADING	100%	98%	95%	90%	80%	70%	60%

REVOLVERS: PERCUSSION

1842 PATERSON - .36 cal. perc., No. 5 Holster Model with hinged loading lever, 5 shot, 7.5 inch octagon barrel, steel backstrap, period-style scrollwork with punch-dot background on both sides of barrel lug, frame, standing breech, loading lever rod tip, hammer, and backstrap. Mfg. 1998-2002.

$3,895	$3,050	$2,550

Last MSR was $4,500.

This model took approximately four months to manufacture and hand engrave.

TEXAS PATERSON - .36 cal. perc., No. 5 Holster Model with hinged loading lever, 5 shot, 7.5 inch octagon barrel, and steel backstrap. Standard model without engraving. Mfg. 2002 only.

$1,080	$920	$740

Last MSR was $1,200.

1847 WALKER - .44 cal. perc., 9 in. barrel, color case hardened frame, hammer, and loading lever, 73 oz. Mfg. 1994-2002.

$675	$605	$545

Last MSR was $750.

GRADING	100%	98%	95%	90%	80%	70%	60%

1847 WALKER NICKEL - .44 cal. perc., 9 in. barrel, nickel finish, 73 oz. Mfg. 2002 only.

	$765	$685	$615

Last MSR was $850.

1847 WALKER 150TH ANNIVERSARY EDITION - .44 cal. perc., 9 in. barrel, color case hardened frame, hammer, and loading lever, 73 oz. "A COMPANY No. 1" on barrel lug, frame and cylinder. Serial numbers begin with #221. Limited production model. Mfg. 1997-2002.

	$810	$730	$655

Last MSR was $900.

WHITNEYVILLE HARTFORD DRAGOON - .44 cal. perc., 7.5 in. barrel, oval bolt cuts in cylinder, color case hardened 3 screw frame, loading lever, plunger, and hammer, silver plated gripstrap and square back trigger guard, one-piece walnut grips. Mfg. 1996-2002.

	$675	$605	$545

Last MSR was $750.

1ST MODEL DRAGOON - .44 cal. perc., 7.5 in. barrel, oval bolt cuts in cylinder, color case hardened frame, loading lever, plunger, and hammer, square back trigger guard, one-piece walnut grips. Mfg. 1998-2002.

	$675	$605	$545

Last MSR was $750.

2ND MODEL DRAGOON - .44 cal. perc., 7.5 in. barrel, rectangular bolt cuts in cylinder, color case hardened frame, loading lever, plunger, and hammer, square back trigger guard, one-piece walnut grips. Mfg. 1998-2002.

	$675	$605	$545

Last MSR was $750.

3RD MODEL DRAGOON BRASS CIVILIAN MODEL - .44 cal. perc., 7.5 in. barrel, rectangular bolt cuts in cylinder, color case hardened frame, loading lever, plunger, and hammer, brass backstrap and round trigger guard, one-piece walnut grips. Mfg. 1996-2002.

	$675	$605	$545

Last MSR was $750.

This model was also available in a steel frame, military four screw variation with blue steel backstrap, cut for optional shoulder stock, fluted cylinder, silver plated backstrap, and round trigger guard.

3RD MODEL DRAGOON COCHISE COMMEMORATIVE - .44 cal. perc., 7.5 in. barrel, rectangular bolt cuts in cylinder, color case hardened frame, loading lever, plunger, and hammer, 24Kt. gold-plated backstrap and round trigger guard, 24Kt. gold inlays on barrel, lug, and frame, one-piece carved black horn grips. Mfg. 1997-2002.

	$1,165	$1,050	$945

Last MSR was $1,295.

3RD MODEL DRAGOON MARINE COMMEMORATIVE - .44 cal. perc., 7.5 in. barrel, rectangular bolt cuts in cylinder, silver plated frame and barrel, 24Kt. gold plated cylinder, loading lever, plunger, wedge, trigger, hammer, backstrap, and square back trigger guard, one-piece walnut grips. Semper Fidelis engraved on backstrap. 950 mfg. 1997.

	$1,400	$1,260	$1,135

Last MSR was $895.

GRADING	100%	98%	95%	90%	80%	70%	60%

1848 BABY DRAGOON - .31 cal. perc., 5-shot, 4 in. barrel, unfluted straight cylinder, color case hardened frame, short frame, no loading lever, silver plated backstrap and square back trigger guard, walnut grips, 1.5 lbs. Mfg. 1998-2002.

$605 $545 $490

Last MSR was $675.

1849 POCKET - .31 cal. perc., 5-shot, 4 in. barrel, unfluted straight cylinder, color case hardened frame, short frame, silver plated backstrap and round trigger guard, walnut grips, 1.5 lbs. Disc. 2002.

$605 $545 $490

Last MSR was $675.

1849 POCKET 150TH ANNIVERSARY GOLD RUSH EDITION - .31 cal. perc., 5-shot, 4 in. barrel, unfluted straight cylinder, color case hardened frame, short frame, 24Kt. gold plated backstrap and round trigger guard, walnut grips, gold-plated cylinder with engraved prospecting scenes, Gold Rush medallion inlaid in the walnut grips, engraved "150th ANNIVERSARY GOLD RUSH" along the face of the barrel, 1.5 lbs. Limited Edition. Mfg. 1999-2002.

$805 $725 $650

Last MSR was $895.

1851 NAVY - .36 cal. perc., 7.5 in. octagon barrel, color case hardened frame, loading lever, plunger, and hammer, silver plated backstrap, square trigger guard, one-piece grip, 42 oz. Mfg. 1994-2002.

$625 $560 $505

Last MSR was $695.

* *1851 Navy London Model* - features original London barrel address. Mfg. 1997-2002.

$625 $560 $505

Last MSR was $695.

1851 NAVY 150TH ANNIVERSARY 1851-2001 COMMEMORATIVE - .36 cal. perc., 7.5 in. octagon barrel. The 1851 Navy commemorative has the seldom seen round trigger guard, and is hand engraved in a nautical theme with 70% coverage and genuine ivory grips showing a carved fouled anchor. The barrel and frame are Colt Royal Blue finish and all other parts are 24Kt. gold plated. Limited Edition. Mfg. 2000-02.

$4,500 $4,050 $3,645

Last MSR was $5,000.

This model took approximately four months for production and hand engraving.

1860 ARMY - .44 cal. perc., 8 in. round blue barrel, color case hardened, frame, loading lever, plunger, and hammer, round brass trigger guard, walnut stock, 2.75 lbs. Five versions were manufactured – one with a roll engraved rebated cylinder, one with blue fluted cylinder, the Officer's Model with hand-crafted brilliant blue finish and traditional crossed sabers in 24Kt. gold above the wedge pin, cut for shoulder stock, the U.S. Cavalry Gold with 24Kt. gold plated cylinder engraved with crossed saber emblem, and U.S. 1860, and 1860 in nickel finish.

* *1860 Army w/Rebated Cylinder* - Mfg. 1994-2002.

$625 $560 $505

Last MSR was $695.

* *1860 Army w/Fluted Cylinder* - Mfg. 1995-2002.

$625 $560 $505

Last MSR was $695.

GRADING	100%	98%	95%	90%	80%	70%	60%

❋ *1860 Army Officer's Model* - fluted cylinder, gold U.S. 1860 and crossed sabers on barrel, gold trigger guard. Mfg. 1995-2002.

	$675	$605	$545				

Last MSR was $750.

❋ *1860 Army Gold U.S. Cavalry Model* - gold rebated cylinder with U.S. 1860 and crossed sabers, two gold bands around muzzle, gold-plated backstrap and trigger guard. Mfg. 1996-2002.

	$720	$645	$580				

Last MSR was $800.

❋ *1860 Army w/Nickel Finish* - Mfg. 1997-2002.

	$675	$605	$545				

Last MSR was $750.

1860 ARMY HEIRLOOM - .44 cal. perc., made to order Tiffany-style revolver, with creeping-style loading lever, 6 shot 24Kt. gold plated, roll engraved, rebated cylinder, 8-inch round barrel, 100% coverage with L.D. Nimschke style scrollwork, silver and 24Kt. gold plated, silver plated Tiffany-style grips. Mfg. 1998-2002.

	$5,400	$4,850	$4,370				

Last MSR was $6,000.

This model took approximately four months for production and hand engraving.

1861 NAVY - .36 cal. perc, 7.5 in. round barrel, color case hardened frame, loading lever, plunger, and hammer, steel backstrap and trigger guard, roll-engraved cylinder and barrel, one-piece walnut grips. 42 oz. Mfg. 1995-2002.

	$625	$560	$505				

Last MSR was $695.

❋ *1861 Navy General Custer Edition* - .36 cal. perc., 7.5 in. round barrel, antique silver finish, 70% coverage Nimschke-style vine scroll engraving, carved rosewood stock bearing the eagle and shield. Mfg. 1996-2002.

	$1,165	$1,050	$945				

Last MSR was $1,295.

1862 POCKET NAVY - .36 cal. perc., 5.5 in. octagon barrel, color case hardened frame, loading lever, plunger, and hammer, silver plated backstrap and round trigger guard, rebated roll engraved cylinder. 25 oz. Mfg. 1996-2002.

	$605	$545	$490				

Last MSR was $675.

1862 POCKET POLICE - .36 cal. perc., 5.5 inch round barrel with creeping-style loading lever, color case hardened frame, loading lever, plunger, and hammer, 5 shot semi-fluted cylinder, silver plated backstrap and square back trigger guard, 25 oz. Mfg. 1997-2002.

	$605	$545	$490				

Last MSR was $675.

1862 TRAPPER MODEL - .36 cal. perc., 3.5 in. round barrel, color case hardened frame, and hammer, silver plated backstrap and trigger guard, no loading lever but supplied with 4.65 in. brass ramrod. Disc. 2002

	$605	$545	$490				

Last MSR was $675.

GRADING	100%	98%	95%	90%	80%	70%	60%

RIFLES: PERCUSSION

1861 MUSKET - .58 cal. perc., 40 in. round barrel with 3 barrel bands, all metal parts bright finished white steel, one-piece oil finished walnut stock. Mfg. 1995-2002.

$900 $810 $730

Last MSR was $1,000.

* **1861 Musket Artillery Model** - with 31.5 in. barrel with two barrel bands. Mfg. 1996-2002.

$900 $810 $730

Last MSR was $1,000.

Add $100 for Colt 1861 bayonet with scabbard.

* **1861 Musket 1 of 1,000** - this edition is serialized, and includes wood presentation box. Disc. 2001.

$2,270 $2,045 $1,835

Last MSR was $2,165.

CONNECTICUT VALLEY ARMS (CVA)

Current manufacturer/distributor located in Norcross, GA. A division of Blackpowder Products, Inc. Catalog and dealer sales.

PISTOLS: FLINTLOCK & PERCUSSION

All CVA pistols have color case hardened finishes with solid brass trim.

COLONIAL PISTOL - .45 cal. perc., 6.75 in. octagon barrel, 31 oz. Mfg. 1989-1994.

$125 $105 $85

Last MSR was $115.

HAWKEN PISTOL - .50 cal. flintlock or perc., 9.75 in. octagon barrel, 50 oz.

MSR $168 $153 $130 $100

Add $10 for flintlock.

KENTUCKY PISTOL - .45 or .50 cal. perc., 10.25 in. octagon barrel, brass blade front sight, 40 oz.

MSR $168 $153 $130 $100

MOUNTAIN PISTOL - .45 or .50 cal. perc., 9 in. octagon barrel, German silver wedge plate with pewter cap, 40 oz.

$135 $115 $90

PHILADELPHIA DERRINGER - .45 cal. perc., 3.25 in. octagon barrel, 16 oz. Disc. 1994.

$90 $75 $60

Last MSR was $90.

SIBER PISTOL - .45 cal. perc., 10.5 in. octagon, white steel engraved barrel, lock also engraved white steel, checkered walnut grip, 38 oz. Disc. 1994.

$400 $345 $260

Last MSR was $440.

TOWER PISTOL - .45 cal. perc., 9 in. octagon barrel (tapers to round at muzzle), antique brass trigger, 36 oz.

$135 $115 $90

REVOLVERS: PERCUSSION

All revolvers have solid brass triggerguards and backstraps, and walnut grips.

WALKER MODEL - .44 cal. perc., 9 in. barrel, color case hardened frame, hammer, and loading lever, 72 oz. Disc. 1996.

$240 $205 $150

Last MSR was $280.

3RD MODEL DRAGOON - .44 cal. perc., 7.5 in. barrel, rectangular bolt cuts in cylinder, color case hardened frame, loading lever, plunger, and hammer, round trigger guard, one-piece grip, 66 oz. Disc. 1994.

$220 $190 $155

Last MSR was $220.

1849 POCKET WELLS FARGO - .31 cal. perc., 3, 4, or 5 in. octagon barrel, 5 shot, color case hardened frame, hammer, no loading lever, brass trim, 1.5 lbs. Disc. 1994.

$115 $100 $80

Last MSR was $130.

1851 NAVY - .36 (disc. 1996) or .44 cal. perc., 7.5 in. octagon barrel, brass frame, 38 oz.

MSR $144 $125 $100 $75

Add $50 for steel frame.

POCKET POLICE - .36 cal. perc., 5.5 in. round barrel, color case hardened frame, loading lever, plunger, and hammer, round trigger guard, fluted cylinder, one-piece grip, 25 oz. Disc. 1996.

$115 $100 $80

Last MSR was $140.

Add $40 for steel frame.
Add $5 for Sheriff's Model.
Add $50 for engraved, nickel plated Sheriff's Model w/matching powder flask.

1860 ARMY - .44 cal. perc., 8 in. round barrel, 6 shot engraved cylinder, color case hardened frame, trigger, and loading lever, 44 oz. Disc. 1996.

$170 $155 $125

Last MSR was $195.

Subtract $40 for brass frame.

1861 NAVY - .36 or .44 cal. perc., 7.5 in. round barrel, 6 shot engraved cylinder, color case hardened frame, trigger, and loading lever, or brass frame (.44 cal. only), 44 oz. New 1986.

$115 $100 $80

Last MSR was $140.

Add $60 for color case hardened steel frame.
Add $60 for presentation grade Sheriff's Model with matching powder flask.
Add $10 for brass frame on Standard Sheriff's Model.
Add $25 for steel frame on Standard Sheriff's Model.

1851 NAVY/1851 SHERIFF'S MODEL (WAR AND PEACE) - .36 cal. perc., includes 1851 Navy and 1851 Sheriff's Models, heavily engraved in rosewood presentation case. Disc. 1994.

$390 $330 $240

Last MSR was $630.

1873 COLT SINGLE ACTION - .44 cal. perc., 7 in. round barrel, brass backstrap and trigger guard, color case hardened frame and cylinder, new in 1991 (this is a ball and cap version of the 1873 Colt SAA). Disc. 1994.

$300 $260 $210

Last MSR was $350.

GRADING	100%	98%	95%	90%	80%	70%	60%

1858 REMINGTON ARMY - .44 cal. perc., 8 in. octagon barrel, color case hardened hammer, steel or brass frame, 38 oz.

MSR	$160	$140	$115	$105			

Add $35 for steel frame.

1858 REMINGTON BISON - .44 cal. perc., brass frame, 10.25 in. octagon barrel, adj. sights, 3 lbs.

	$195	$175	$135				

Last MSR was $200.

NEW MODEL REMINGTON POCKET - .31 cal. perc., 5 shot, 4 in. octagon barrel, brass frame, 15 oz. Mfg. 1989-disc.

	$125	$105	$85				

Last MSR was $150.

1858 REMINGTON TARGET - .44 cal. perc., 12 in. octagon barrel, brass frame and trigger guard, adj. sights, based on 1858 Navy frame, 38 oz.

	$195	$175	$135				

Last MSR was $205.

OFFICER AND THE GENTLEMAN - matched set .44 cal. perc., 1858 Rem. Army and .31 cal. perc. New Model Remington Pocket, heavily engraved in rosewood presentation case. Disc. 1994.

	$500	$425	$300				

Last MSR was $650.

RIFLES: FLINTLOCK & PERCUSSION

BLUNDERBUSS - .69 cal. flintlock, 16 in. tapered to flared muzzle barrel, brass trim, available right or left-hand, 5 lbs. 5 oz. Disc. 1994.

	$240	$195	$155				

Last MSR was $255.

BOBCAT HUNTER RIFLE - .36, .50, or .54 (disc.) cal. perc., 26 in. octagon barrel, (1:48 in. twist) matte black finish, adj. sights, hardwood or synthetic stock. New 1995.

MSR	$105	$95	$85	$75			

Add $40 for .36 cal. Disc.
Subtract $20 for fixed sights.
Add $23 for hardwood stock.

BUSHWACKER RIFLE - .50 cal. perc., 26 in. octagon barrel, color case hardened hammer, lock, and nipple, blue furniture, 7.5 lbs. Disc. 1994.

	$140	$120	$95				

Last MSR was $160.

EXPRESS RIFLE - .50 or .54 cal. perc., double barrel, 28 in. tapered round barrel, color case hardened plate, hammers, and trim, adj. sights. Mfg. 1986-disc.

	$400	$350	$280				

Last MSR was $430.

Add $160 for extra set of 12 ga. barrels.
Add $375 for presentation grade.

GRADING	100%	98%	95%	90%	80%	70%	60%

FRONTIER RIFLE/CARBINE - .45, .50, or .54 cal. flintlock or perc., 28 in. octagon barrel, brass trim, right or left-hand, 7.9 lbs. Disc. 1994.

	$160	$145	$100

Last MSR was $190.

Add $15 for flintlock.
Add $10 for left-hand.
Add $10 for carbine model.

FRONTIER HUNTER CARBINE - .50 or .54 cal. perc., 24 in. blue octagon barrel, color case hardened hammer and lock, blue furniture, adj. rear sight, 7.5 lbs. Disc. 2002.

	$190	$170	$125

Last MSR was $220.

During 1995, a laminated stock became standard on this model.

HAWKEN RIFLE/CARBINE - .50 or .54 cal. flintlock or perc., 28 in. octagon chrome bore barrel, brass trim, beavertail select walnut stock, 7 lbs. 15 oz. Disc. 1994.

	$335	$290	$240

Last MSR was $440.

Add $10 for flintlock.

HAWKEN DEERSLAYER RIFLE/CARBINE - .50 cal. perc., similar to above, 7.5 lbs. Mfg. 1992 only.

	$220	$190	$160

Last MSR was $250.

HUNTER HAWKEN RIFLE/CARBINE - .50 or .54 cal. perc., 24 in. (carbine) or 28 in. octagon barrel, color case hardened lock and nipple, sling swivels, adj. hunting sights. 8 lbs. Disc. 1994.

	$230	$200	$160

Last MSR was $330.

Add $70 for premier grade (.50 cal. only).

KENTUCKY RIFLE/HUNTER - .45 or .50 cal. flintlock or perc., 33.5 in. octagon barrel, color case hardened hammer and plate, antique brass trigger, 7.25 lbs. Disc. 1996.

	$240	$210	$170

Last MSR was $280.

Add $10 for flintlock, or adj. hunting sights.

LYNX RIFLE - .50 or .54 cal. perc., similar to Bobcat Hunter but with camo Realtree gray stock and 1:32 in. twist barrel. Disc. 1996.

	$160	$130	$105

Last MSR was $180.

MISSOURI HUNTER RIFLE - .50 cal. perc., 28 in. octagon barrel, adj. hunting sights, color case hardened hammer and lock, recoil pad, 9 lbs. 6 oz. New 1991. Disc. 1994.

	$200	$175	$140

Last MSR was $300.

MISSOURI RANGER - .50 cal. perc., 28 in. octagon barrel, color case hardened trim, right or left-hand, 7.5 lbs.

	$190	$170	$130

GRADING	100%	98%	95%	90%	80%	70%	60%

MOUNTAIN RIFLE - .50 or .54 cal. flintlock or perc., 32 in. octagon barrel, German silver wedge plate and patch box, pewter or German silver nose cap, 7 lbs. 14 oz. Disc. 1994.

$240 $210 $170

Last MSR was $260.

Add $80 for premier grade (chrome bore and German silver trim).

MOUNTAIN RIFLE CLASSIC - .50 cal. perc., 32 in. brown steel barrel, 1:66 inch rifling twist, brown hardware, German silver wedge plates and blade front sight, buckhorn rear sight, American hard maple stock, 9 lbs. Modeled after the original CVA Mountain Rifle. Made in the USA. In limited quantities.

MSR $400 $350 $285 $225

MOUNTAIN RIFLE HUNTER - .50 cal. perc., 32 in. blue steel barrel, 1:48 inch rifling twist, blue hardware, blade front sight, buckhorn rear sight, hardwood stock, 9 lbs. Modeled after the original CVA Mountain Rifle. Made in the USA. Limited quantities. New 2002.

MSR $260 $210 $185 $155

OVER/UNDER DOUBLE BARREL CARBINE - .50 cal. perc., O/U, 26 in. octagon tapering to round barrels, color case hardened lock, hammers, and triggers, checkered walnut stock, 8.5 lbs. Disc. 1994.

$575 $500 $400

Last MSR was $800.

PANTHER CARBINE - .50 or .54 cal. perc., 24 in. octagon blue barrel, color case hardened hammer (45 degree offset) and lock, modern trigger, adj. rear sight, available in left-hand (.50 cal. only), epoxy coated hardwood stock with recoil pad, 7.5 lbs. Disc. 1994.

$170 $145 $115

Last MSR was $190.

Add $15 for left-hand.

PENNSYLVANIA LONG RIFLE - .50 cal. flintlock or perc., 40 in. octagon barrel, color case hardened hammers and plate, brass trim, 8 lbs. 3 oz. Disc. 1993.

$385 $335 $255

Last MSR was $455.

PLAINSHUNTER RIFLE - .50 cal. flintlock or perc., octagon barrel, 1:48 in. twist, color case hardened hammer and lock, brass nose cap and trigger guard. New 1995. Disc.

$160 $120 $95

Last MSR was $175.

PLAINSMAN RIFLE - .50 cal. flintlock or perc., 26 in. blue octagon barrel, color case hardened lock and nipple, select hardwood stock, 6.5 lbs.

MSR $180 $155 $125 $100

SIERRA STALKER RIFLE - .50 cal. perc., 28 in. blue octagon barrel, color case hardened hammer and lock, adj. sight (rear), 7.25 lbs. Mfg. 1993-94.

$170 $130 $100

Last MSR was $190.

SQUIRREL RIFLE - .32 cal. flintlock or perc., 25 in. octagon barrel, color case hardened hammer and plate, brass trim, stainless steel nipple, 5 lbs. 12 oz. Disc. 1994.

$230 $200 $160

Last MSR was $250.

Add $10 for flintlock or left-hand.

GRADING	100%	98%	95%	90%	80%	70%	60%

ST. LOUIS HAWKEN - .50 or .54 cal. flintlock or perc., 28 in. blue octagon barrel, select hardwood stock, fully adjustable sights, brass trim, buttplate, patch box, 7 lbs. 13 oz. Also available in left-hand percussion model. New 1995.

MSR	$275	$245	$195	$145

Subtract $45 for right-hand percussion model.

STALKER RIFLE - .50 cal. perc., 28 in. octagon barrel, hunting style sight (click adj.) color case hardened hammer and lock, recoil pad, 7 lbs. 4 oz. Mfg. 1991-94.

	$190	$160	$130

Last MSR was $220.

Add $100 for premier grade.
Add $20 for left-hand.

TRACKER CARBINE - .50 cal. perc., 21 in. blue half round/half octagon barrel, color case hardened nipple, hammer and lock, new laminated stock in 1994, 6.5 lbs. Disc. 1994.

	$195	$170	$135

Last MSR was $230.

TROPHY CARBINE - .50 or .54 cal. perc., 24 in. half round/half octagon, similar to above with sling swivel mounts and dark stained Monte Carlo stock, 7.5 lbs. Disc. 1994.

	$230	$200	$140

Last MSR was $260.

VARMINT RIFLE - .32 cal. perc., 24 in. octagon, blue barrel, color case hardened hammer and lock, brass trigger guard and furniture, adj. rear sight, 6.75 lbs. New 1993.

	$200	$170	$135

Last MSR was $220.

WOLF SERIES RIFLES - .50 or .54 cal. perc., 26 in. matte blue barrel, color case hardened hammer and lock, adj. sights, Tuff-Lite stock, 6.5 lbs.

	$140	$125	$100

Last MSR was $170.

Add $15 for Lone Wolf Rifle with better rear sight and vent. recoil pad (.50 cal. only).
Add $25 for Timber Wolf Rifle with RealTree all purpose camo stock (.50 cal. only).
Add $15 for Silver Wolf Rifle with stainless steel barrel & nickel hardware.

WOODSMAN RIFLE - .50 or .54 cal. perc., 26 in. octagon blue barrel, color case hardened hammer and lock, brass tip ramrod, adj. sights, laminated stock, 6.5 lbs.

	$170	$150	$110

Last MSR was $190.

YOUTH HUNTER - .50 cal. perc., 24 in. blue octagon blue barrel, shortened half stock, adj. sights, select hardwood stock, designed according to input from the YMCA, Hunter Education, Boy Scouts of America, 4-H Clubs. 5 lbs.

MSR	$136	$120	$95	$75

ZOUAVE RIFLE - .58 cal. perc., 32.5 in. tapered barrel with bayonet mount, brass trim, and adj. sight, 9.75 lbs. Mfg. 1989-1994.

	$290	$250	$200

Last MSR was $335.

GRADING	100%	98%	95%	90%	80%	70%	60%

RIFLES: IN-LINE IGNITION, APOLLO SERIES

All Apollo models are percussion, and were discontinued in 1997.

APOLLO RIFLE - .50 or .54 cal. perc., 22 in. (carbine), 24, 25, or 27 in. round tapered barrel with chrome bore, straight pull bolt design.

* *Apollo 90 Rifle*

	$240	$210	$170

Last MSR was $260.

* *Apollo 90 Shadow Rifle* - with duragrip synthetic stock.

	$210	$180	$145

Last MSR was $240.

* *Apollo Brown Bear* - with hardwood stock and Williams Hunter sight.

	$200	$170	$140

Last MSR was $224.

* *Apollo Buckmaster* - with camo duragrip synthetic stock.

	$220	$190	$150

Last MSR was $247.

* *Apollo Carbelite* - similar to Apollo 90 models, except has Carbelite stock.

	$200	$170	$140

Last MSR was $350.

* *Apollo Comet* - with duragrip stock and adj. trigger.

	$225	$200	$160

Last MSR was $280.

* *Apollo Dominator* - with Bell & Carlson synthetic stock, stainless steel barrel, and modern adj. trigger.

	$250	$210	$170

Last MSR was $330.

* *Apollo Eclipse* - this is the standard model.

	$180	$160	$130

Last MSR was $208.

* *Apollo Shadow Rifle* - similar to Apollo 90 Shadow model.

	$210	$180	$145

Last MSR was $240.

* *Apollo Sporter* - with standard sporter stock and 25 in. barrel.

	$200	$170	$140

Last MSR was $225.

* *Apollo Stag Horn* - basic version of Apollo rifle with duragrip synthetic stock.

	$170	$150	$120

Last MSR was $185.

* *Apollo Starfire* - with duragrip stock and stainless steel barrel.

	$230	$200	$160

Last MSR was $270.

GRADING	100%	98%	95%	90%	80%	70%	60%

ACCUBOLT RIFLE - .50 cal. perc., 24 in. round barrel, synthetic standard thumbhole stock. 7.5 lbs.

$305 $260 $230

Last MSR was $340.

＊ *Accubolt Pro with Thumbhole Stock*

$500 $425 $325

Last MSR was $560.

BLAZER I/II RIFLE - .50 cal. perc., 28 in. octagon barrel, stainless steel nipple, brass tipped ramrod, 6.75 lbs. Disc. 1994.

$135 $115 $95

Last MSR was $210.

Subtract $10 for Blazer II.

ECLIPSE SERIES - .50 or .54 cal. perc., 24 in. round blue barrel, regular or black synthetic stock. 7 lbs. New 1998.

$155 $130 $110

Last MSR was $180.

Subtract $10 for black synthetic stock.

ECLIPSE 209 MAGNUM - .45 or .50 cal. perc., 24 in. round matte blue MonoBlock barrel, adjustable fiber optic sights, black synthetic, Mossy Oak Break-Up, Timber Blue, or Bigwoods Blue stock, 3-way ignition – #209 shot shell primer, musket cap, and No. 11 percussion cap, 6 lbs.

MSR $150 $130 $105 $80

Add $30 for Mossy Oak Break-Up, Bigwoods, or Timber Blue stock.

FIREBOLT RIFLE - .50 or .54 cal. perc., 24 in. round barrel, synthetic standard stock. 7 lbs. New 1998.

$245 $195 $160

Last MSR was $280.

＊ *FireBolt Stainless*

$260 $215 $175

Last MSR was $300.

＊ *Firebolt Thumbhole* - with steel barrel.

$245 $195 $160

Last MSR was $280.

FIREBOLT TEFLON RIFLES - .50 or .54 cal. perc., 24 in. round Teflon coated barrel, Teflon coating on all metal parts, synthetic standard stock. 7 lbs. New 1998.

$260 $215 $175

Last MSR was $300.

FIREBOLT LEFT-HAND RIFLE - .50 cal. perc., 24 in. round matte blue barrel, hardwood stock. 7.5 lbs. New 1998.

$260 $215 $175

Last MSR was $300.

FIREBOLT 209 ULTRAMAG - .45 or .50 cal. perc., 26 in. flutted round matte blue or nickel finish barrel, bolt-action, black FiberGrip synthetic, Mossy Oak Break-Up, Bigwoods Blue (disc.), or Timber Blue (disc.) stock, adjustable fiber optic sights, ventilated recoil pad, 3-way ignition – #209 shot shell primer, musket cap, and No. 11 percussion cap, 7 lbs. New 2001.

MSR $240 $200 $175 $150

GRADING	100%	98%	95%	90%	80%	70%	60%

Add $20 nickel barrel.
Add $40 for Mossy Oak Break-Up stock.
Add $60 for Bigwoods Blue, or Timber Blue stock.

HUNTERBOLT 209 MAGNUM RIFLES - .45 or .50 cal. perc., 26 in. round matte blue or nickel finish barrel, adjustable fiber optic sights, black synthetic or Mossy Oak Break-Up stock, 3-way ignition – #209 shot shell primer, musket cap, and No. 11 percussion cap, 7 lbs. .45 cal. models new 2002.

MSR	$190	$165	$135	$105

Add $15 nickel barrel.
Add $35 for Mossy Oak Break-Up, Bigwoods Blue, or Timber Blue stock.

MONSTER BUCK RIFLE - .50 or .54 cal. perc., 24 in. round matte blue barrel, synthetic X-Tra Brown camo stock. 7 lbs.

	$250	$205	$165

Last MSR was $290.

OPTIMA 209 MAGNUM BREAK-ACTION - .45 or .50 cal., #209 primer ignition, break-action, interchangeable 26 in. round blue or nickel finish barrel, 1:28 in. twist rifling, solid composite black or Mossy Oak Breaqk-Up finish stock, adj. Illuminator fiber optic sights, ventilated recoil pad, 8.2 lbs. New 2003.

MSR	$200	$170	$145	$120

Add $15 for nickel barrel.
Add $35 for Mossy Oak Break-Up stock.
Add $83 for additional blue barrel.
Add $98 for additional nickel barrel.

OPTIMA PRO 209 MAGNUM BREAK-ACTION - .45 or .50 cal., #209 primer ignition, break-action, interchangeable 29 in. fluted round blue or nickel finish barrel, 1:28 in. twist rifling, solid composite black FiberGrip or Mossy Oak Breaqk-Up finish stock, all metal adj. Dura-Bright fiber optic sights, ventilated recoil pad, 8.8 lbs. New 2003.

MSR	$260	$220	$180	$140

Add $20 for nickel barrel.
Add $40 for Mossy Oak Break-Up stock.
Add $95 for additional blue barrel.
Add $110 for additional nickel barrel.

ROCKY MOUNTAIN ELK FOUNDATION RIFLE - .54 cal. perc., Apollo action, designed to commemorate the Rocky Mountain Elk Foundation. Standard or thumbhole camo. stocks. 7.5 lbs.

	$270	$225	$185

Last MSR was $330.

Add $50 for thumbhole stock.

STAG HORN SERIES - .50 or .54 cal. #209 primer ignition, 24 in. round blue barrel, synthetic stock. 7 lbs.

MSR	$122	$105	$85	$65

SHOTGUNS: PERCUSSION

BRITTANY SHOTGUN SxS - 12 ga. perc., 28 in. barrels, 7 lbs. 7 oz. Disc. 1989.

	$275	$230	$185

Last MSR was $295.

BRITTANY SHOTGUN II SxS - .410 bore perc., 24 in. barrels, 6 lbs. 4 oz. Disc. 1989.

	$275	$230	$185

Last MSR was $210.

GRADING	100%	98%	95%	90%	80%	70%	60%

CLASSIC TURKEY SxS - 12 ga. perc., 28 in. round barrels, color case hardened lock, stainless steel nipple, recoil pad, 9 lbs.

$390 $360 $280

Last MSR was $460.

NWTF GOBBLER SERIES - 12 ga., 28 in. single chrome-lined blue barrel, color case hardened hammer and lock, select hardwood stock with laser engraved, full color Tom flying down from the roost, lock plate with official seal of the NWTF, 6 lbs. Limited production with a portion of all sales donated to the NWTF. Mfg. 2001-02.

$330 $280 $225

Last MSR was $368.

SHOTGUN SxS - 12 ga. or .410 bore perc., 28 in. (24 in. on .410 bore) barrels, 6 lbs. 10 oz (6 lbs. 4 oz. on .410 bore). Mfg. 1987-89.

$275 $230 $185

Last MSR was $275.

Subtract $85 for .410 bore.
Add $350 for Presentation grade.

TRAPPER SHOTGUN - 12 ga., 28 in. single chrome-lined blue barrel, color case hardened hammer and lock, select hardwood stock, 6 lbs. New 1988.

MSR $288 $240 $200 $160

CUMBERLAND MOUNTAIN ARMS, INC.

Previous manufacturer located in Winchester, TN. Dealer and consumer direct sales.

RIFLES: IN-LINE IGNITION

MOUNTAIN MUZZLE LOADER - .50 cal., utilizes #209 primer ignition, falling block action, 22 or 28 in. heavy round barrel, manual safety, adj. rear sights, gold front sight, walnut stock.

$895 $815 $650

Last MSR was $950.

D SECTION

DAVIDE PEDERSOLI & C. Snc

Please refer to the Pedersoli listing in the P section of this text.

DALY, CHARLES

Current trademark previously imported and distributed by K.B.I., Inc., located in Harrisburg, PA. and previously distributed by Outdoor Sports Headquarters, in Dayton, OH.

GRADING	100%	98%	95%	90%	80%	70%	60%

RIFLES: FLINTLOCK & PERCUSSION

All Charles Daly rifles feature adj. sights, investment cast brass trim, patch boxes, color case hardened hammer and locks, octagon rifle barrels, adj. double set triggers, and European hard wood stocks.

DELUXE HAWKEN RIFLE - .50 or .54 cal. perc. or flintlock, 29 in. barrel, right and left-hand. Disc. 2000.

	100%	98%	95%
	$340	$290	$230

Last MSR was $390.

Add $20 for left-hand.
Subtract $50 for percussion.

HAWKEN CARBINE - .50 cal. flintlock, 22 in. barrel. Disc. 1994.

	100%	98%	95%
	$250	$205	$160

Last MSR was $240.

HAWKEN RIFLE - .45, .50, or .54 cal. perc., 29 in. barrel, right-hand only. Disc. 2000.

	100%	98%	95%
	$250	$205	$160

Last MSR was $270.

Add $70 for Hunter Carbine Model.

DEER CREEK MFG.

Previous manufacturer located in Waldron, IN. Previously sold exclusively by Mountain States Muzzle Loading in Williamstown, WV.

For current Deer Creek Mfg. listings, refer to Mowrey Gun Works, Inc.

RIFLES: PERCUSSION

HIGHLANDER RIFLE - .50 or .54 cal. perc., 32 in. brown octagon barrel, brown furniture, hammer, lock, and patchbox, maple half stock, 7.5-7.75 lbs. Disc. 1994.

	100%	98%	95%
	$200	$180	$160

Last MSR was $280.

ROUGHRIDER RIFLE - .45, .50, or .54 cal. perc., 32 in. octagon blue barrel, pewter nosecap, German silver cap box and wedge plates, maple half stock, 7.5-7.75 lbs. Disc. 1994.

	100%	98%	95%
	$200	$180	$160

Last MSR was $280.

DIXIE GUN WORKS, INC.

Current importer and catalog house located in Union City, TN, established in 1954. Dixie is one of the oldest suppliers of black powder arms, and offers a complete line of flintlock, percussion lock, and cap and ball revolvers manufactured by F.lli Pietta, Uberti, and Palmetto, as well as an extensive selection of longarms, bayonets, Civil War uniforms, sabers, military accouterments, holsters, presentation cases, period camping supplies, and

tents. **Consumer direct (store or mail order) and dealer sales.**

Dixie offers an extensive line of hard to find Confederate models such as the Dance, Spiller & Burr, and LeMat revolvers. Please contact Dixie Gun Works, Inc. directly (see Trademark Index) to receive a catalog.

Short descriptions are for models of standard configuration. Also, since 1986, many models are imported from A. Uberti (see Uberti section.).

REVOLVERS: PERCUSSION

TEXAS PATERSON - .36 cal. perc., 9 in. barrel, has hidden trigger and no loading lever. Mfg. by Pietta.

MSR	$495	$400	$350	$300

HOLSTER MODEL PATERSON - .36 cal. perc., 7.5 in. barrel, has hidden trigger and no loading lever. Mfg. by Uberti.

MSR	$360	$295	$255	$220

WALKER - .44 cal. perc., 9 in. barrel, 6 shot, color case hardened frame, hammer, and loading lever, brass trim, 4.5 lbs. Mfg. by Palmetto & Uberti.

MSR	$325	$265	$230	$195

Subtract $75 for Palmetto Walker.

1ST MODEL DRAGOON - .44 cal. perc., 6 shot, brass grip straps, color case hardened frame, hammer, and loading lever, brass trim, 3.9 lbs. Mfg. by Uberti.

MSR	$320	$265	$225	$185

2ND MODEL DRAGOON - .44 cal. perc., 6 shot, brass grip straps, color case hardened frame, hammer, and loading lever, brass trim, 3.9 lbs. Mfg. by Uberti.

MSR	$320	$265	$225	$185

3RD MODEL DRAGOON - .44 cal. perc., 7 3/8 in. barrel, color case hardened frame, hammer, and loading lever, brass trigger guard and back strap. Mfg. by Uberti.

MSR	$320	$265	$225	$185

1848 BABY DRAGOON - .31 cal. perc., 6 in. barrel, color case hardened frame. Mfg. by Uberti.

MSR	$265	$215	$185	$155

1849 POCKET - .31 cal. perc., with loading lever, 3, 4, or 5 in. barrel, 5 shot, color case hardened frame, hammer, and loading lever, brass trim, 1.5 lbs. Mfg. by Uberti and Palmetto.

MSR	$275	$225	$195	$160

Subtract $104 for models mfg. by Palmetto.

1851 NAVY - .36 cal. perc., 7.5 in. octagon barrel, brass frame or color case hardened frame, hammer, and loading lever, brass trigger guard and back strap. Also available with antique finish (disc. 2003).

MSR	$163	$135	$115	$95

Subtract $25 for brass frame model.
Add $50 for antique finish. Mfg. by Pietta.
Add $100 for Mfg. by Uberti.

1851 LONDON NAVY - .36 cal. perc., 7.5 in. octagon barrel, color case hardened frame, hammer, and loading lever, blue trigger guard and back strap. New 2003.

MSR	$270	$220	$190	$160

1851 NAVY .44 - .44 cal. perc., 7.5 in. octagon barrel, antiqued finish, steel frame. Disc. 2003.

	$170	$145	$115

Last MSR was $200.

GRADING	100%	98%	95%	90%	80%	70%	60%

1851 NAVY "WYATT EARP" .44 REVOLVER - .44 cal. perc., 12 in. octagon barrel, brass backstrap, trigger guard, and frame. Mfg. By Pietta.

	MSR	$160	$140	$120	$95

Add $145 for detachable shoulder stock.

1860 ARMY - .44 cal. perc., 8 in. barrel, color case hardened hammer, frame, and loading lever, and brass trigger guard, cut for shoulder stock, also available in antique finish. Mfg. by Pietta and Uberti.

	MSR	$270	$220	$190	$160

Add $145 for detachable shoulder stock.
Subtract $70 for Pietta mfg.

1861 NAVY - .36 cal. perc., 5 in. barrel, many styles, brass back strap or trigger guard, stainless steel or color case hardened frame, hammer, and loading lever, 2.5 lbs. Mfg. by Uberti.

	MSR	$270	$220	$190	$160

Add $15 for silver plated backstrap and trigger guard.
Add $15 for fluted military cylinder.
Add $50 for stainless steel.
Add $145 for shoulder stock.

1862 POLICE - .36 cal. perc., 4.5, 5.5, or 6.5 in. barrel, stainless steel or color case hardened frame, hammer, and loading lever, cylinder, semi-fluted or engraved, 1.6 lbs. Mfg. by Uberti.

	MSR	$280	$230	$195	$170

Add $15 for silver plated backstrap and trigger guard.
Add $50 for stainless steel.

1862 POCKET NAVY - .36 cal. perc., similar to 1862 Police, except octagon barrel and rebated engraved cylinder. 1.6 lbs. Mfg. by Uberti. New 2003.

	MSR	$240	$195	$170	$145

REMINGTON 44 REVOLVER - .44 cal. perc., 8 in. octagon barrel, blue finish. Mfg. by Euro Arms.

	MSR	$200	$170	$145	$115

1858 REMINGTON - .44 cal. perc., 8 in. octagon barrel, oversize frame and grips, blue or antique (disc. 2003) finish. Mfg. by Pietta.

	MSR	$265	$215	$185	$155

1858 REMINGTON NEW MODEL ARMY SHOOTERS REVOLVER - .44 cal. perc., 8 in. octagon barrel with progressive rifling, blued steel frame, silver plated trigger guard, blue steel backstrap.

	MSR	$450	$365	$320	$275

REMINGTON NAVY - .36 cal. perc., 6.25 in. octagon barrel, .36 cal. variation of the 1858 Remington, 2.5 lbs. Mfg. by Pietta.

	MSR	$170	$138	$120	$100

REMINGTON NEW MODEL ARMY - .44 cal. perc., similar to 1858 Remington, except stainless steel. Mfg. by Uberti. New 2003.

	MSR	$350	$285	$250	$215

REMINGTON NEW MODEL POCKET - .31 cal. perc., 3.5 in. octagon barrel, spur trigger, brass frame, nickel plated or color case hardened hammer and trigger, 1 lb. Mfg. by Palmetto.

	MSR	$165	$138	$120	$100

Add $10 for nickel plated model.

GRADING	100%	98%	95%	90%	80%	70%	60%

LEMAT ARMY, NAVY, & CAVALRY - .44 cal. perc., includes 16 ga. smoothbore shotgun barrel, 6.75 in. octagon barrel, blue steel furniture, case hardened hammer and trigger, barrel marked "Col. LeMat," checkered grips, lanyard ring, round or spur (Cavalry Model) trigger guard, 3.5 lbs., Mfg. by Pietta.

	MSR	$525	$465	$380	$300

Add $40 for Army and Navy with round trigger guard.

1861-62 DANCE & BROTHERS - .44 cal. perc., 7.75 in. octagon to round barrel, steel frame Confederate copy of the Colt 1851 Navy. The Dance differs from the Colt design in that it has a Dragoon-style barrel and lacks a recoil shield behind the cylinder. Mfg. By Pietta.

	MSR	$250	$210	$180	$140

LEECH and RIGDON - .36 cal. perc., 7 in. round barrel, Confederate copy of the Colt Navy, 2.75 lbs. New in 1989. Mfg. by Uberti.

	MSR	$240	$215	$185	$150

ROGERS & SPENCER - .44 cal. perc., 6 shot, 7.5 octagon barrel, walnut grips, 3 lbs. Mfg. by Euroarms.

	MSR	$275	$225	$195	$165

SPILLER and BURR - .36 cal. perc., octagon barrel, color case hardened hammer and loading lever, brass frame and trigger guard. Mfg. by Pietta.

	MSR	$150	$125	$105	$90

STARR ARMS CO. DOUBLE ACTION AND SINGLE ACTION 1858 ARMY - .44 cal. perc., 6 in. tapered round barrel DA model, 8-in round barrel SA model, all blue steel frame, backstrap and trigger guard. Unique Starr top break design for takedown. DA model fires double action or single action. Mfg. by Pietta.

	MSR	$325	$275	$235	$190

1873 COLT SAA PERCUSSION REVOLVER - .44 cal. perc., 6 shot, 5.5 in. barrel, color case hardened frame. Designed by Uberti for countries where black powder is legal and cartridge-firing pistols are not, the authentic-looking Colt SAA has a black powder cylinder and an optional loading tool.

	MSR	$245	$190	$160	$130

Add $25 for loading tool.

PISTOLS: FLINTLOCK & PERCUSSION, SINGLE SHOT

ABILENE DERRINGER - .41 cal. perc., 2 3/8 in. round steel blue finish barrel, color case hardened frame and hammer. New 2003.

	MSR	$98	$85	$70	$55

BLACK WATCH SCOTTISH PISTOL - .577 cal. flintlock, 7 in. smooth bore barrel.

	MSR	$250	$165	$140	$115

CHARLES MOORE ENGLISH DUELING PISTOL - .36, .44, or .45 cal. flintlock (.44 (disc.) or .45 cal.) or perc. (.36 (disc.) or .45 cal.), 11 in. octagon barrel, white steel hammer and lock (flintlock), color case hardened (percussion), brass furniture, adj. trigger, hand checkered walnut stock, 2.5 lbs. Mfg. by Pedersoli. Disc. 2002.

		$370	$325	$265

Last MSR was $425.

Subtract $50 for percussion model.

CHARLEVILLE PISTOL - .69 cal. flintlock, 7.5 in. white steel barrel. Disc. 1994.

		$225	$145	$120

Last MSR was $195.

GRADING	100%	98%	95%	90%	80%	70%	60%

ENGLISH DUELING PISTOL - .45 cal. perc., 11 in. octagon barrel, silver thimble and nose cap. Mfg. by Pedersoli.

		$425	$325	$225			

Last MSR was $310.

1805 HARPERS FERRY - .58 cal. flintlock, 10 in. barrel, color case hardened hammer and lock. Mfg. by Pedersoli.

MSR	$295	$295	$250	$215			

KENTUCKY PISTOL - .45 cal. flintlock or perc., 10.25 in. blue barrel, color case hardened hammer and lock, brass furniture, 2.25 lbs. Disc. 1993.

		$225	$170	$140			

Last MSR was $150.

KENTUCKY-PENNSYLVANIA PISTOL - .45 cal. flintlock or perc., 10.25 in. blue barrel, color case hardened hammer and lock, brass furniture, Mfg. by Pedersoli.

MSR	$195	$160	$135	$110			

LE PAGE DELUXE TARGET PISTOL - .45 cal. flintlock or perc., 9.25 in. white steel barrel, Mfg. by Pedersoli.

MSR	$625	$550	$450	$375			

Add $110 for Flintlock International Pistol.

LE PAGE DUELING PISTOL - .45 cal. perc., 10 in. octagonal barrel, fluted grip, European walnut, brass furniture silver plated, lock in the white, engraved lockplate, double set triggers. Mfg. by Armi Sport.

MSR	$450	$365	$320	$275			

LINCOLN DERRINGER - .41 cal. perc., 2 in. barrel, with case. Mfg. By Palmetto. Disc., reintroduced 2000.

MSR	$425	$350	$295	$240			

MANG IN GRAZ TARGET PISTOL - .38 cal. perc., 11.5 in. octagon brown barrel, white steel hammer and lock, color case hardened furniture, fluted grip. Mfg. by Pedersoli.

MSR	$895	$835	$770	$675			

MOORE AND PATRICK PISTOL - .45 cal. flintlock, 10 in. brown octagon barrel, white steel hammer and lock, silver plated trigger guard checkered walnut grip.

		$310	$270	$215			

Last MSR was $335.

MURDOCK SCOTTISH HIGHLANDERS PISTOL - .52 cal. flintlock, 7.75 in. white steel barrel, hammer, lock, and furniture, 4 lbs. Mfg. 1989-1991, reintroduced 2003.

MSR	$350	$285	$245	$215			

PENNSYLVANIA PISTOL - .44 cal. flintlock or perc., 10 in. barrel, brass furniture, white steel hammer and lock. Mfg. by Pedersoli.

		$195	$140	$100			

Last MSR was $175.

Add $5 for flintlock.

QUEEN ANNE PISTOL - .50 cal. flintlock, 7.5 in. bronzed steel barrel. Mfg. by Pedersoli.

MSR	$245	$210	$185	$155			

SCREW BARREL DERRINGER - .44 cal. perc., 2 3/8 in. round steel barrel, .5 lb. Mfg. by Pedersoli.

MSR	$115	$107	$91	$73			

GRADING	100%	98%	95%	90%	80%	70%	60%

TORNADO TARGET - .44 cal. perc., 10 in. octagon barrel. Built on Remington 1860 Army frame.

	$195	$170	$135

Last MSR was $215.

WILLIAM PARKER PISTOL - .45 cal. flintlock, 11 in. barrel, hand checkered half stock, 2 lbs. 8 oz.

	$270	$235	$190

Last MSR was $335.

RIFLES: FLINTLOCK & PERCUSSION

AUSTRIAN LORENZ - .54 cal. perc., 28 in. tapered octagon barrel, full stock of select hardwood, Armory bright steel furniture, open-style adjustable rear sight, dovetailed front blade, barrel marked "Lorenz 1854 cal. 13.9 m/m." Reproduction of Austrian model (often referred to as the "Austrian Enfield") imported and used by both Federal and Confederate troops during the Civil War, 9 lbs. Mfg. by Arms-Moravia, Ltd., Czech Republic.

MSR	$825	$700	$575	$460

BRITISH OFFICERS LIGHT INFANTRY FUSIL - .67 cal. flintlock, 37.25 in. white tapered round barrel, fullstock of select American walnut with gloss finish, brass furniture, lock in the white, lockplate marked with a crown, single trigger, steel sling swivels on trigger guard and forearm. A continuation of the legendary "Officers' Model Musket" developed by the late "Curley" Gostomski, founder of North Star Gun Company. Four years in development this latest version is produced by Bob Rathburn and Bill Wescombe, who were chosen by Gostomski to succeed him. The musket is custom manufactured to original British government specifications, 8 lbs. Mfg. By North Star West/USA.

MSR	$1,165	$1,000	$850	$695

BROWN BESS MUSKET 2ND MODEL - .75 cal. flintlock, 42 in. tapered round barrel, one-piece European walnut stock, brass furniture, lockplate border line engraved "GRICE 1762" on tail, crown over "GR" ahead of hammer, single trigger, sling swivels, 9 lbs. The traditional British longarm for nearly a century. Mfg. by Pedersoli.

MSR	$725	$625	$535	$435

BROWN BESS TRADE MODEL - .75 cal. flintlock, 30.5 in. brown barrel, one-piece European walnut stock, brass furniture, serpentine sideplate, brown engraved lockplate, lock marked "GRICE 1762," crown over "GR" under pan, 7 lbs. 8 oz. Carbine version of the English Brown Bess Musket originally made from surplus guns bought from the British government in the early 1700s. The trade gun became a favorite of American Indians in the 1700s.

MSR	$750	$650	$550	$450

BRISTLEN MORGES - .44 cal. perc., 29.5 in. tapered octagon barrel, color case hardened hammer and lock, European walnut halfstock, palm rest, Creedmoor-style rear sight, color case hardened furniture. 15.5 lbs. Mfg. by Pedersoli.

MSR	$1,500	$1,350	$1,200	$950

BUFFALO HUNTER - .58 cal. perc., 26 in. barrel.

	$400	$340	$270

C.S. RICHMOND MUSKET - .58 cal. perc., 40 in. round barrel, white steel hammer and lock, brass buttplate and end cap, walnut stock, 10.5 lbs.

MSR	$675	$550	$450	$350

COOK & BROTHER CARBINE - .58 cal. perc., 24 in. barrel, adj. front sight (windage only), 2 barrel bands, walnut stock, 7.5 lbs. Mfg. By Euro Arms.

MSR	$575	$450	$375	$300

GRADING	100%	98%	95%	90%	80%	70%	60%

CHARLEVILLE 1766 MUSKET - .69 cal. flintlock, 44.5 in. Armory bright tapered round barrel, all steel hammer, lock, and furniture. Lockplate marked "Charleville," 10.5 lbs. Mfg. by Pedersoli.

MSR	$865	$775	$705	$610

Subtract $230 for earlier models mfg. By Miroku.

CHARLEVILLE 1777 FRENCH MODEL - .69 cal. flintlock, 44.75 in. Armory bright tapered round barrel, all steel hammer, lock, and furniture. Lockplate marked "St. (84 over crown over E) Etienne", 10.25 lbs. Mfg. by Pedersoli.

MSR	$825	$705	$610	$530

DELUXE CUB RIFLE - .40 and .45 cal. flintlock or perc., 28 in. octagon barrel, color case hardened hammer, plate and triggers, brass trim and patch box, double set triggers. Mfg. by Pedersoli.

MSR	$450	$390	$345	$280

Subtract $10 for .45 cal. models.

1853 3-BAND ENFIELD - .58 cal. perc., 3 barrel bands, 10 lbs. 8 oz. Mfg. by Euro Arms.

MSR	$565	$475	$400	$320

1858 2-BAND ENFIELD - .58 cal. perc., 2 barrel bands, 9 lbs. 4 oz. Mfg. by Euro Arms.

MSR	$525	$425	$375	$300

ENFIELD MUSKETOON LONDON ARMORY - .58 cal. perc., 24 in. round barrel, color case hardened hammer and lock, brass buttplate, trigger guard, and nose cap. Mfg. by Armi San Paolo.

MSR	$500	$410	$360	$250

ENGLISH MATCHLOCK - .72 cal. matchlock, 44 in. octagon to round barrel (with cannon type muzzle), all white steel, walnut stock.

MSR	$895	$800	$680	$580

HAWKEN RIFLE - .45, .50, .54, or .58 cal. perc., color case hardened hammer and lock, brass patch box. Mfg. by Armi San Marco.

MSR	$250	$230	$200	$160

HARPERS FERRY RIFLE - .54 or .58 cal. flintlock, 35.5 in. octagon to round barrel, color case hardened hammer and lock, brass trigger guard and patchbox. Mfg. by Armi San Paolo.

MSR	$795	$650	$525	$410

Subtract $75 for .58 cal.

INDIAN MODEL - similar to Brown Bess Musket, except has 31 in. barrel. Mfg. by Pedersoli.

MSR	$750	$635	$555	$445

JAPANESE TANEGASHIMA MATCHLOCK RIFLE - .50 cal. matchlock, smoothbore barrel, all brass furniture, trigger guard, trigger and matchlock, buttstock was held against shooter's cheek, cherry stock, OAL 54.75 in., 8.5 lbs. Mfg. by Miroku.

MSR	$625	$500	$450	$395

JAEGER RIFLE - .54 cal. flintlock, or perc., 27 5/8 in. matte brown octagon barrel, matte brown hammer, lock, and trigger guard, sliding wooden patchbox, double set triggers, 8.25 lbs. Mfg. by Pedersoli. New 2000.

MSR	$750	$590	$510	$410

J.P. MURRAY ARTILLERY CARBINE - .58 cal. perc., 23.5 in. round barrel, color case hardened hammer and lock, brass buttplate trigger guard and barrel bands (2), factory sling swivels. Mfg. by EuroArms.

MSR	$575	$475	$395	$340

GRADING	100%	98%	95%	90%	80%	70%	60%

KENTUCKIAN RIFLE/CARBINE - .45 cal. flintlock or perc., 27.5 (carbine, disc. 1993) or 33.5 in. octagon barrel, color case hardened hammer and lock, brass patch box, trigger guard and furniture. Carbine disc. 1993. Mfg. by Armi Sport.

	MSR	$395	$325	$255	$225

Add $10 for flintlock.

KENTUCKY RIFLE - .45 cal. flintlock or perc., 33.5 in. barrel, brass patch box and furniture. Disc. 1994.

		$300	$255	$200

Last MSR was $270.

Add $10 for flintlock.

KODIAK DOUBLE RIFLE SxS - .50, .54, or .58 (combo barrels .50 x 12 ga. and .58 x 12 ga.) cal. perc., 28 in. barrels, hand checkered walnut stock, adj. sights. Mfg. By Pedersoli.

	MSR	$785	$700	$645	$550

KODIAK MKIII RIFLE/SHOTGUN COMBO - .50 or .58 cal. perc., similar to Kodiak Double Rifle, except has one 12 ga. barrel. Mfg. By Pedersoli.

	MSR	$785	$700	$645	$550

KODIAK EXPRESS DOUBLE RIFLE SxS - .72 cal. perc., 25.5 in. barrels, hand checkered walnut half stock, adj. Sights, 10.5 lbs. Mfg. By Pedersoli.

	MSR	$725	$620	$530	$430

LANCASTER COUNTY RIFLE - .45 cal. flintlock or perc., similar to Pennsylvania Rifle, except less ornate trigger guard and patch box.

		$300	$250	$190

Add $5 for flintlock.

1857 MAUSER RIFLE - .547 cal. perc. patterned after the Mauser rifles manufactured by The Royal Wurttemburg Gun Factory in Oberndorf from 1857–1862. Fullstock of European walnut, Armory bright 39 3/8 in. octagon to tapered round barrel, adjustable rear sight for elevation and windage, steel blade front sight on upper barrel band, steel furniture, color case hardened lock and barrel tang, engraved lockplate "KÖNIGI.WÜRT FABRIK." Mfg. by Pedersoli. New 2001.

	MSR	$925	$805	$685	$550

MISSISSIPPI RIFLE - .58 cal. perc. patterned after the U.S. Rifle Model 1841, 33.5 in. barrel, color case hardened hammer and lock, solid brass furniture, similar to Zouave with nose cap replacing front barrel band. Mfg. by Armi San Paolo.

	MSR	$595	$525	$450	$390

MORTIMER RIFLE - .54 cal. flintlock, 36.25 in. octagon to round barrel, color case hardened hammer, lock and trigger guard, waterproof pan, 8 7/8 lbs. Mfg. by Pedersoli.

	MSR	$795	$700	$605	$485

MORTIMER WHITWORTH RIFLE - .451 cal. perc., 32 in. blue octagonal to round barrel, European walnut half stock, checkered wrist and forearm, dovetailed front sight with hood, adjustable rear peep sight on wrist, lock marked "MORTIMER". Target version of standard Mortimer. This rifle won World Muzzleloading Championship gold medals in 1989, 1991, and 1992. Mfg. by Pedersoli.

	MSR	$795	$700	$605	$485

PENNSYLVANIA RIFLE - .45 cal. flintlock or perc., 41.5 in. octagon barrel, brown hammer, lock and barrel, brass patchbox and furniture walnut full stock, 8 lbs. Mfg. by Pedersoli.

	MSR	$525	$480	$430	$360

GRADING	100%	98%	95%	90%	80%	70%	60%

REVOLVING CARBINE - .44 cal. perc., 18 in. tapered octagon barrel, brass trigger guard and buttstock. Reproduction of 1866-1879 Remington revolving carbine. Mfg. by Uberti.

MSR	$375	$345	$300	$240

SANFTL SCHUETZEN TARGET RIFLE - .45 cal. perc., 29 in. barrel, adj. sights. Disc. 1991.

	$700	$600	$480

Last MSR was $595.

SHARPS RIFLE/CARBINE - .54 cal. perc.. 22 (carbine, single barrel band) or 30 in. barrel with 3 bands, patchbox in stock. Mfg. by Pedersoli.

MSR	$965	$875	$750	$625

Subtract $150 for carbine.

SHARPS MILITARY CARBINE - .54 cal. perc. 22.25 in. tapered round barrel. Closely resembles Confederate "Robinson Sharps," N/SSA approved. Mfg. by IAB/Italy.

MSR	$595	$535	$455	$365

SHARPS SPORTING RIFLE - .54 cal. perc.. 29.25 in. octagonal barrel. European walnut stock, color case hardened lock, receiver, and buttplate, double set/double phase triggers, 9 lbs. Mfg. by IAB/Italy.

MSR	$595	$535	$455	$365

SMITH CARBINE - .50 cal. perc., 21.5 in. octagon to round barrel, walnut buttstock and forearm, blue steel folding leaf rear sight with sliding elevator, blue steel furniture, color case hardened receiver and hammer. Cavalry model with saddle bar and ring on left side of receiver, Artillery model has sling swivel on buttstock and barrel band. Mfg. by Pedersoli.

MSR	$695	$625	$555	$475

1842 SPRINGFIELD MUSKET - .69 cal. perc., 42 in. round tapered smoothbore barrel, white steel furniture, 9 lbs. 4 oz. Mfg. By Armi Sport.

MSR	$495	$425	$360	$290

Add $100 for rifled barrel.

1855 SPRINGFIELD RIFLE-MUSKET - .58 cal. perc., 40 in. round tapered barrel, white steel furniture, 10 lbs. 8 oz. Mfg. By Euro Arms.

MSR	$795	$700	$605	$485

1861 SPRINGFIELD MUSKET - .58 cal. perc., 40 in. round tapered barrel, white steel furniture, 10 lbs. 8 oz. Mfg. by Miroku Japan, and Euro Arms.

MSR	$595	$505	$430	$340

Subtract $130 for Euro Arms model.

1863 SPRINGFIELD MUSKET - .58 cal. perc., 41.5 in. barrel. Mfg. by Miroku Japan and Euroarms.

MSR	$595	$575	$500	$400

Subtract $130 for Euro Arms model.

TENNESSEE MOUNTAIN/SQUIRREL RIFLE - .32 (squirrel rifle) or .50 cal. perc. or flintlock, 41.5 in. brown barrel, brown furniture, cherry full stock, 8.5 or 9.5 lbs., right or left-hand. Mfg. by Miroku. Disc. 2002.

	$575	$510	$420

Last MSR was $625.

TRYON RIFLE - .50 cal. perc., 32 in. octagon barrel, color case hardened furniture and patch box, chrome bore, 9.5 lbs. Mfg. by Pedersoli.

MSR	$525	$450	$395	$305

TRYON CREEDMOOR RIFLE - .50 cal. perc., 32 in. octagon all black barrel, matte finish furniture and patchbox adj. Creedmoor sights, 9.5 lbs. Mfg. by Pedersoli.

MSR	$795	$695	$605	$540

U.S. MODEL 1816 FLINTLOCK MUSKET AND COLT STYLE CONVERSION - .69 cal. flintlock or perc., 42 in. round tapered smoothbore barrel, Armory bright steel furniture, brass pan on lock, lock marked "Harpers Ferry 1816" on tail w/American eagle over "U.S." ahead of hammer. 9.75 lbs. Available with Colt style conversion to percussion lock. Mfg. by Pedersoli.

MSR	$825	$700	$630	$565

WAADTLANDER RIFLE - .44 cal. perc., 31 in. octagon brown barrel, color case hardened hammer, lock, trigger guard, and heavy buttplate, adj. sights, professional target model. Mfg. by Pedersoli.

MSR	$1,550	$1,440	$1,280	$1,000

WHITWORTH MILITARY TARGET RIFLE - .451 cal. perc., 36 in. tapered round barrel, color case hardened lockplate, brass buttplate, trigger guard and nosecap, flip-up adj. blue steel rear sight. This is a reproduction of the long-range Whitworth rifle used by Confederate snipers during the Civil War, and is accurate up to 1,000 yards! Mfg. by Euroarms.

MSR	$850	$700	$600	$450

VOLUNTEER TARGET RIFLE (2 BAND AND 3 BAND) - .451 cal. perc., 33 in. round barrel with 2 barrel bands, 36 in barrel with 3 bands, color case hardened hammer and lock, brass furniture, adj. rear and hooded front sights, walnut stock, 10.5 lbs, 11.5 lbs. New 1993.

MSR	$795	$695	$605	$540

Add $45 for 3 Band model.

WESSON RIFLE - .50 cal. perc., 28 in. barrel, adj. sights. Disc. 1994. Returned 2002.

MSR	$595	$525	$450	$390

YORK COUNTY RIFLE - .45 cal. flintlock or perc., 36 in. barrel. Disc. 1987.

	$270	$230	$175

Last MSR was $210.

Add $15 for flintlock.

ZOUAVE RIFLE - .58 cal. perc., 33.5 in. blue barrel, color case hardened lock, hardwood stock, 9 lbs. 8 oz. Mfg. by Armi Sport and Euro Arms.

MSR	$415	$360	$295	$245

Add $57 for Euro Arms version with European Walnut stock, color case hardened hammer, trigger, and lock.

RIFLES: CARBINE

IN-LINE CARBINE - .50 or .54 cal. perc., 22 in. round barrel, three-quarter length walnut stock, adj. single trigger, open adj. rear sight, 7 lbs. Mfg. by Pedersoli.

MSR	$350	$325	$295	$240

SHOTGUNS: FLINTLOCK & PERCUSSION

MAGNUM SxS - 10 or 12 ga. perc., 28 in. barrels, chrome bore, color case hardened hammer and lock, (engraved white steel on 10 ga.), checkered walnut stock. 7.5 lbs. Mfg. by Pedersoli.

MSR	$525	$450	$395	$305

Add $25 for 10 ga.

GRADING	100%	98%	95%	90%	80%	70%	60%

MAGNUM CAPE - 12 ga. perc., 32 in. barrel, engraved with walnut stock, 5.5 lbs. Mfg. by Armi San Paolo. Disc. 2002.

	$365	$325	$260				

Last MSR was $395.

MORTIMER - 12 ga. flintlock, similar to Mortimer Rifle listed in rifle section, 7 lbs. Mfg. by Pedersoli.

MSR	$795	$695	$605	$540			

NORTHWEST TRADE - 20 ga. flintlock, 36 in. octagon tapering to round barrel, brown barrel and lock assembly, 11 lbs. Mfg. 1989-1991.

	$425	$370	$295				

Last MSR was $495.

PEDERSOLI SxS - .20 ga. perc., brown 27.5 in. tapered round barrels, European walnut stock, color case hardened steel furniture and lock (except blue trigger guard and buttplate), engraved locks, tang, and trigger-plate, two single triggers, 6.75 lbs.

MSR	$525	$450	$395	$305			

PEDERSOLI COACH GUN - .12 ga. perc., brown 20 in. tapered blue round barrels, European walnut half stock, checkered wrist, color case hardened locks, trigger guard, tang, entry thimble and wedge plates. Engraved locks and tang, 6.75 lbs. New 2001. Mfg. By Pedersoli.

MSR	$500	$450	$385	$305			

NOTES

E SECTION

E.M.F. COMPANY

Current importer and distributor located in Santa Ana, CA. Consumer direct and dealer sales.

E.M.F. is one of the oldest names in the black powder industry, and has been importing and selling revolvers and longarms for more than 41 years. The majority of E.M.F. revolvers are manufactured in Italy. These are the most affordable black powder reproductions on the market, and are frequently used in Civil War reenactments.
E.M.F. is well known for its extensive line of cartridge-firing revolvers and longarms, holsters, accessories, and presentation cases.

GRADING	100%	98%	95%	90%	80%	70%	60%

PISTOLS: FLINTLOCK & PERCUSSION

1775 BLACK WATCH SCOTTISH PISTOL - .58 cal. flintlock, 7 in. smooth bore white steel barrel, brass frame, ram's horn grips with round ball trigger. Disc. 1994.

	$180	$155	$110

Last MSR was $260.

CHARLES MOORE - .45 cal. flintlock, 10 in. octagon barrel, 2 lbs. Disc. 1994.

	$340	$295	$235

Last MSR was $400.

1777 CHARLEVILLE PISTOL - .69 cal. flintlock, 7.5 in. white steel barrel, brass frame. Disc. 1994.

	$190	$165	$110

Last MSR was $315.

CORSAIR PISTOL SxS - .36 or .44 cal. perc., color case hardened hammers and locks, brass trim. Disc. 1987.

	$265	$210	$135

Last MSR was $160.

HARPERS FERRY - .58 cal. flintlock, brass mounted brown barrel. Disc. 1994.

	$270	$230	$180

Last MSR was $405.

HAWKEN PISTOL - .54 cal. perc., 9 in. octagon barrel, adj. trigger, 2 lbs. 9 oz. Disc. 1994.

	$230	$195	$150

Last MSR was $370.

KENTUCKY PISTOL - .44 cal. flintlock or perc., available engraved or with brass barrel. Disc. 1994.

	$205	$170	$140

Last MSR was $250.

Add $30 for flintlock.
Add $20 for brass barrel.
Add $25 for engraved percussion.

LE PAGE PISTOL - .45 cal. perc., 9 in. octagon white steel barrel and trim, adj. sights, 2 lbs. 2 oz. Disc. 1994.

	$170	$145	$120

Last MSR was $400.

REMINGTON STYLE TARGET PISTOL - .44 cal. perc., 9 in. octagon barrel, factory engraved, adj. sights (windage only), based on Rem. frame, 43 oz. Disc. 1994.

	$200	$180	$145

Last MSR was $310.

GRADING	100%	98%	95%	90%	80%	70%	60%

WM. PARKER PISTOL - .45 cal. perc., 10 in. octagon barrel, German silver lock and trim, double set triggers, 2.5 lbs. Disc. 1994.

| | **$270** | **$235** | **$190** |

Last MSR was $400.

REVOLVERS: PERCUSSION

E.M.F. percussion revolvers are available in two series – the Standard and Hartford. The Hartford Series, introduced in 1993, features German silver plated backstrap and trigger guard, and walnut grips with original type inspector's cartouche. Also available in cased sets. E.M.F. models are manufactured in Italy by Uberti, and Pietta.

1847 WALKER - .44 cal. perc., 9 in. barrel, color case hardened frame and loading lever, brass trim, 4 lbs. 8 oz.

| MSR | **$280** | **$230** | **$195** | **$155** |

1ST MODEL DRAGOON - .44 cal. perc., 7.5 in. barrel, color case hardened frame, brass trim, engraved cylinder, 4 lbs. 2 oz. Disc.

| | **$285** | **$240** | **$190** |

Last MSR was $315.

1848 2ND MODEL DRAGOON - .44 cal. perc., 7.5 in. barrel, color case hardened frame, brass trim, engraved cylinder, 4 lbs.

| MSR | **$260** | **$220** | **$190** | **$150** |

3RD MODEL DRAGOON - .44 cal. perc., 7.5 in. barrel, color case hardened frame and loading lever, brass trim, engraved cylinder, 4 lbs. 2 oz., adj. target sights. Disc.

| | **$285** | **$240** | **$190** |

Last MSR was $350.

Add $25 for Buntline model.
Add $15 for Texas Dragoon Model (Tucker and Sherrard and Co., Confederate States, Texas Star engraved on cylinder, square brass trigger guard).

1848 BABY DRAGOON - .31 cal. perc., 5 shot, 4 and 6 in. barrel, color case hardened frame and loading lever, brass trim.

| MSR | **$165** | **$135** | **$110** | **$95** |

1849 WELLS FARGO - .31 cal. perc., 5 shot, 5 in. barrel, w/o loading lever. Disc.

| | **$200** | **$180** | **$140** |

Last MSR was $255.

1851 NAVY - .36 or .44 cal. perc., 7.5 in. barrel, brass or steel frame, color case hardened hammer, and loading lever, factory engraved cartouche in walnut grips. Standard Hartford model has brass frame.

| MSR | **$140** | **$115** | **$95** | **$80** |

Add $10 for case hardened steel frame.
Add $140 for Shoulder stock.
Subtract $105 if w/o engraving.

1851 NAVY "BUNTLINE" BUFFALO - .44 cal. perc., similar to 1851 Navy Brass, except with 12 in. barrel.

| MSR | **$165** | **$135** | **$115** | **$95** |

Add $140 for shoulder stock.

1851 NAVY SHERIFF - .44 cal. perc., 5.5 in. barrel, brass or steel frame, color case hardened hammer, and loading lever, factory engraved cartouche in walnut grips. Standard Hartford model has brass frame.

| MSR | **$140** | **$115** | **$95** | **$80** |

Add $45 for case hardened steel frame.

GRADING	100%	98%	95%	90%	80%	70%	60%

1851 GRISWOLD CONFEDERATE - .36 or .44 cal. perc., 7.5 in. round barrel, brass frame, 2 lbs. 12 oz. Disc.

| | | | 100% $110 | 98% $95 | 95% $75 | | |

Last MSR was $145.

1860 ARMY - .44 cal. perc., 8 in. barrel, brass or steel frame, blue finish, walnut grips. Standard Hartford model has brass frame.

| MSR $145 | | $120 | $100 | $85 | | | |

Add $40 for case hardened frame.
Add $140 for shoulder stock.

1860 ARMY SHERIFF - .44 cal. perc., 5.5 in. barrel, steel frame, blue finish, walnut grips. Standard Hartford model has brass frame.

| MSR $185 | | $150 | $130 | $105 | | | |

Add $140 for shoulder stock.

1861 NAVY - .36 cal. perc., steel frame, 7.5 in. round barrel, color case hardened frame, hammer and loading lever. Disc. Reintroduced 2003.

| MSR $210 | | $175 | $150 | $120 | | | |

1862 POLICE - .36 cal. perc., 5 shot, 5.5 in. round barrel, color case hardened frame, hammer and loading lever, blue finish, walnut grips.

| MSR $200 | | $170 | $145 | $115 | | | |

1862 POLICE BRASS - .36 cal. perc., 5 shot, brass frame, blue finish, walnut grips. Disc.

| | | | $150 | $130 | $100 | | |

Last MSR was $170.

1862 POCKET NAVY - .36 cal. perc., 5 shot, color case hardened frame. Disc.

| | | | $190 | $175 | $140 | | |

Last MSR was $200.

NAVY SQUAREBACK - .36 or .44 cal. perc., 7.5 in. barrel, color case hardened frame and loading lever, Dragoon style square back trigger guard. Disc. 1994.

| | | | $135 | $120 | $100 | | |

Last MSR was $130.

Additional options are priced similar to the Model 1851 Navy.

1858 REMINGTON ARMY - .44 cal. perc., 8 in. barrel, stainless steel frame, blue finish, 2 lbs. 8 oz.

| MSR $280 | | $240 | $200 | $160 | | | |

1858 REMINGTON ARMY BRASS - .44 cal. perc., 8 in. barrel, brass or steel frame, blue finish, 2 lbs. 8 oz.

| MSR $180 | | $150 | $130 | $105 | | | |

Add $15 for blue frame and blue barrel.

1863 REMINGTON POCKET PISTOL - .31 cal. perc., 4 in. barrel, brass frame, blue barrel.

| MSR $165 | | $140 | $120 | $95 | | | |

RIFLES: FLINTLOCK & PERCUSSION

BOSTONIAN - .45 cal. perc. Mfg. 1989-disc.

| | | | $220 | $190 | $150 | | |

Last MSR was $285.

| GRADING | 100% | 98% | 95% | 90% | 80% | 70% | 60% |

ALAMO COMMEMORATIVE - .45 cal. perc., embellished to commemorate the anniversary of the Alamo. Mfg. 1989-1994.

	100%	98%	95%
	$420	$380	$300

Last MSR was $435.

DELUXE BROWN BESS MUSKET - .75 cal. flintlock. Disc. 1994.

	100%	98%	95%
	$630	$550	$440

Last MSR was $850.

Add $60 for bayonet.

HAWKEN RIFLE - .50 cal. perc., brass trim, color case hardened lock and hammer, adj. sights, and stainless steel nipple. Disc. 1996.

	100%	98%	95%
	$230	$200	$160

Last MSR was $325.

KENTUCKY RIFLE - .36, .44, or .45 cal. perc. or flintlock, factory engraved, brass trim, color case hardened lock and hammer.

	100%	98%	95%
	$300	$255	$200

Add $10 for flintlock.
Add $30 for deluxe model.
Add $50 for deluxe engraved.

LONDON ARMORY ENFIELD - .58 cal. perc.

	100%	98%	95%
	$445	$390	$310

Last MSR was $575.

Subtract $20 for Musketoon Model.

MINUTEMAN KENTUCKY RIFLE - .45 cal. flintlock or perc., 36 in. octagon barrel, brass blade front sight, brass trim, color case hardened lock, hammer, and trigger.

	100%	98%	95%
	$300	$255	$200

Add $15 for engraving, $15 for flintlock.

PENNSYLVANIA KENTUCKY RIFLE - .50 cal. perc., brass trim, color case hardened lock, hammer, and trigger. Disc. 1994.

	100%	98%	95%
	$410	$360	$290

Last MSR was $440.

PLAINSMAN KENTUCKY RIFLE - .44 cal. perc., shorter forearm than Pennsylvania with more ornate finish. Disc. 1994.

	100%	98%	95%
	$345	$300	$225

Last MSR was $450.

PURDEY DELUXE RIFLE/CARBINE - .50 cal. perc., half stock English style, select checkered walnut, color case hardened nose cap, lock, tang, buttplate and patch box, adj. sights, double set triggers.

	100%	98%	95%
	$345	$300	$225

SAN FRANCISCO TO ST. LOUIS COMMEMORATIVE - .45 cal. perc., Kentucky rifle, highly embellished, made to commemorate the 130th anniversary of the stage coach crossing "2,400 miles in 24 days." Mfg. 1989-1991.

	100%	98%	95%
	$380	$330	$240

Last MSR was $395.

GRADING	100%	98%	95%	90%	80%	70%	60%

SHARPS RIFLE/CARBINE - .54 cal. perc., 22 (round carbine) or 28 (octagon rifle) in. blue barrel, case hardened receiver, hammer and lever, standard falling block action, 9.5 (rifle) or 7.75 (carbine) lbs. Mfg. by Industria Armi Bresciane.

MSR	$665	$656	$480	$385

Add $55 for blue octagonal barrel.

WESSON BERDAN RIFLE - .45 cal. perc., engraved brass frame.

	$385	$335	$260

ZOUAVE RIFLE DELUXE - .58 cal. perc., brass trim, color case hardened lock and hammer, blue finish, adj. "Sniper Sight." Disc.

	$440	$400	$300

Last MSR was $625.

SHOTGUNS: PERCUSSION

SHOTGUN SxS - 12 ga. perc., based on early English design, brown barrel, color case hardened lock and hammer, imported from Italy. Disc. 1994.

	$430	$390	$310

Last MSR was $535.

SHOTGUN O/U - 12 ga. perc. Mfg. 1989-1991.

	$470	$410	$310

Last MSR was $640.

EASTERN MUZZLELOADERS SUPPLY

Current importer/distributor located in Bear, Delaware. Dealer and catalog sales.

RIFLES

CRISTOFORO COLOMBO QUINCENTENARY MATCHLOCK - classic period matchlock styling, rear sight is a dolphin (a sign of good luck) the front sight, a stylized dolphin. The hammer is shaped like a sea monster (trigger being the tail), walnut stock, 500 scheduled to be mfg. and serial numbered CC1492–CC1992, custom mfg. by Pedersoli.

MSR	$780	$745	$645	$515

FRENCH MODEL 1777 NAVY MUSKET - .69 cal. flintlock, 42.5 in. white steel barrel, brass furniture, split ring iron center barrel band, non-corrosive brass priming pan, walnut stock, 8.5 - 9.5 lbs. (similar to Charleville Musket) custom mfg. by Pedersoli.

	$630	$550	$440

EUROARMS ITALIA S.r.l.

Current manufacturer located in Concesio Italy. Armi San Paolo S.r.l. changed its name to Euroarms Italia S.r.l. in January 2002. Euroarms Italia S.r.l. (formerly Armi San Paolo) also owns Euroarms of America and is currently imported by Cabela's, located in Sydney, NE, Euroarms of America located in Winchester, VA, Dixie Gun Works, Inc. located in Union City, IN, and Navy Arms Co. located in Union City NJ. Dealer and catalog sales.

PISTOLS: PERCUSSION

BOOMER "LUDWIG II" - .58 cal. perc., 7.25 in. smooth bore, brass or steel barrel.

	$260	$220	$175

Last MSR was $300.

GRADING	100%	98%	95%	90%	80%	70%	60%

REVOLVERS: PERCUSSION

1851 NAVY SCHNEIDER & GLASSICK - .36 or .44 cal. perc., 5 or 7 in. octagon barrel, brass frame.

	$115	$100	$80

Last MSR was $125.

1851 NAVY GRISWOLD & GUNNISON - .36 or .44 cal. perc., 7.5 in. octagon round barrel, brass frame. Disc. 1987.

	$115	$100	$80

Last MSR was $100.

1851 NAVY - .36 or .44 cal. perc., 7.5 in. barrel, steel frame, 39-43 oz.

	$130	$110	$90

Last MSR was $156.

Add $10 for square back trigger.
Add $25 for silver strap.
Subtract $24 for brass frame.

1851 NAVY POLICE - .36 cal. perc., 5 or 7.5 in. octagon barrel, steel frame, 5 shot fluted cylinder, 38-41 oz. Disc. 1994.

	$130	$110	$90

Last MSR was $135.

1851 NAVY SHERIFF'S MODEL - .36 or .44 cal. perc., 5 in. barrel, steel frame, 39 oz. Disc. 1994.

	$130	$110	$90

Last MSR was $105.

1860 ARMY - .44 cal. perc., 5 or 8 in. barrel, brass or steel frame, 41 oz.

	$159	$135	$105

Last MSR was $177.

Subtract $32 for brass frame.

1861 NAVY - .36 cal. perc., 7.5 in. barrel, steel frame, 42 oz.

	$160	$130	$100

Last MSR was $245.

1862 POLICE - .36 cal. perc., 7.5 in. barrel, steel frame, 40 oz. Disc. 1987.

	$160	$130	$100

Last MSR was $135.

REMINGTON 1858 ARMY - .36 or .44 cal. perc., 8 in. octagon barrel, 40 oz.

	$185	$160	$130

Last MSR was $200.

Add $75 for engraving, and $48 for stainless steel.

REMINGTON 1858 NAVY - .36 cal. perc., 6.5 in. octagon barrel, 40 oz. Disc.

	$185	$160	$130

Last MSR was $200.

ROGERS & SPENCER - .44 cal. perc., 7.5 in. octagon barrel, high gloss blue finish, 47 oz. Winner of the Product Merit Award for 1977 from the National Association of Federally Licensed Firearms Dealers, the Euroarms Rogers & Spencer recreates an historic Civil War era pistol in authentic detail. Available through Dixie Gun Works and Navy Arms.

NO MSR	$300	$255	$215	$175

GRADING	100%	98%	95%	90%	80%	70%	60%

RIFLES: FLINTLOCK & PERCUSSION

BROWN BESS MUSKET (TOWER FLINTLOCK) - .75 cal. flintlock, 41.75 in. barrel, smooth bore. Disc. 1994.

	$520	$430	$335

Last MSR was $755.

BUFFALO CARBINE - .58 cal. perc., 26 in. round barrel, color case hardened hammer and lock, brass patchbox and furniture, 7.75 lbs.

	$380	$325	$260

Last MSR was $440.

C.S. RICHMOND MUSKET - .58 cal. perc., 40 in. round barrel, white steel hammer and lock, brass buttplate and end cap, walnut stock, 10.5 lbs.

NO MSR $525 $485 $425 $340

CAPE RIFLE - .50 cal. perc., 32 in. barrel, engraved with walnut stock. Mfg. 1989-1991.

	$420	$360	$290

Last MSR was $515.

CHARLEVILLE 1777 FLINTLOCK MUSKET - .69 cal. flintlock, 44.75 in. white steel barrel, smooth bore. Disc. 1994.

	$600	$510	$410

Last MSR was $835.

COOK & BROTHER RIFLE/CARBINE - .58 cal. perc., 24 in. barrel, adj. front sight (windage only), 2 barrel bands, walnut stock, 7.5 lbs.

	$375	$330	$265

Last MSR was $447.

Add $33 for rifle.

1853 ENFIELD RIFLE MUSKET (PARKER-HALE) - .58 cal. perc., 39 in. barrel, adj. rear sight), 3 barrel bands, walnut stock, 9.5 lbs.

NO MSR $495 $465 $410 $315
Add $40 for satin finish.

1858 ENFIELD RIFLE MUSKET (LONDON ARMORY CO.) - .58 cal. perc., 33 in. barrel, adj. rear sight, 2 barrel bands, walnut stock, 7.5 lbs.

NO MSR $475 $440 $385 $305

1861 ENFIELD ARTILLERY CARBINE MUSKETOON - .58 cal. perc., 24 in. barrel, adj. rear sight, 2 barrel bands, walnut stock, 7.5 lbs.

NO MSR $450 $425 $375 $285

MODEL 1803 HARPER'S FERRY FLINTLOCK - .54 or .58 cal. flintlock, 32.5 in. brown barrel, walnut stock, 9 lbs.

MSR $645 $590 $515 $405

HAWKEN RIFLE - .58 cal. perc., 28 in. oct. barrel, double set triggers, target model, 9 lbs. 6 oz. Disc. 1989.

	$265	$225	$180

Last MSR was $295.

1862-1864 CONFEDERATE CARBINE (J.P. MURRAY) - .58 cal. perc., 23 in. round barrel, color case hardened hammer and lock, brass patch box and furniture, 7.75 lbs.

NO MSR $450 $410 $345 $275

GRADING	100%	98%	95%	90%	80%	70%	60%

MATCHLOCK SMOOTHBORE - .63 cal. perc., 42 in. barrel.

$555 $470 $375

Last MSR was $637.

MISSISSIPPI RIFLE MODEL 1841 - .54 or .58 cal. perc., 33 in. barrel, 9 lbs. 8 oz.

NO MSR $500 $460 $395 $305

PENNSYLVANIA RIFLE - .45 or .50 cal. flintlock or perc., 36 in. barrel, adj. rear sight (windage only), walnut stock, 7 lbs. Disc. 1987.

$330 $280 $220

Last MSR was $285.

Add $30 for flintlock.

1862 REMINGTON RIFLE - .58 cal. perc., 33 in. barrel, 3 leaf folding rear sight, 3 barrel bands, beechwood stock, 9.5 lbs. Disc. 1987.

$310 $260 $210

Last MSR was $285.

SPRINGFIELD RIFLE MUSKET - .58 cal. perc., 40 in. barrel with 3 bands.

$530 $440 $380

Last MSR was $564.

U.S. MODEL 1855 RIFLE MUSKET - .58 cal. perc., 40 in. barrel.

NO MSR $650 $560 $480 $385

VOLUNTEER TARGET RIFLE (2 BAND) - .451 cal. perc., 33 in. round barrel, color case hardened hammer and lock, two barrel bands, brass furniture, adj. rear and hooded front sights, walnut stock, 9.5 lbs. New 1993.

NO MSR $750 $650 $560 $460

VOLUNTEER TARGET RIFLE (3 BAND) - .451 cal. perc., same as above except with 3 bbl. bands and longer barrel.

NO MSR $795 $690 $590 $475

WHITWORTH MILITARY TARGET RIFLE (3 BAND) - .451 cal. perc., 36 in. barrel.

NO MSR $825 $715 $610 $490

1863 REMINGTON ZOUAVE RIFLE - .58 cal. perc., brass trim, color case hardened lock and hammer, blue finish, adj. sniper sight.

NO MSR $452 $390 $310 $260

Add $115 for "Range" grade Target Model.

SHOTGUNS: PERCUSSION

MAGNUM CAPE - 12 ga. perc., 32 in. barrel, engraved with walnut stock, 5.5 lbs.

$365 $325 $260

Last MSR was $395.

DUCK MODEL - 8, 10, or 12 ga. perc., 33 in. round barrel, color case hardened hammer and lock, brass patchbox and furniture, 8.5 lbs. Mfg. 1989-1992.

$360 $300 $235

Last MSR was $455.

STANDARD SxS - 12 ga. perc., 28 in. barrels, engraved with walnut stock, 6 lbs. Disc. 1994.

$340 $285 $225

Last MSR was $405.

F SECTION

FABER BROTHERS

Current distributor located in Chicago, IL. Dealer sales.

Faber Brothers is currently marketing customized C.V.A. (see Connecticut Valley Arms) and InvestArms Hawken rifles. These rifles come drilled and tapped for scope with offset hammers and chrome bores. Faber Brothers rifles may command a slight premium over similar configurations from C.V.A. & InvestArms.

FEDERAL ORDNANCE CORPORATION

Previous manufacturer/importer located in South El Monte, CA. All black powder models were discontinued during 1990.

PISTOLS: FLINTLOCK & PERCUSSION

DURS EGG SAW HANDLED PISTOL - .45 cal. flintlock or perc., 9.5 in. blue octagon barrel, unique stock, hand checkered, German silver trim, white steel hammer and lock. Disc. 1994.

$210	$175	$150

Last MSR was $225.

F. ROCHATTE - .45 cal. perc., single set trigger, hand checkered stock. Disc. 1994.

$250	$210	$160

Last MSR was $250.

KENTUCKY PISTOL - .45 cal. perc., 10.25 in. octagon barrel, brass blade front sight, 40 oz. Disc. 1994.

$205	$170	$140

Last MSR was $110.

WILLIAM MOORE PISTOL - .45 cal. flintlock or perc., 10 in. octagon barrel, white steel hammer and lock, silver plated trim, 2 lbs. Disc. 1994.

$310	$270	$215

Last MSR was $230.

Add $10 for flintlock.

NAPOLEON LE PAGE PISTOL - .45 cal. perc., 10 in. octagon white steel barrel and lock, brass trim, adj. double set triggers, fluted grip, 2 lbs. 7 oz. Disc. 1994.

$170	$145	$120

Last MSR was $185.

WILLIAM PARKER PISTOL - .45 cal. flintlock or perc., 11 in. octagon brown barrel, silver plated furniture, double set triggers. Disc. 1994.

$270	$235	$190

Last MSR was $200.

Add $10 for flintlock.

REVOLVERS: PERCUSSION

1858 REMINGTON - .44 cal. perc., 7.5 in. octagon barrel, 6 shot, brass frame and trigger guard, 2 lbs. 10 oz. Disc. 1994.

$85	$65	$50

Last MSR was $110.

Add $30 for steel.
Add $100 for stainless steel frame.
Add $75 for target model.

GRADING	100%	98%	95%	90%	80%	70%	60%

1860 ARMY - .44 cal. perc., 8 in. barrel, 6 shot, color case hardened hammer, lock, and loading lever, brass backstrap and trigger guard. Disc 1994.

$175 $165 $140

Last MSR was $125.

Add $15 for Sheriff's Model.
Add $75 for shoulder stock.

1862 POCKET NAVY - .36 cal. perc., 6.5 in. barrel, color case hardened frame, hammer and loading lever, cylinder semi-fluted, or engraved. 1 lb. 9 oz. Disc. 1994.

$160 $130 $100

Last MSR was $205.

ROGERS & SPENCER - .44 cal. perc., 7.5 in. octagon barrel, blue steel, 3 lbs. Disc. 1994.

$200 $170 $135

Last MSR was $200.

RIFLES: FLINTLOCK & PERCUSSION

1853 ENFIELD (3-BAND) - .58 cal. perc., 39 in. round barrel, color case hardened hammer and lock, brass trim, blue bands, adj. rear sight, 9.5 lbs. Disc. 1994.

$460 $400 $300

Last MSR was $400.

1858 ENFIELD (2-BAND) - similar to 1853 3-Band Enfield, except has 33 in. round barrel, 10 lbs. Disc. 1994.

$435 $380 $300

Last MSR was $340.

ENFIELD MUSKETOON - .58 cal. perc., 24 in. barrel, adj. rear sight (windage only), 2 barrel bands, walnut stock, 8 lbs. Disc. 1994.

$460 $400 $300

Last MSR was $480.

HARPERS FERRY FLINTLOCK - .58 cal. flintlock, 35 in. round barrel, color case hardened hammer and lock, brass trim, 8.5 lbs. Disc. 1994.

$585 $400 $300

Last MSR was $440.

HAWKEN RIFLE - .45 or .50 cal. flintlock or perc., 28.5 in. octagon barrel, color case hardened hammer and lock, double set triggers, 7¾ lbs. Disc. 1994.

$265 $225 $180

Last MSR was $220.

KENTUCKY RIFLE - .45 cal. perc., color case hardened hammer and lock, percussion cap holder in stock, brass trim. Disc. 1994.

$300 $255 $200

Last MSR was $210.

J.P. MURRAY CARBINE - .58 cal. perc., 23.5 in. brown round barrel, color case hardened hammer and lock, brass trim and bands, 7.5 lbs. Disc. 1994.

$395 $340 $270

Last MSR was $370.

GRADING	100%	98%	95%	90%	80%	70%	60%

MISSISSIPPI RIFLE - .58 cal. perc., 33 in. brown round barrel, color case hardened hammer and lock, brass trim and bands, 9.5 lbs. Disc. 1994.

$450 $390 $300

Last MSR was $410.

SANFTL SCHUETZEN RIFLE - .45 cal. perc., 31 in. octagon barrel, both aperture and iron sights, Schuetzen buttplate and trigger guard, brass furniture. Disc. 1994.

$800 $700 $600

Last MSR was $590.

ZOUAVE RIFLE - .58 cal. perc., 32.5 in. round barrel, color case hardened hammer, lock and trigger, brass trim, adj. rear sight, 9 lbs. Disc. 1994.

$290 $250 $200

Last MSR was $360.

FEINWERKBAU

Current manufacturer established circa 1951, and located in Oberndorf, Germany. Feinwerkbau firearms have had limited importation by Beeman Precision Airguns, located in Huntington Beach, CA.

PISTOLS: SINGLE SHOT

BILLINGHURST MODEL - .36 cal., perc., under hammer, high polish blue, walnut grips, 10.1 in. barrel, adj. sight, 2.4 lbs. Limited U.S. importation beginning 2002.

As this edition went to press, U.S. availability had yet to be established on this model.

FORT WORTH FIREARMS

Previous manufacturer located in Fort Worth, TX 1995-2000.

RIFLES: PERCUSSION

PECOS RIFLE - .50 cal. perc., 22 in. tapered round stainless steel barrel, adj. sights and trigger, trigger safety, checkered black composite stock with recoil pad, 6.5 lbs.

$450 $380 $300

Last MSR was $500.

Add $35 for black stainless steel.
Add $50 for camo stock.

RIO GRANDE RIFLE - .50 cal. perc., 22 or 24 in. tapered round stainless steel barrel, adj. sights and trigger, checkered black composite stock with recoil pad, 6.5 lbs.

$450 $380 $300

Last MSR was $500.

Add $35 for black stainless steel.
Add $50 for thumbhole or camo stock.

BRAZOS - .50 cal. perc., in-line ignition, 22 in. tapered round stainless steel barrel, adj. sights, checkered black composite stock with recoil pad, 6.5 lbs.

$270 $220 $175

Last MSR was $300.

GRADING	100%	98%	95%	90%	80%	70%	60%

SABINE RIFLE - .22 cal. perc., in-line ignition, 16.25 round blue barrel, safety, Monte Carlo walnut finish stock, 3.5 lbs.

$170 $145 $110

Last MSR was $190.

FREEDOM ARMS

Current manufacturer located in Freedom, WY. Dealer sales.

REVOLVERS

STAINLESS MINI-REVOLVER - .22 cal. perc., 5 shot, 1, 1¾, or 3 in. barrel, stainless steel. Disc. 1994.

$250 $210 $170

Add $15 for 3 in. barrel.
Add $40 for brass buckle.

Last MSR was $205.

G SECTION

GIBBS RIFLE COMPANY

Current manufacturer, importer, and distributor located in Martinsburg, WV.

Founded in 1991, the Gibbs Rifle Company has purchased the rights to manufacture the Parker-Hale Enfield black powder replicas from Parker-Hale located in Birmingham, England. Navy Arms remains the only distributor of Parker-Hale black powder replicas. Beginning in 1996, Parker-Hale Enfield rifles are bring manufactured by Euroarms Italia S.r.l. (formally Armi San Paolo) under license.

GONIC ARMS

Current manufacturer located in Gonic, NH. Dealer and consumer direct sales.

Gonic Arms has designed a true hunter's Magnum rifle. Equipped with an ambidextrous safety, it eliminates the noisy "click" often associated with bringing a hammer back from half cock or setting the first of double set triggers. A specially designed firing pin and housing allow spent caps to blow out the bottom of the rifle, thus eliminating the need to "dig out" the spent cap from the breech. This, combined with its modern appearance and newly designed loading system, makes it a true hunters rifle without the problems associated with most black powder arms. Gonic also produces black powder Magnum barrels to fit the Thompson Contender frame, easily converting the T.C. single shot pistol into a black powder model with in-line ignition, and an optional Contender shoulder stock can be included.

GRADING	100%	98%	95%	90%	80%	70%	60%

PISTOLS: BARREL ASSEMBLIES

MODEL 90 MAGNUM PISTOL BARREL - .45 or .50 cal. perc., #11 percussion cap or #209 primer ignition, 16 or 24 in. blue or stainless steel barrel, 1:22 (.45 cal.) or 1:24 in. twist, designed to fit into a Thompson Contender frame, standard Thompson forearm must also be replaced.

MSR	$276	$245	$215	$180

Add $28 for 24 in. barrel.
Add $32 for stainless steel barrel.
Additional features are available, call for pricing.

RIFLES: IN-LINE IGNITION

MODEL 87 RIFLE/CARBINE - .308 Spitfire, .38, .44, .458 Express, .50 cal., (rifle only), .54, and 20 ga., 26 in. round barrel, (24 in. carbine custom shop only) single stage trigger with left or right safety, cap is placed in breech, 6 lbs. Disc. 1987.

$500	$420	$340

Last MSR was $570.

Add $25 for sights.
Add $20 for Deluxe.
Add $70 for laminated stock.
Add $250 for 1-1,000 limited edition.

MODEL 87 MAGNUM - .45 or .50 cal. perc., similar to Model 87, Deluxe Model, American walnut stock, checkered with 1 in. recoil pad.

$675	$600	$480

Last MSR was $800.

Add $25 for open sights.
Add $40 for aperture sights.

MODEL 90 CARBINE - .45 or .50 cal. perc., #11 percussion cap or #209 primer in-line ignition, 24 in. blue or stainless steel barrel, 1:22 (.45 cal.) or 1:24 in. twist, walnut, black, or grey laminated wood stock and forearm, recoil pad. New 2003.

MSR	$982	$875	$785	$650

Add $26 for grey laminated stock.
Add $42 for stainless steel barrel.
Additional features are available, call for pricing.

MODEL 93 MAGNUM - .45 (new 2003) or .50 cal. perc., 24 or 26 (new 2003) in. barrel, 1:22 (.45 cal.) or 1:24 in. twist, adj. trigger, drilled and tapped for scope, adj. fiber optic sights, hardwood stock, recoil pad, sling swivel studs, approx. 6.5-7 lbs.

MSR $720	$650	$575	$465

Add $62 for stainless steel barrel (new 1994).
Additional features are available, call for pricing.

MODEL 93 MAGNUM DELUXE - .45 (new 2003) or .50 cal. perc., similar to Model 93 Magnum.

MSR $950	$850	$765	$615

Add $62 for stainless steel barrel.
Additional features are available, call for pricing.

MODEL 93 MAGNUM SAFARI - .50 cal. perc., in-line action, similar to Model 93 Magnum Standard, except is available with any or all options (built to the purchasers specifications). Disc.

$1,300	$1,100	$880

Last MSR was $1,560.

MODEL 93 MAGNUM SAFARI CLASSIC - .50 cal., in-line action, similar to Model 93 Magnum Safari, except has classic cheek piece, walnut stock with hand checkering, available with all options (built to the purchaser's specifications). Disc.

$1,450	$1,225	$900

Last MSR was $1,612.

MODEL 93 MAGNUM MOUNTAIN CLASSIC RIFLE - .50 cal, in-line ignition, custom version of Model 93 Magnum Standard, available with any or all options (built to purchaser's specifications). Available with thumbhole stock at no additional charge. Disc.

$1,775	$1,400	$1,000

Last MSR was $2,132.

MODEL 93 THUMBHOLE RIFLE - .45 (new 2003) or .50 cal. perc., custom version of Model 93 Magnum Standard, available with any or all options (built to purchaser's specifications). New 2003.

MSR $2,600	$2,350	$2,075	$1,700

MODEL SS-01 - .50 cal. perc., inline ignition, 26 in. satin stainless steel barrel, 1:24 in. twist, adj. stights and detacable scope bases, adj. trigger, grey laminated stock, 1 in. Pachmayer Decelerator recoil pad, sling swivel studs, approx. 7-8 lbs. New 2003.

MSR $1,050	$950	$850	$675

Additional features are available, call for pricing.

MODEL SS-01-T - .50 cal. perc., inline ignition, similar to Model SS-01, except includes the best of all available features. New 2003.

MSR $2,700	$2,450	$2,175	$1,775

GUN WORKS

Current manufacturer located in Springfield, OR. Specializing in English pistols, English sporting rifles, Hawken rifles, North West Trade guns, Pennsylvania rifles, and American Fowlers.

GRADING	100%	98%	95%	90%	80%	70%	60%

PISTOLS: FLINTLOCK & PERCUSSION

ENGLISH FLINTLOCK AND PERCUSSION PISTOLS - .32, .36, .40, .45, or .50 cal. flintlock or perc., single set trigger, walnut or maple stock, iron furniture, 2 lb. 10 oz. Left-hand versions available.

MSR	$450	$405	$365	$300

Add $25 for Flintlock.
Add $50 for select wood stock.

RIFLES: PERCUSSION

ENGLISH SPORTING RIFLE - .45, .50, .54, .58, .62, or .69 cal perc., 28 in. to 36 in. Oregon Barrel Co. tapered octagon barrels, single trigger, brown lock, hammer, furniture, and trigger guard, walnut or maple stock.

MSR	$1,500	$1,375	$1,200	$1,030

Add $150 for select wood.
Add $300 for select plus wood.

HAWKEN RIFLE - .54 cal. perc., 34 in. octagon barrel, brown lock, hammer, furniture, and trigger guard, adj. rear sight, presentation grade curly maple stock.

MSR	$1,375	$1,275	$1,130	$980

Add $200 for select wood.
Add $300 for select plus wood.

PENNSYLVANIA RIFLE - .32, .36, .40, .45, .50, or .54 cal. perc. or flintlock, 38 in. swamped barrel, double set triggers, iron or brass furniture, optional patchbox.

MSR	$1,500	$1,365	$1,180	$980

Add $150 for select wood.
Add $300 for select plus wood.

SHOTGUNS: FLINTLOCK & PERCUSSION

NORTH WEST TRADE GUN - 20, 24, or 28 ga. perc., smoothbore, 42 in. barrel, maple stock.

MSR	$950	$855	$725	$580

AMERICAN FOWLER - 20, 24, or 28 ga. flintlock or perc., smoothbore or rifled, 38 in. barrel, maple or walnut stock.

MSR	$1,400	$1,265	$1,125	$945

Add $100 for select wood.
Add $200 for select plus wood.
Add $75 for rifled barrel.

NOTES

H SECTION

HATFIELD

Previous trademark manufactured by Mountain River Rifle Works, and by Hatfield Gun Co. Inc. until 1996.

GRADING	100%	98%	95%	90%	80%	70%	60%

RIFLES: FLINTLOCK & PERCUSSION

MOUNTAIN RIFLE - .50 or .54 cal. perc., 32 in. octagon barrel, brown furniture, half stock, 9 lbs.

$575 **$500** **$360**

Last MSR was $665.

During 1992-93, extensive work was done to all internal working parts to insure greater longevity for target or field use. All internal parts were U.S. made.

SQUIRREL RIFLE - .32, .36, .45, or .50 cal. flintlock or perc., 39 in. barrel, adj. sights, double set triggers, brass trim, 7.5 lbs.

$520 **$450** **$360**

Last MSR was $600.

Add $20 for flintlock.
Add $65 for extra fancy maple Grade II.
Add $175 for hand selected fancy Grade III.
Custom models could run 200% over standard.

HAWKEN SHOP

Current manufacturer of original Hawken rifles, located in Oak Harbor, WA. Dealer or consumer direct sales.

The Hawken Shop (owned by the Dayton Traister Company) has purchased the rights and machinery to manufacture the original Hawken Rifle from Arthur Ressel. Mr. Ressel had previously purchased the rights to manufacture these rifles from the heirs of John Gemmer, who purchased S. Hawken Manufacturing directly from Samuel Hawken in 1860. Because of the continual lineage of ownership, these models are considered original Hawken rifles.

Standard Hawken rifles in new condition (100%) are selling for $2,000+, with the Hawken Commemorative Plains Rifle (1 of 50) selling in excess of $4,000.

HEGE

Currently manufactured by Hege Jagd und Sporthandels GmbH, located in Überlingen, Germany. No current importation.

PISTOLS: PERCUSSION

HEGE-SIBER PISTOL - .33 or .44 cal. perc., 10 in. blue octagon barrel, exceptional finish, color case hardened hammer and lock. Importation disc. 1994.

$1,055 **$905** **$720**

Last MSR was $1,000.

FRENCH STYLE HEGE-SIBER PISTOL - .33 or .44 cal. perc., 10 in. blue octagon barrel, exceptional finish, London grey finish, 24Kt. gold inlays, blue trigger guard. Importation disc. 1994.

$1,850 **$1,575** **$1,260**

Last MSR was $1,795.

* **Matched set** - same serial numbers. Importation disc. 1994.

$3,700 **$3,140** **$2,510**

Last MSR was $2,995.

GRADING	100%	98%	95%	90%	80%	70%	60%

RIFLES: FLINTLOCK

HEGE-MANTON - .44 cal. flintlock, 6 lbs. Importation disc. 1994.

$1,800 $1,525 $1,225

Last MSR was $1,695.

Add $100 for engraving.

HIGH STANDARD

Previous manufacturer located in New Haven, Hamden, and East Hartford, CT. High Standard Mfg. Co was founded in 1926. They purchased Hartford Arms and Equipment Co. in 1932. The original plant was located in New Haven, CT. During WWII High Standard operated plants in Hew Haven and Hamden. After the war the operations were consolidated in Hamden. In 1968 the company was sold to the Leisure Group, Inc. The Leisure group sold High Standard to High Standard Inc. in January 1978. A final move was made to East Hartford, CT in 1977 where they remained until the doors closed in late 1984.

The author and publisher wish to thank Mr. John J. Stimson, Jr. for the following information in this edition of *Blue Book of Modern Black Powder Values*.

LIMITED/SPECIAL EDITIONS

These guns were a series of .36 caliber cap and ball revolvers which began production in 1974 and ran through 1976. These are reproductions of the Confederate copies of the Colt Model 1851 Navy Revolver. Note most Confederate copies of the Colt had round barrels not the octagonal barrel found on the Colt. The frames were made by High Standard and the balance of the parts by Uberti. The guns were assembled and finished by High Standard.

GRISWOLD & GUNNISON - .36 cal., perc., SA, six shot copy of Confederate Revolver, 7.5 in. barrel, blue finish w/brass frame. Commemorative gun in a pine presentation case w/brass belt plate depicting the Georgia State seal. Catalog no. 9333 Commemorative (S/N 00001-00500), Catalog no. 9331 (S/N 00501-02600). Mfg. 1974 only.

$275 $220 $175

Last MSR was $145.

Add 30% for case and accessories.

LEECH & RIGDON - .36 cal., perc., SA, six shot, blue finish with steel frame. Commemorative gun cased with reproduction of a Civil War belt buckle. Catalog no. 9334 Commemorative (S/N 00001-00500), Catalog no. 9332 (S/N 00501-01199). Mfg. 1974 only.

$275 $220 $175

Last MSR was $145.

Add 30% for case and accessories.

SCHNEIDER & GLASSICK - .36 cal. perc., SA, six shot, blued finish w/steel frame, cased w/Confederate "D guard" Bowie knife. Catalog no. 9335 (S/N 0-1000). Mfg. 1975 only.

$375 $300 $200

Last MSR was $325.

BICENTENNIAL BLACK POWDER - .36 cal. perc., SA, six shot, 1776-1976 Bicentennial Edition, two versions, pine case marked High Standard and the trigger logo on the lid with a powder flask and silver dollar sized medallion inside, or brown leatherette covered case with American Bicentennial 1776-1976 and contains a pewter Bicentennial belt buckle. Catalog no. 9336 (S/N A 0000-A 2028).

$350 $275 $175

I SECTION

IVER JOHNSON

Previous manufacturer located in Jackson, AR.

GRADING	100%	98%	95%	90%	80%	70%	60%

RIFLES: PERCUSSION, O/U

MODEL BP50HB - .50 cal. perc., double hammers and triggers, color case hardened hammers and furniture.

$400 $300 $250

I.A.B. srl

Current manufacturer (Industria Armi Bresciane) of modern firearms, black powder replicas, and historycal Sharps rifles located in Gardone, Valtrompia, Brescia, Italy. Currently imported by Kiesler's, located in Jeffersonville, IN, E.M.F. & Co., located in Santa Ana, CA, Dixie GunWorks, located in Union City, TN, Tristar Sporting Arms, located in Kansas City, MO.

Please refer to individual importer/distributor listing in this text for model information and pricing.

NOTES

J SECTION

J.P. GUN STOCK, INC.

Current manufacturer located in Las Vegas, NV. Previously distributed by Mountain States Muzzleloading Supplies, Inc. located in Williamstown, WV.

GRADING	100%	98%	95%	90%	80%	70%	60%

RIFLES: FLINTLOCK & PERCUSSION

J.P. BECK RIFLE - .50 cal. flintlock, 42 in. oct. barrel. Pennsylvania long rifle style, brass furniture, 9 lbs.

		100%	98%	95%
MSR	$795	$795	$715	$650

J.P. HENRY TRADE RIFLE - .54 cal. flintlock, 35 in. oct. brown barrel, brass trigger guard, buttplate and patchbox, curly maple stock, 10 lbs.

		100%	98%	95%
MSR	$795	$795	$715	$650

J.P. MCCOY SQUIRREL RIFLE - .32 or .45 cal. flintlock or perc., 42 in. brown barrel, brown hammer and lock, brass buttplate and trigger guard, full length select curly maple stock, 7.5 lbs.

		100%	98%	95%
MSR	$700	$690	$600	$480

Add $20 for flintlock.

NOTES

K SECTION

K.B.I.

Current importer/distributor located in Harrisburg, PA. K.B.I. discontinued all black powder arms during late 1994, and are currently importing firearms only.

For more information and current pricing on both new and used K.B.I. firearms, please refer to the 24th Ed. *Blue Book of Gun Values* by S.P. Fjestad (now online also).

GRADING	100%	98%	95%	90%	80%	70%	60%

REVOLVERS: PERCUSSION

1851 NAVY - .44 cal. perc., 7.5 in. barrel, brass frame, 39-43 oz. Disc. 1994.

	100%	98%	95%
	$115	$100	$70

Last MSR was $150.

Add $30 for engraving, or for Pony Express Sheriff Model.

1860 ARMY - .44 cal. perc., 5 or 8 in. barrel, steel frame, 41 oz. Disc. 1994.

	100%	98%	95%
	$170	$150	$120

Last MSR was $240.

1858 REMINGTON ARMY - .36 or .44 cal. perc., 6.5 or 8 in. oct. barrel, 40 oz. Disc. 1994.

	100%	98%	95%
	$135	$115	$100

Last MSR was $170.

Add $25 for steel frame.
Add $140 for stainless steel.
Add $20 for 12 in. Buffalo Model.

RIFLES: FLINTLOCK & PERCUSSION

HAWKEN RIFLE - .45, .50, .54, or .58 cal. flintlock or perc., 28 in. oct. barrel, color case hardened hammer and lock, 9 lbs. Disc. 1994.

	100%	98%	95%
	$265	$225	$180

Last MSR was $300.

Add $30 for flintlock.
Add $10 for left-hand.
Subtract $45 for Field Grade.

KENTUCKY RIFLE - .50 cal. perc., 35 in. oct. barrel, color case hardened hammer and lock, brass furniture and trigger guard, 7 lbs. Disc. 1994.

	100%	98%	95%
	$300	$255	$200

Last MSR was $420.

KAHNKE/DENALI GUN WORKS

Current trademark manufactured by Mid-Western Outdoor Specialties, Inc. located in Joplin, MO. Previously named Kahnke Gun Works and located in Redwood Falls, MN.

Kahnke has developed a lightweight contemporary style .50 cal. rifle and a companion .54 cal. single-shot model. Both feature in-line ignition and resemble the Thompson Contender in appearance. The first version was introduced in 1982.

PISTOLS: IN-LINE IGNITION

KAHNKE .54 CAL. MODEL - .54 cal. perc., single-shot hunting pistol, adj. sights, unusual combination of both old and new technologies, walnut grips. 3.5 lbs. Mfg. 1988-disc.

	100%	98%	95%
	$345	$315	$240

Last MSR was $295.

GRADING	100%	98%	95%	90%	80%	70%	60%

MODEL 82 - .36, .45, .50, or .54 cal. perc., hammer block safety, 10.5, 12, or 14 in. barrel, drilled and tapped for scope mounts, Millett adj. sights, Herrett's walnut grips.

MSR	$389	$350	$310	$250

Add $20 for stainless steel.

RIFLES: IN-LINE IGNITION

MODEL 94 - .50 cal. perc., 24 in. barrel, adj. sights, walnut stock and forearm, 6 lbs.

MSR	$529	$475	$425	$345

Add $20 for stainless steel.

KNIGHT RIFLES

Current manufacturer and distributor located in Centerville, IA. Previously located in Lancaster, MO. Available through dealers, catalog houses or consumer direct.

The Knight MK Series is the forerunner of the modern black powder rifle designed as a true hunting/sporting rifle. These black powder rifles feature a straight through Posi-Fire ignition system, double safety, in-line bolt assembly, and Timney deluxe trigger system. Current Knight rifles use the Knight Disc system, which holds the primer in an easily managed plastic disc. Knight's new "Full Plastic Jacket" (FPJ) completely seals the #209 primer against moisture.

PISTOLS: IN-LINE IGNITION

HAWKEYE - .50 cal. perc., 12 in. round barrel, adj. trigger, drilled and tapped for scope, synthetic stock, also available in stainless, 3.25 lbs. Mfg. 1993-98.

	$360	$305	$245

Last MSR was $400.

Subtract $25 for black composite stock.
Add $40 for stainless steel.

RK-88 HAWK - .45, .50 or .54 cal. perc., same action as MK rifles, modern (swept back) black composite stock. Mfg. 1991-92 only. Disc. 1994.

	$365	$290	$230

Last MSR was $430.

RIFLES: IN-LINE IGNITION

AMERICAN KNIGHT - .50 cal. perc., #209 primer (FPJ) ignition system (new 2003), 22 in. blue round barrel, 1:28 in. twist, adj. Fiber-Lite rear and fiber optic front sights, drilled and taped for scope, double safety, black solid composite stock w/sling swivel studs, 6.5 lbs.

MSR	$198	$180	$155	$125

BLACK LEGEND/BLACK LEGEND PLUS - .50 cal. perc., 22 in. round blue barrel (24 in. on Black Legend Plus), double safety, fiber-tuff, walnut stained hardwood, or black Prolight stock, 6.25 lbs. Disc. 1994.

	$260	$220	$175

Last MSR was $290.

Add $45 for stained hardwood stock or Black Legend Plus Model with 24 in. barrel.

BH-99 BIGHORN - .50 cal. perc., 22 in. or 26 in. blue or stainless round barrel, double safety, black, camo, or black thumbhole composite stock, right or left-hand versions, 7 lbs. Disc. 2001.

	$315	$265	$215

Last MSR was $350.

Add $50 for camo stock.
Add $30 for thumbhole stock.
Add $60 for stainless steel barrel.

GRADING	100%	98%	95%	90%	80%	70%	60%

Add $20 for 26 in. barrel.

BK-89 SQUIRREL - .36 cal. perc., 24 in. barrel, Monte Carlo stock, double safety, 5.5 lbs. Disc. 1992.

$445 $380 $310

Last MSR was $500.

BK-92 BLACK KNIGHT - .50 or .54 cal. perc., 24 in. blue barrel, wood, epoxy coated wood, or composite Monte Carlo stock (standard 1995-96), double safety, under 7 lbs. Mfg. 1991-96.

$310 $250 $200

Last MSR was $400.

Subtract $40 for standard wood stock.

DELUXE RIFLE WITH DISC SYSTEM - .50 cal. perc., 22 in. round barrel, disc system allows the shooter the choice of a #11 percussion cap or a standard #209 primer, either can be pre-loaded into a disc for fast loading and higher grain loads, double safety, adj. trigger and sights, black composite stock. Designed to use the disc system in conjunction with Pyrodex pellets. Disc. 1997.

$350 $275 $225

Last MSR was $400.

Add $45 for camo stock.
Add $60 for stainless steel.
Add $40 for deluxe.

DISC ELITE - .45 or .50 cal. perc., #209 primer (FPJ) ignition system, bolt-action, 26 in. fully contoured blue or stainless steel barrel, 1:30 (.45 cal.) or 1:28 in. twist, drilled and taped for scope, black, Mossy Oak Break-Up, or HD Hardwoods Green composite stock with recoil pad and sling swivel studs, adj. trigger, approx. 7.4 lbs. New 2003.

MSR $510 $465 $410 $335

Add $70 for stainless steel.
Add $40 for Mossy Oak Break-Up or HD Hardwoods Green stock.

DISC EXTREME - .45, .50, or .52 (new 2003) cal. perc., #209 primer (FPJ) ignition system, bolt-action, 26 in. fluted (.45 cal.) blue or stainless steel barrel, 1:30 (.45 cal.) or 1:28 in. twist, adj. Metallic fiber optic sights, drilled and taped for scope, walnut, black composite with or without thumbhole, laminated hardwood, Mossy Oak Break-Up (new 2003), or HD Hardwoods Green (new 2003) stock with recoil pad and sling swivel studs, adj. trigger, approx. 7.8 lbs. New 2002.

MSR $550 $510 $450 $350

Add $82 for .45 cal.
Add $50 for .52 cal.
Add $82 for stainless steel.
Add $77 for walnut stock.
Add $82 for laminated stock.
Add $55 for Mossy Oak Break-Up or HD Hardwoods Green stock.

✳ *Disc Extreme Master Hunter* - .45 or .50 cal. perc., #209 primer (FPJ) ignition system, similar to Disc Extreme, except Cryogenically accurized 26 in. fluted stainless steel barrel, black composite and laminated hardwood thumbhole stock, (comes with both stocks) 7.5 lbs. New 2002.

MSR $1,045 $950 $835 $675

Add $50 for .45 cal.

DISC (ORIGINAL) - .45 and .50 cal. perc., #209 primer (Original Disc) ignition system, 24 or 26 in. blue or stainless steel barrel, 1:30 (.45 cal.) or 1:28 in. twist, adj. Metallic fiber optic sights, drilled and taped for scope, adj. trigger, black composite stock with recoil pad and sling swivel studs, 7.8 lbs. New 1998.

MSR $440 $395 $350 $285

GRADING	100%	98%	95%	90%	80%	70%	60%

Add $55 for Mossy Oak Break-Up or Advantage Timber HD stock.
Add $22 for 26 in. barrel.
Add $110 for .45 cal.
Add $90 for stainless steel.

❋ *Disc (Original) Master Hunter* - .45 or .50 cal. perc., 26 in. fluted stainless steel barrel, bolt-action, black composite thumbhole and laminated hardwood stock, (comes with both stocks) 7.44 lbs. Mfg. 2000-02.

$900 $765 $615

Last MSR was $1,000.

GRAND AMERICAN - .50 or .54 cal. perc., hand selected deluxe model of MK-85 Hunter, with thumbhole stock and gold inlaid barrel. Special order only. Disc. 2000.

$1,170 $995 $795

Last MSR was $1,300.

LKII WOLVERINE II - .50 or .54 cal. perc., 22 in. blue or stainless round barrel, double safety, full length composite stock in black, camo, or with thumbhole, 6.69 lbs. Disc. 2001.

$200 $170 $135

Last MSR was $270.

Add $40 for camo stock.
Add $40 for thumbhole stock.
Add $60 for stainless steel barrel.

MK-85 BACK COUNTRY CARBINE - .45, .50, or .54 cal. perc., 20 in. round barrel, Monte Carlo stock, double safety, 6.63 lbs. Disc. 1992.

$430 $365 $300

Last MSR was $520.

Add $60 for stainless steel.

MK-85 GRIZZLY (PLB) - .54 cal. perc., brown laminate stock, double safety. Mfg. 1991-92.

$475 $410 $330

Last MSR was $650.

Add $100 for stainless steel.

MK-85 HUNTER - .45, .50, or .54 cal. perc., 24 in. round barrel drilled and tapped for scope, walnut stock, double safety system, under 7 lbs. Disc. 2001.

$390 $330 $260

Last MSR was $550.

MK-85 KNIGHT HAWK - .50 or .54 cal. perc., 24 in. blue barrel, blue steel, synthetic thumbhole stock, tapped for scope, double safety system, (6.75 lbs. stainless) 7.25 lbs. Disc. 2001.

$550 $460 $410

Last MSR was $770.

Add $70 for stainless.

MK-85 LIGHT KNIGHT - .50 or .54 cal. perc., 20 in. round barrel, walnut or black composite stock, lightweight version of MK-85 Hunter. Disc. 1993.

$445 $380 $310

Last MSR was $500.

Add $20 for composite stock.

GRADING	100%	98%	95%	90%	80%	70%	60%

MK-85 PREDATOR - .50 or .54 cal. perc., 20 or 24 in. round barrel, black synthetic stock, double safety system, under 7 lbs. Disc 2001.

$585 $495 $390

Last MSR was $650.

Add $40 for camo composite stock.
Add $25 for forest green or shadow black laminate.

MK-85 STALKER - .45, .50, or .54 cal. perc., 22 or 24 in. round barrel, Monte Carlo stock, double safety system, under 7 lbs. Disc. 2001.

$515 $435 $350

Last MSR was $570.

Add $40 for camo composite stock.
Add $25 for forest green or shadow black laminate.

MK-86 MBS (MULTI-BARREL SYSTEM) - .50 cal., .54 cal., or 12 ga. perc., 22 in. round rifle or shotgun barrel, double safety, adj. trigger, black composite stock, 7.75 lbs. (6.75 shotgun). Disc. 2000.

$500 $440 $370

Last MSR was $600.

Add $150 for combo, .50, .54, or 12 ga. barrel.

MK-93 WOLVERINE - .50 or .54 cal. perc., 22 in. blue or stainless round barrel, double safety, composite stock in black, camo, or with thumbhole, 6 lbs. Disc. 1999.

$200 $170 $135

Last MSR was $270.

Add $50 for camo stock.
Add $70 for stainless steel barrel.

MK-95 MAGNUM ELITE - .50 or .54 cal. perc., unique new posi-fire system which uses a Magnum rifle primer, 24 in. round stainless steel barrel, all parts stainless steel, black composite or Realtree camo stock, 6.75 lbs. Mfg. 1994-98.

$665 $565 $455

Last MSR was $740.

Add $60 for Realtree camo stock.

T-5 WOODSMAN - .50 or .54 cal. perc., 20 in. round barrel, hardwood stock, double safety, adj. sights, approx. 7 lbs. Mfg. 1991-92.

$230 $195 $160

Last MSR was $230.

T-BOLT RIFLE - .50 cal. perc., 22 or 26 in. blue or stainless round barrel, double safety, composite stock in black or camo, 7.88 lbs. Disc. 2000.

$360 $305 $245

Last MSR was $400.

Add $50 for camo stock.
Add $70 for stainless steel barrel.
Add $20 for 26 in. barrel.

WOLVERINE 209 - .45 (new 2003) or .50 cal. perc., #209 primer (FPJ) ignition system, 22 or 26 (new 2003) in. blue or stainless round barrel, double safety, adj. metallic fiber optic sight, drilled and taped for scope, adj. trigger, black with or without thumbhole, Mossy Oak Break-Up, Hardwoods Green HD (new 2003), or Advantage Timber HD (disc. 2002) composite stock with recoil pad and sling swivel studs, 7 lbs. Left-hand model available. New 2002.

MSR	$302	$270	$240	$195

Add $45 for Mossy Oak Break-Up stock.
Add $60 for stainless steel.
Add $33 thumbhole stock.
Add $44 for Advantage Timber HD or Realtree Hardwoods Green Rocky Mountain Elk Foundation model.
Add $20 for 26 in. barrel.

SHOTGUNS: IN-LINE IGNITION

TK 2000MC - 12 ga., #209 primer (FPJ) ignition system (new 2003), 26 in. blue or Advantage Timber HD barrel, adj. metallic fiber optic sight, adj. trigger, black or Advantage Timber HD composite stock with recoil pad and sling swivel studs, 7.5 lbs. New 2000.

MSR	$396	$355	$310	$250

Add $44 for Advantage Timber HD.

L SECTION

LOVEN-PIERSON, INC.

Previous trademark of the Appalachia Arsenal located in Appalachia, NY.

GRADING	100%	98%	95%	90%	80%	70%	60%

RIFLES: PERCUSSION

All rifles have rotating over and under set of barrels to facilate a fast 2nd shot.

MODEL 10 - .45 cal. perc., swivel breech, 22 (carbine) or 28 in. (rifle) octagon or half round barrel, blue furniture, maple stock, 7.75–8.5 lbs. Disc. 1994.

	100%	98%	95%
	$300	$255	$200

Last MSR was $330.

MODEL 13 - .45, .50, or .54 cal. perc., similar to Model 10, except brass furniture and walnut stock. Disc. 1994.

	100%	98%	95%
	$400	$340	$270

Last MSR was $440.

MODEL 16 - .45, .50, or .54 cal. perc., similar to Model 10, except has color case hardened lock and furniture, brown barrels and curly or birds eye maple or figured walnut stock. Disc. 1994.

	100%	98%	95%
	$600	$540	$430

Last MSR was $880.

LYMAN PRODUCTS CORP.

Current manufacturer located in Middletown, CT. Lyman Products Corp. also carries a complete line of black powder accessories. Dealer and consumer direct sales.

PISTOLS: PERCUSSION

1851 NAVY - .36 cal. perc. Disc.

	100%	98%	95%
	$110	$95	$75

Last MSR was $165.

1858 REMINGTON .36 NAVY - .36 cal perc., 6 shot, 5.5 in. barrel. Disc.

	100%	98%	95%
	$125	$110	$90

Last MSR was $170.

1858 REMINGTON .44 ARMY - .44 cal perc., 6 shot. Disc.

	100%	98%	95%
	$125	$110	$90

Last MSR was $170.

1860 ARMY - .44 cal. perc. Disc.

	100%	98%	95%
	$160	$145	$110

Last MSR was $170.

PLAINS PISTOL - .50 or .54 cal. perc., color case hardened hammer and lock, brass trigger guard, blue otagonal barrel, walnut stock, 3.1 lbs.

MSR	100%	98%	95%
$245	$210	$175	$140

GRADING	100%	98%	95%	90%	80%	70%	60%

RIFLES: FLINTLOCK & PERCUSSION

DEERSTALKER - .50 or .54 cal. flintlock or perc. 24 in. octagon barrel, color case hardened hammer and lock, sling swivels, adj. sights, available right or left-hand action, and in stainless steel, 10.1 lbs.

MSR	$305	$230	$195	$155

Add $45 for flintlock model.
Add $90 for stainless steel percussion model with stainless steel barrel, lock, trigger guard, escutcheons and wedge.
Add $25 for left-hand.

GREAT PLAINS RIFLE - .50 or .54 cal. flintlock or perc., color case hardened hammer and lock, blackened steel furniture, 32 in. octagon barrel, right or left-hand action, 11.38 lbs.

MSR	$475	$370	$335	$275

Add $25 for flintlock.

TRADE RIFLE - .50 or .54 cal. perc. or flintlock, 28 in. octagon barrel, color case hardened hammer and lock, right or left-hand action, 10.8 lbs.

MSR	$315	$245	$210	$170

Add $25 for flintlock.

RIFLES: IN-LINE IGNITION

COUGAR RIFLE - .50 or .54 cal. perc., 22 in. blue barrel, dual safety, rubber recoil pad, walnut stock with swivels, 7.25 lbs. New 1996.

$260 $225 $180

Last MSR was $300.

M SECTION

MANDALL SHOOTING SUPPLIES, INC.

Current retailer and dealer located in Scottsdale, AZ. Dealer or consumer direct sales.

GRADING	100%	98%	95%	90%	80%	70%	60%

FRENCH DUELING PISTOL - .44 cal. perc., single trigger, classic fluted handle, sold with velvet lined display case and accessories. Disc. 1994.

	$450	$390	$310				

Last MSR was $295.

NAPOLEON CANNON - .69 cal., wick ignition, detailed scaled down model of the original used by both the Union and Confederacy during the Civil War, brass furniture, with carriage, 18 lbs. Disc. 1994.

	$450	$390	$310				

Last MSR was $290.

MARKESBERY MUZZLE LOADERS, INC.

Current manufacturer located in Florence, KY. Dealer and consumer direct sales.

These in-line ignition rifles with a modular design allow for custom tailoring with a wide selection of stocks from traditional one-piece and two-piece designs to Monte Carlo, thumbhole pistol grip versions, black laminate, and camo finishes. All models feature a crossbolt safety system, "Spit-Fire" nipple threaded into the rear of the breech plug at a 45 degree angle for positive ignition, stainless steel trigger, interchangeable, precision rifled Green Mountain barrels, and investment cast receiver.

PISTOLS: IN-LINE IGNITION

MARKESBERY MODEL KM82 - .36 (10.5 in. barrel only), .45, .50 & .54 cal. perc., 10.5, 12, or 14 in. blue or stainless steel barrel. Mfg. 1994-98.

	$460	$400	$270				

Last MSR was $539.

Add $30 for stainless steel.
Add $30 for Goncalo Alves grip.
Add $10 for Lamo Gamo grips.

RIFLES: IN-LINE IGNITION

MARKESBERY MODEL KM94 - .45, .50, or .54 cal. perc., 24 in. blue or stainless steel barrel, straight or pistol grip stock, rifle version of Model KM82. Many styles, 6.5 lbs.

	$490	$425	$360				

Last MSR was $525.

KM BLACK BEAR - .36, .45, .50, or .54 cal. perc., 24 in. 1:26 in. twist barrel, blue or matte stainless steel finish, adj. sights, black composite or walnut Monte Carlo two-piece stock w/PG, 6.5 lbs.

MSR	$537	$480	$410	$330			

Add $16 for stainless steel.
Add $4 for black or green laminate stock.
Add $20 for camo stock.
Subtract $4 for black composite stock.
Markesbery will donate $10 to the NRA Foundation for every Black Bear NRA Foundation Commemorative Rifle w/NRA Foundation, Inc. logo on frame, new 2003.

KM BROWN BEAR - .36, .45, .50, or .54 cal. perc., similar to KM Black Bear, except one-piece black or crotch walnut composite thumbhole stock, 6.75 lbs.

MSR	$659	$600	$510	$410			

Add $16 for stainless steel.

GRADING	100%	98%	95%	90%	80%	70%	60%

Add $4 for black or green laminate stock.

Add $25 for camo stock.

KM GRIZZLY BEAR - .36, .45, .50, or .54 cal. perc., similar to KM Black Bear, except two-piece black or crotch walnut composite thumbhole stock, 6.5 lbs.

MSR	**$643**	**$578**	**$490**	**$393**			

Add $16 for stainless steel.

Add $4 for black or green laminate stock.

Add $25 for camo stock.

KM POLAR BEAR - .36, .45, .50, or .54 cal. perc., similar to KM Brown Bear, except one-piece black composite or walnut Monte Carlo pistol grip stock, 6.75 lbs.

MSR	**$539**	**$485**	**$412**	**$330**			

Add $16 for stainless steel.

Add $4 for black or green laminate stock.

Add $25 for camo stock.

COLORADO ROCKY MOUNTAIN - .36, .45, .50, or .54 cal. perc. 24 in. blue or stainless steel barrel, straight grip traditional walnut carbine stock with two bands, hammer action spur, 6.5 lbs.

MSR	**$545**	**$490**	**$415**	**$330**			

Add $16 for stainless steel.

Add $4 for black or green laminate stock.

MARLIN

Current manufacturer established in 1870, and located in North Haven, CT. Distributor sales only.

RIFLES: IN-LINE IGNITION

MLS-50 - .50 cal. perc., 22 in. round stainless steel barrel, unique reversible cocking handle for right or left-hand shooters, adj. rear sights, composite stock, auto safety, 6.5 lbs. Disc. 1999.

		$355	**$285**	**$235**			

Last MSR was $411.

MLS-54 - .54 cal. perc., 22 in. round stainless steel barrel, unique reversible cocking handle for right or left-hand shooters, adj. rear sights, composite stock, auto safety, 6.5 lbs. Disc. 1999.

		$355	**$285**	**$235**			

Last MSR was $411.

MICHIGAN ARMS CORPORATION

Previous manufacturer located in Troy, MI.

Michigan Arms designed an extremely accurate and reliable ignition system, and was the first company to utilize a #209 shotgun primer as a source of ignition. It is not known how many of this variation were actually produced, and as a result, secondary marketplace pricing could be unpredictable.

RIFLES: IN-LINE IGNITION

WOLVERINE RIFLE - .45, .50 or .54 cal., #209 primer ignition, 25.25 in. octagon barrel, adj. sights, Dayton Traister rifle trigger with adj. pull, 8 lbs. Disc. 1994.

		$420	**$355**	**$260**			

Last MSR was $400.

FRIENDSHIP SPECIAL MATCH - .45, .50 or .54 cal., #209 primer ignition, 25.25 in. octagon barrel, fully adj. target sights with custom maple stock, Dayton Traister rifle trigger with adj. pull, 8 lbs. Disc. 1994.

		$495	**$410**	**$325**			

Last MSR was $600.

GRADING	100%	98%	95%	90%	80%	70%	60%

SILVERWOLF - similar to Wolverine, except only available in stainless steel. Disc. 1994.

$525 $445 $345

Last MSR was $600.

MID-WESTERN OUTDOOR SPECIALTIES, INC.

Current manufacturer and distributor located in Joplin, MO.

RIFLES: IN-LINE IGNITION

DENALI SUPER MAG - .45, .50, or .54 cal. perc., #209 primer ignition, closed breech hinged frame w/trigger guard release, 26 in. matte blue (Grade I) or matte stainless steel (Grade II) round barrel, 1:28 in. twist, adj. Williams Fire Sights fiber optic sights, drilled and tapped for scope, matte blue (Grade I) or matte stainless steel (Grade II) frame, carbon fiber (Grade I) or Mossy Oak Break-Up (Grade II) finish compostit stock and forearm, recoil pad, sling swivel studs, 7 lbs. New 2003.

* *Grade I* - matte blue finish and cardon fiber finish composite stock and forearm.

  MSR $400 $350 $295 $250

* *Grade II* - matte stainless steel finish and Mossy Oak Break-Up composite stock and forearm.

  MSR $430 $385 $345 $280

MILLENNIUM DESIGNED MUZZLELOADERS, LTD.

Current manufacturer and distributor of custom built in-line percussion rifles, located in Maidstone, VT. Previously located in Limington, ME.

Millennium Designed Muzzleloaders (MDM), manufactures a complete line of custom-built in-line rifles under the names M2K and Buckwacka. Designed for magnum loads (three 50gr. Pyrodex Pellets), the .50 caliber M2K rifles are bedded in a similar fashion as that of high powered rifles, utilizing two attachment points of stock to receiver. All barrels and receivers are precision machined from ordnance grade 400 series stainless steel. Barrels are rifled with a 1 in 24 in. right hand twist. All barrels feature a recessed crown for muzzle protection. The M2K's receiver qualifies the rifle as an open breech design, while still allowing maximum protection to the ignition system in harsh, wet, realistic hunting conditions.

All models feature an interlocking safety design, and a fully adj. trigger. M2K models were built for either left or right-hand shooters at no additional charge. Choice of two ignition systems, standard Spitfire nipple for #11 percussion caps, or Spitfire magnum musket nipple which accepts today's hot musket caps. The Buckwacka is a closed breech, break-open-action design offering a choice of calibers or a 12 ga. shotgun system. An ambidextrous design, Buckwacka lends itself to either right or left-handed shooters. Features include a multi-safety system with a primary transfer bar safety, and "Incinerating Ignition System" designed to use a #209 shotgun primer, musket caps, or #11 percussion caps.

PISTOLS: IN-LINE IGNITION

MINI-WACKA - .50 cal. perc., 15 in. blue barrel, rubber grips and black forearm. Uses #209 shotgun primer. Disc. 2002.

$279 $250 $225

Last MSR was $310.

RIFLES: IN-LINE IGNITION, PERCUSSION

BUCKWACKA - .45 cal. Nitro Magnum or .50 cal., #209 MDM Incinerating Ignition system, break-open-action, 23 (.50 cal.) or 25 in. blue or stainless steel barrel, 1:24 (.50 cal.) or 1:20 in. twist, adj. sights, black, walnut, Mossy Oak Break-Up, Trebark Superflauge, or Skyline Excel finished stock w/recoil pad and sling swivel studs, 6 (.50 cal.) or 6.5 lbs.

MSR $320 $285 $250 $205

Add $50 for Mossy Oak Break-Up, Skyline Excel, or TreBark Superflauge stock.
Add $30 for stainless steel.

GRADING	100%	98%	95%	90%	80%	70%	60%

COMPETITOR - .45 cal. or .50 cal., #209 primer Magnum Nitro Ignition system, bolt action, 24 in. blue barrel, 1:28 (.50 cal.) or 1:20 in. twist, adj. sights, matte black or Mossy Oak Break-Up finished stock w/recoil pad and sling swivel studs, 7 lbs. New 2003.

	MSR	$199	$175	$150	$125

Add $40 for Mossy Oak Break-Up stock.

M2K - .50 cal. perc., 24 in. stainless steel barrel, Shadow Black laminate stock or walnut stock, 7.75 lbs. Right or left-hand models. Disc. 2002.

$475	$405	$325

Last MSR was $529.

M2K CARBINE - .50 cal., 21 in. stainless steel barrel, Shadow Black laminate stock or walnut stock, 7-7.5 lbs. Right or left-hand models. Disc. 2002.

$475	$405	$325

Last MSR was $529.

M2K DELUXE/DELUXE CARBINE - .50 cal., 21 (carbine) or 24 in. stainless steel barrel, Deluxe Shadow Black laminate stock, 7.75 lbs. Right or left-hand models. Disc. 2002.

$495	$425	$355

Last MSR was $549.

M2K LADIES/YOUTH MODEL - .50 cal., 21 or 24 in. stainless steel barrel, Shadow Black laminate stock, 7-7.5 lbs. Right or left-hand models. Disc. 2002.

$495	$425	$355

Last MSR was $549.

M2K SPORTER RIFLE/CARBINE - .50 cal., 21 (carbine) or 24 in. stainless steel barrel, Nylon composite stock, 7.5 lbs. Right or left-hand models. Disc. 2002.

$495	$425	$355

Last MSR was $549.

SHOTGUNS: IN-LINE, PERCUSSION

BUCKWACKA SHOTGUN - 12 ga. perc., 28 in. barrel, walnut finish or black finish stock, 6 lbs. Disc. 2002.

$330	$290	$245

Last MSR was $359.

Add $130 for camo finish stock and barrel.

TOMWACKA - 12 ga. perc. #209 MDM Incinerating Ignition system, break-open-action, 24 in. blue or Mossy Oak Break-Up barrel with screw-in choke system, ivory bead sight, walnut or Mossy Oak Break-Up stock with recoil pad and sling swivel studs, 5 lbs. New 2003.

MSR	$370	$335	$285	$245

Add $100 for Mossy Oak Break-Up.

MITCHELL ARMS

Current importer located in Fountain Valley, CA. Distributor and dealer sales only.

In 1993, Mitchell Arms discontinued the importation of black powder arms. All revolvers were imported from Pietta. Please refer to the Pietta section for pricing guidelines on similar models/configurations.

MODERN MUZZLELOADING, INC.

Please refer to Knight Rifles in the K section of this text for more information.

MOUNTAIN STATE MANUFACTURING

Current importer/distributor/manufacturer of accessories for black powder shooters located in Williamstown, WV.

Beginning 2002, Mountain State Muzzleloading Supplies, Inc. change their name to Mountain State Manufacturing. See Mountain State Muzzleloading Supplies, Inc. for more information.

MOUNTAIN STATE MUZZLELOADING SUPPLIES, INC.

Previous importer/distributor located in Williamstown, WV. Mountain State Muzzleloading changed the mane to Mountain State Manufacturing during 2002, and continues to primarily markets accessories for black powder shooters, repair parts, period clothing, holsters, leather goods, bullets and bullet molds, and previously a modest line of pistols and pistol kits, available from manufacturers such as CVA. Dealer and consumer direct sales.

Mountain State also made an exclusive line of high quality American-made flint and percussion rifles under the trade name All American Golden Classic and All American Silver Classic. These were traditional antique-style muzzle loading rifles reminiscent of early 1800s Leman-Lancaster rifles manufactured in Pennsylvania. They featured fancy curly maple full stocks, hand finished in traditional satin reddish brown, a high cheekpiece, polished brass or nickel silver buttplate and trigger guard, antiqued rust brown barrel and lock, and double set triggers.

RIFLES: FLINTLOCK & PERCUSSION

GOLDEN CLASSIC - .50 cal. perc. or flintlock, 35 in. octagon barrel, authentic sand cast brass finish or nickel-silver furniture, 1: 66 in. twist rifling, 7.5 lbs. Disc. 2000.

$675   **$570**   **$450**

Last MSR was $750.

SILVER CLASSIC - .50 cal. perc. or flintlock, 42 in. octagon barrel, nickel-silver (white bronze) furniture, 1:66 in. twist rifling, fancy side plates, chevron nose cap, 8 lbs. Built to commemorate Mountain State Muzzleloading's 25th anniversary in 1997. Disc. 2000.

$895   **$750**   **$575**

Last MSR was $995.

MOWREY GUN WORKS, INC.

Current manufacturer and distributor located in Waldren, IN. Previously manufactured in Saginaw, TX. Previously distributed exclusively by Mountain State Muzzle Loaders Supplies, Inc. in Williamstown, WV. Dealer and consumer direct sales.

Mowrey Gun Works has recreated the guns designed by Ethan Allen and marketed under the name Allen and Thurber in the early and mid 1800s. The models themselves are beautifully hand crafted with "cut rifled" brown barrels (each groove cut individually using as many as 20 passes) and actions using only five moving parts creating exceptional accuracy and reliability. The 1:30 in. twist rifling was designed specifically to stabilize conical bullets. Each specimen is available with a number of features and options (listed below).

Mowrey Gun Works standard rifle features include: curly maple stocks and forearms, front blade-buckhorn rear sights, hand rubbed finish, and brass or brown steel receivers. Options include: premium curly maple, cherry or walnut stock and forearm, custom barrel lengths from 22-40 in., primitive fixed sight, target sights, and Scheutzen style buttplate. Beginning 1994, Mowrey Gun Works also began making reproductions of Hopkins & Allen underhammer rifles.

Add $30 for Fancy Grade Curly Maple.

Add $25 for fancy brass or steel Scheutzen buttplate, or shotgun buttplate.

RIFLES: FLINTLOCK

CLASSIC - .50 cal. flintlock or perc., copy of early Leman-Lancaster rifle, 35 in. brown octagon barrel, high relief checkered on beautiful curly maple full stock, brass furniture, brown hammer and lock, brass buttplate

GRADING	100%	98%	95%	90%	80%	70%	60%

and trigger guard.

* *Golden Classic*

MSR	$750	$695	$600	$500

* *Silver Classic* - with nickel silver furniture

MSR	$995	$895	$750	$600

RIFLES: PERCUSSION

1:30 TWIST CONICAL RIFLE - .45, .50 or .54 cal. perc., 28 in. octagon barrel, brass furniture, special 1:30 in. twist rifling for conical bullets, 8 lbs. Disc. 1998.

	$325	$280	$200

Last MSR was $360.

PLAINS RIFLE - .50 or .54 cal. perc., 28 or 32 in. full octagon barrel, brass furniture, 10 lbs. Only available in kit form.

MSR	$345	$300	$250	$170

ROCKY MOUNTAIN HUNTER - .50 or .54 cal. perc., 28 in. full octagon barrel, all brown steel furniture, 8 lbs. Available only in kit form.

MSR	$345	$300	$250	$170

SILHOUETTE RIFLE - .40 cal. perc., 28 or 32 in. octagon barrel, brass furniture. Available only in kit form.

MSR	$345	$300	$250	$170

SQUIRREL RIFLE - .32, .36, or .45 cal. perc., 28 in. full octagon barrel, brass furniture, 7 lbs. Available only in kit form.

MSR	$345	$300	$250	$170

RIFLES: PERCUSSION, HOPKINS & ALLEN DESIGN

HERITAGE RIFLE - .36, .45, or .50 cal. perc., 32 in. octagon barrel, all metal is brown, dark stained maple stock, unique underhammer design. Available only in kit form.

MSR	$239	$215	$180	$145

BUGGY RIFLE - .36, .45, or .50 cal. perc., 26 in. octagon barrel, all metal is brown, dark stained maple, unique underhammer design, approx. 6 lbs. Available only in kit form.

MSR	$239	$215	$180	$145

SHOTGUNS: PERCUSSION, SINGLE SHOT

12 GAUGE - 12 ga. perc., 32 in. full octagon barrel, brass or steel furniture, 7.5 lbs. Disc. 1998.

	$325	$280	$200

Last MSR was $360.

28 GAUGE - 28 ga. perc., 28 in. full octagon barrel, brass or steel furniture, built on squirrel frame, 7.5 lbs. Disc. 1994.

	$320	$280	$200

Last MSR was $350.

MUZZLELOADING TECHNOLOGIES, INC.

Previous trademark of manufacturer located in Roosevelt, UT 1997-2000. During 2000 Split Fire Sporting Goods, LLC located in Orem, UT acquired Muzzleloading Technologies, Inc. During 2001 Split Fire Sporting Goods, LLC changed the name to White Rifles LLC. For current information and model availability refer to these trademarks.

GRADING	100%	98%	95%	90%	80%	70%	60%

MTI offered two series of in-line muzzleloading rifles: Model 97 Whitetail Hunter, and Model 98 Elite Hunter. Both feature Doc White's new "MultiSystem Technology." Whitetail Hunter and Elite Hunter are constructed of ordnance-grade stainless steel, and feature a side-cocking action, large recoil absorption block and a two-point stock engagement system to increase accuracy and reduce felt recoil with heavy loads. These rifles are handcrafted and come with either checkered black composite or smooth black laminate stocks with straight comb, slender pistol grip, and English-styledbutt stock.

RIFLES: IN-LINE IGNITION

MODEL 97 WHITETAIL HUNTER - .41, .45, or .50 cal. perc., 22 in. straight tapered barrel, 1:16 in. twist (.41 cal.), 1:20 in. twist (.45 cal.), 1: 24 in. twist (.50 cal.), fully adj. hunting sights, aluminum ramrod with integral bullet puller. 6.5 lbs. Mfg. 1998-2000.

$480   **$410**   **$328**

Last MSR was $550.

Add $30 for black laminate stock.

MODEL 98 ELITE HUNTER - .41, .45, or .50 cal. perc., 24 in. straight tapered barrel with two ramrod guides, 1:16 in. twist (.41 cal.), 1:20 in. twist (.45 cal.), 1:24 in. twist (.50 cal.), custom fiber optic high visibility fully adj. hunting sights, aluminum ramrod with integral bullet puller. Mfg. 1998-2000.

$610   **$520**   **$415**

Last MSR was $700.

Add $30 for black laminate stock.

MUZZLE LOADERS, INC.

Previous importer/distributor located in Burke, VA.

PISTOLS: FLINTLOCK & PERCUSSION

DELUXE KENTUCKY PISTOL - .44 cal. perc. or flintlock, 10.25 in. octagon barrel, brass blade front sight, 2.5 lbs.

$205   **$170**   **$140**

Add $15 for flintlock mfg. by Armi San Paolo.

REVOLVERS: PERCUSSION

1847 WALKER - .44 cal. perc., charcoal finish, color case hardened frame, hammer, and loading lever, brass trim, engraved cylinder, 4.4 lbs. Mfg. by Uberti.

$275   **$240**   **$165**

1848 1ST MODEL DRAGOON - .44 cal. perc., 6 shot, brass grip straps, color case hardened frame, hammer, and loading lever, brass trim, 3.9 lbs. Mfg. by Uberti.

$265   **$235**   **$180**

1850 2ND MODEL DRAGOON - .44 cal. perc., 6 shot, brass grip straps, color case hardened frame, hammer, and loading lever, brass trim, 3.9 lbs. Mfg. by Uberti.

$265   **$235**   **$180**

1851 3RD MODEL DRAGOON - .44 cal. perc., 6 shot, brass grip straps, color case hardened frame, hammer, and loading lever, brass trim, 3.9 lbs.

$265   **$235**   **$180**

Add $15 for silver plated straps, or cut for stock.
Add $35 for Military Model (mfg. by Uberti).

GRADING	100%	98%	95%	90%	80%	70%	60%

1851 NAVY - .36 or .44 cal. perc., 7.5 in. octagon barrel, engraved (roll) cylinder, color case hardened frame and loading lever, silver plated brass backstrap and square back trigger guard. Sheriff's Model has 5 in. barrel, brass trigger guard and backstrap.

	$130	**$110**	**$90**				

Subtract $10 for Sheriff Model.
Subtract $20 for brass backstrap and trigger guard.
Subtract $25 for brass frame (mfg. by Armi San Paolo).

1860 ARMY - .44 cal. perc., 8 in. round barrel, color case hardened frame, hammer and loading lever, 2.56 lbs. Mfg. by Armi San Paolo.

	$175	**$165**	**$130**				

Subtract $50 for brass frame.

1862 POLICE - .36 cal. perc., 5.5 in. round barrel, color case hardened frame, loading lever, plunger, and hammer, round trigger guard, fluted cylinder, one-piece stock, 1.56 lbs. Mfg. by Armi San Paolo.

	$160	**$130**	**$100**				

1858 REMINGTON - .36 or .44 cal. perc., blue or brass frame, brass trigger guard, steel backstrap, 6 shot, 2.44 lbs.

	$185	**$160**	**$130**				

Add $30 for stainless.
Subtract $50 for brass frame (mfg. by Armi San Paolo).

ROGERS & SPENCER - .44 cal. perc., 7.5 in. octagon barrel, 2.94 lbs. Mfg. by Armi San Marco.

	$200	**$170**	**$135**				

Add $15 for target sights, and $25 for engraved London grey finish.

RIFLES: FLINTLOCK & PERCUSSION

1858 2-BAND ENFIELD - .58 cal. perc., 33 in. barrel, 2 barrel bands. Mfg. by Armi San Paolo.

	$435	**$380**	**$300**				

DELUXE HAWKEN RIFLE - .45 or .50 cal. perc. or flintlock, color case hardened hammer and lock, percussion cap holder in stock, chrome lined barrels. Mfg. by Uberti.

	$385	**$330**	**$265**				

DELUXE KENTUCKY RIFLE - .45 or .50 cal. perc. or flintlock, color case hardened hammer and lock, percussion cap holder in stock, chrome lined barrels, brass trim.

	$345	**$280**	**$210**				

Add $15 for flintlock (mfg. by Pedersoli).

ST. LOUIS HAWKENS - .50 cal. perc., color case hardened hammer and lock, 28 in. octagon barrel, brass trim, 7.94 lbs. Mfg. by CVA.

	$200	**$175**	**$140**				

ZOUAVE RIFLE - .58 cal. perc., brass trim, color case hardened hammer and lock, blue finish. Mfg. by Armi San Paolo.

	$290	**$250**	**$200**				

Identifying Popular Modern Black Powder Revolvers

by Dennis Adler

After Sam Colt patented the Paterson in 1836, (distinguished by its folding trigger and absence of a trigger guard), his fortunes faded, and by 1842 his Paterson, New Jersey manufacturing company was out of business. Undaunted, he soldiered back, quite literally, with the most powerful military revolver of the early 19th century, the 1847 Walker. This massive and unmistakable .44 caliber pistol played a significant role in the War with Mexico. Sam Colt and Captain Samuel Walker, who convinced the U.S. government to place its initial order for the mighty sidearm, worked together on the gun's design. Tragically, Walker was killed in action, but is remembered more than 150 years later by the guns that bear his name.

The Walker was a handful, and Sam Colt returned to his Paterson roots briefly by following the big .44 with two small pocket pistols, the .31 caliber 1848 Baby Dragoon and the 1849 Pocket Dragoon, which is differentiated by having a loading lever. Both resemble a small version of the 1st Model Dragoon.

The need for a lighter weight but still potent revolver led to the 1st, 2nd, and 3rd Model Dragoons in the late 1840s, which were a slightly smaller .44 caliber evolution of the Walker, and one of the most successful of the Colt percussion era.

Both the U.S. military and civilian market were clamoring for an even lighter but sufficiently powerful revolver by the end of the 1840s, and in 1851 Sam Colt brought out the most famous gun of his career, the 1851 Navy, chambered in .36 caliber. This distinctive firearm is recognized by its smaller frame and elegant octagon barrel. Two basic versions were offered, one with a square back trigger guard, and another with a round trigger guard.

The 1860 Army chambered in .44 caliber came next and is often considered the best looking gun ever built. A great departure from the squared lines of the Dragoons and Navy models, the Army had a slender round barrel and new loading leaver design, and either a rebated or fluted cylinder. A slightly scaled down version, the 1861 Navy, fitted with the 1851 Navy's rebated cylinder, followed in .36 caliber.

Colt's again returned to its pocket pistols around 1862 with the addition of the compact .36 caliber Police model, resembling a scaled down 1861 Navy with a half rebated, half fluted cylinder. The Pocket model of Navy size caliber followed in 1865, also chambered in .36 caliber, and resembling a compact 1851 Navy. This marked the end of new percussion models for Colt's.

The Colt's patent for the revolving cylinder had prevented other American gun manufacturers from producing revolvers until 1858, whereupon Remington introduced the .44 caliber Army model and .36 caliber Navy. Both can be distinguished by their use of a top strap design and fixed barrel.

Another popular model from the 1850s that has been reproduced in Italy is the Starr single and double action revolver. A distinctive design, the Starr has a break open frame secured by a screw. The guns have an easily recognizable profile.

The most elegant pistol design of the percussion era was the LeMat, set apart by its sheer size, large nine-shot .44 caliber cylinder, and 20-gauge shotgun barrel! Once you've seen a LeMat, you'll never forget it.

There are other Civil War reproductions built today, such as the Dance, which resembles an 1851 Navy without a recoil shield, and the Rogers & Spencer, which is similar in appearance to the 1858 Remington Army. The identification guide presented, however, should help in recognizing the majority of models currently available for black powder shooters. ■

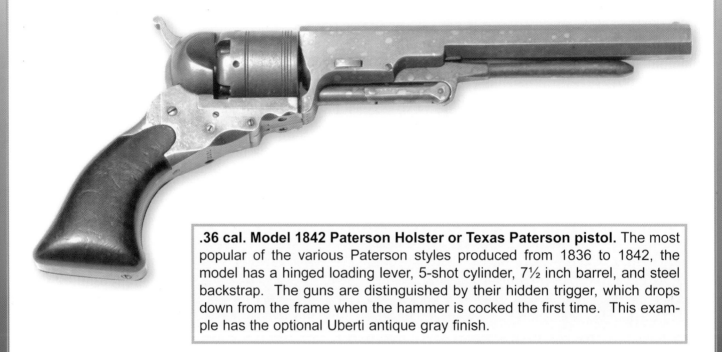

.36 cal. Model 1842 Paterson Holster or Texas Paterson pistol. The most popular of the various Paterson styles produced from 1836 to 1842, the model has a hinged loading lever, 5-shot cylinder, 7½ inch barrel, and steel backstrap. The guns are distinguished by their hidden trigger, which drops down from the frame when the hammer is cocked the first time. This example has the optional Uberti antique gray finish.

.44 cal. Model 1847 Walker Revolver, with hinged loading lever, 6 shot, 9½ in. half round, half octagon barrel, steel backstrap, brass square back trigger guard, "US 1847" stamped above wedge screw, NY address.

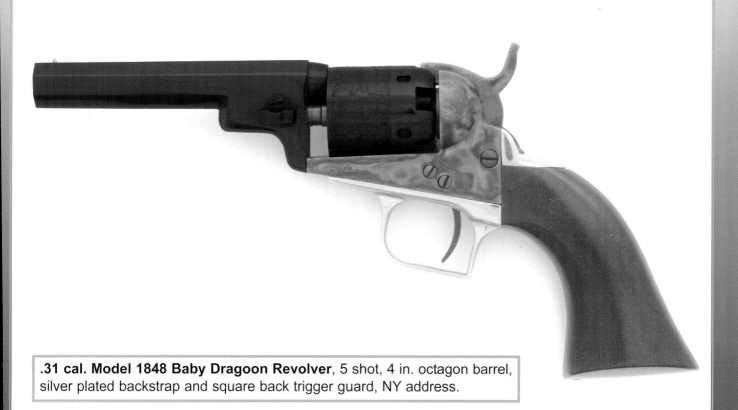

.31 cal. Model 1848 Baby Dragoon Revolver, 5 shot, 4 in. octagon barrel, silver plated backstrap and square back trigger guard, NY address.

.44 cal. 3rd Model Dragoon Revolver with hinged and latched loading lever, 6 shot, 7½ in. half-round, half-octagon barrel, rectangular cylinder stop slots, brass backstrap civilian model with round trigger guard, NY address.

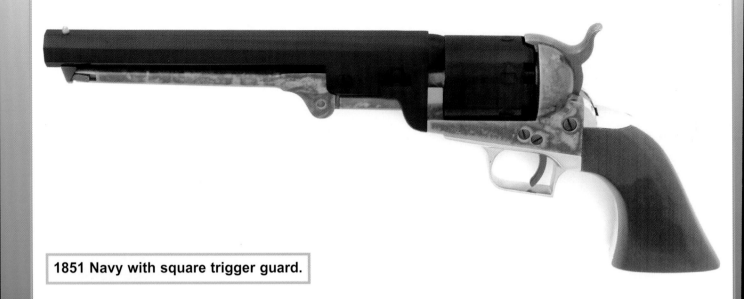

1851 Navy with square trigger guard.

.36 cal. Model 1851 Navy Revolver, with hinged and latched loading lever, 6 shot, 7½ in. octagon barrel, silver plated backstrap and square back trigger guard, NY address.

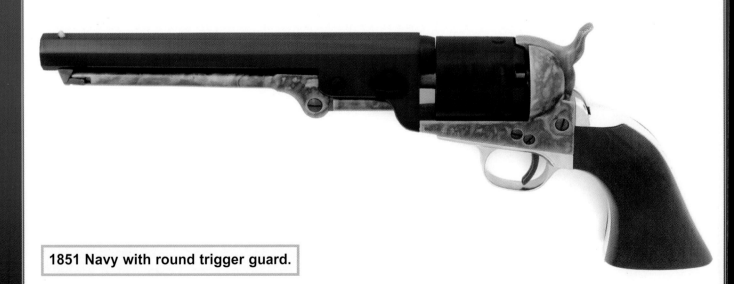

1851 Navy with round trigger guard.

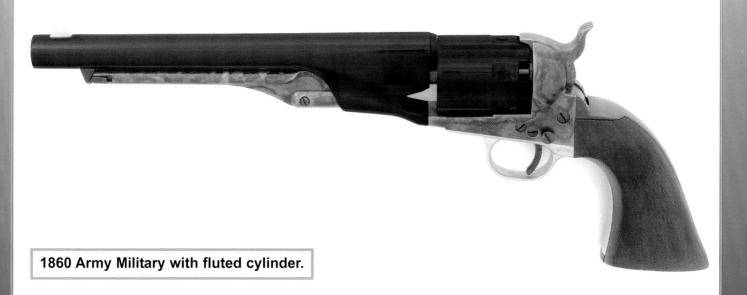

1860 Army Military with fluted cylinder.

.44 cal. Model 1860 Army Revolver with creeping style loading lever, 6 shot rebated or fluted cylinder, 8 in. round barrel, steel backstrap and brass trigger guard, NY U.S. America address.

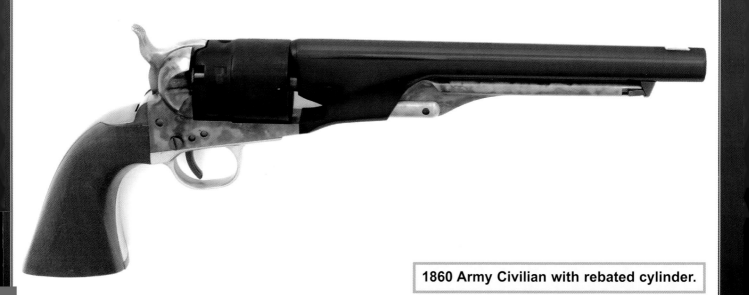

1860 Army Civilian with rebated cylinder.

.36 cal. Model 1861 Navy Revolver with creeping style loading lever, 6 shot non-rebated cylinder, 7½ in. round barrel, steel backstrap and trigger guard, NY address.

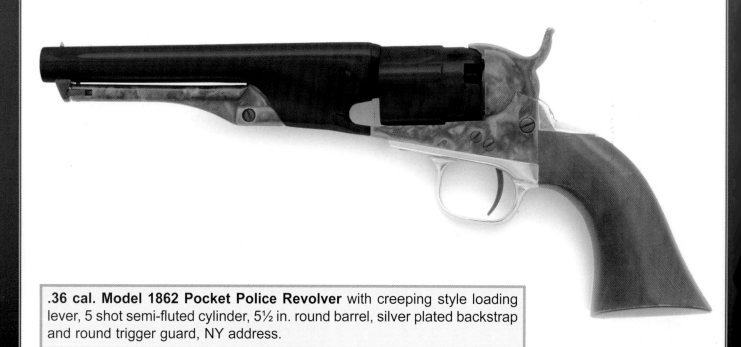

.36 cal. Model 1862 Pocket Police Revolver with creeping style loading lever, 5 shot semi-fluted cylinder, 5½ in. round barrel, silver plated backstrap and round trigger guard, NY address.

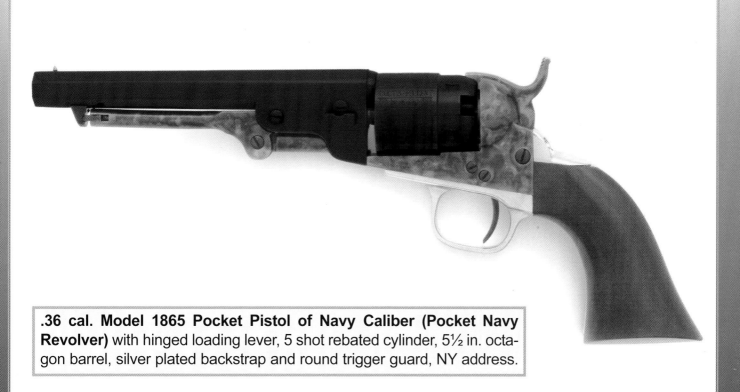

.36 cal. Model 1865 Pocket Pistol of Navy Caliber (Pocket Navy Revolver) with hinged loading lever, 5 shot rebated cylinder, 5½ in. octagon barrel, silver plated backstrap and round trigger guard, NY address.

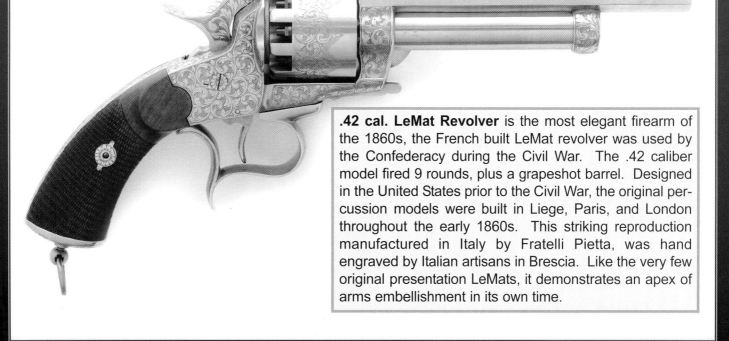

.42 cal. LeMat Revolver is the most elegant firearm of the 1860s, the French built LeMat revolver was used by the Confederacy during the Civil War. The .42 caliber model fired 9 rounds, plus a grapeshot barrel. Designed in the United States prior to the Civil War, the original percussion models were built in Liege, Paris, and London throughout the early 1860s. This striking reproduction manufactured in Italy by Fratelli Pietta, was hand engraved by Italian artisans in Brescia. Like the very few original presentation LeMats, it demonstrates an apex of arms embellishment in its own time.

.44 cal. 1858 Remington Revolver. Following the Colt 1851 Navy and 1860 Army in popularity, the 1858 Remington is one of the most heavily produced pistols manufactured in Italy.

.44 cal. Starr revolver. Fratelli Pietta in Brescia, Italy, produces these authentic reproductions of the Starr single and double action .44 cal. revolvers used during the Civil War. The Starr was one of the very first double action revolvers built and could be fired either single or double action. This example has a custom antique finish that has fooled some experts. Pietta also offers the Starr with an antique gray patina.

N SECTION

NAVY ARMS CO.

Current manufacturer/importer/distributor established in 1958, and located in Union City, NJ.

Navy Arms is one of the oldest black powder importers and distributors in the United States. In addition to black powder pistols and longarms, Navy Arms also sells black powder cartridge conversions of Colt pistols, western cartridge-firing pistols, rifles and shotguns, edged weapons, muzzle loading accessories, Civil War leather accessories, accouterments, and presentation cases. Navy Arms black powder pistols are principally manufactured by A. Uberti & Co., and by F.lli Pietta. Dealer, catalog, and consumer direct sales.

Val Forgett, Sr., president of Navy Arms Co., is given credit for starting the Italian black powder reproduction and replica business. When in Italy on a gun tour during 1959, he placed the first American order for a quantity of Colt 1851 Navy reproductions. These black powder reproductions and replicas are marked "Navy Arms Co." on the top of the barrel, "Made In Italy" on the right side of the barrel, and "NAVY ARMS CO." on the frame.

He also ordered and purchased Uberti's first gun, a Colt 1860 Navy, which was entered into the Uberti factory log book on Oct. 14, 1959. Forgett was also the first supplier of components for Colt Industries and produced the earliest examples of the 2nd Generation Colt 1851 Navy models.

For more information and current pricing on both new and used Navy Arms Co. firearms, please refer to the 24th Ed. *Blue Book of Gun Values* by S.P. Fjestad (now online also).

GRADING	100%	98%	95%	90%	80%	70%	60%

PISTOLS: FLINTLOCK & PERCUSSION

1775 BLACK WATCH SCOTTISH PISTOL - .58 cal. flintlock, 7 in. smooth bore white steel barrel, brass frame, ram's horn grip with round ball trigger. Disc. 1994.

$180 $155 $110

Last MSR was $200.

BRITISH DRAGOON PISTOL - .614 cal. flintlock, white steel with brass trim, first 240 production pistols were used in Governor's palace restoration, Colonial Williamsburg. Disc. 1994.

$360 $300 $240

Last MSR was $395.

Add $100 for official Williamsburg crest.

1777 CHARLEVILLE PISTOL - .69 cal. flintlock, 7.5 in. white steel smooth bore barrel, brass furniture, belt hook, walnut stock, 2.75 lbs. Disc. 1994.

$190 $165 $110

Last MSR was $225.

DURS EGG SAW HANDLED PISTOL - .45 cal. flintlock, 9.5 in. blue octagon barrel, unique stock, hand checkered, German silver trim, white steel hammer and lock. Disc. 1994.

$210 $175 $140

Last MSR was $235.

1805 HARPERS FERRY PISTOL - .58 cal. flintlock, 10 in. browned barrel, color case hardened lock and hammer, brass trim, 2.6 lbs. New 2002.

MSR $355 $310 $265 $220

1806 HARPERS FERRY PISTOL - .58 cal. flintlock, 11.75 in. barrel, color case hardened lock and hammer, brass trim, 3 lbs. 14 oz. Mfg. by Pedersoli. Disc. 2002.

$305 $265 $220

Last MSR was $345.

GRADING	100%	98%	95%	90%	80%	70%	60%

J.S. HAWKINS PISTOL - .50 or .54 cal. perc., 9 in. octagon barrel, German silver trim, blue barrel, adj. trigger, 2 lbs. 9 oz. Disc. 1994.

	$230	$195	$150				

Last MSR was $200.

KENTUCKY PISTOL - .44 cal. flintlock or perc., 10.13 in. barrel, color case hardened lock and hammer, brass trim, 2 lbs. Mfg. by Pedersoli.

	$215	$175	$145				

Last MSR was $235.

Add $15 for brass barrel.
Subtract $10 for percussion.

❋ *Cased*

	$310	$275	$235				

Last MSR was $355.

❋ *Double cased set*

	$530	$460	$360				

Last MSR was $600.

LE PAGE PISTOL - .45 cal. flintlock or perc., 9 in. octagon white steel barrel and trim, adj. sights, engraved spur type trigger guard, 2 lbs. 2 oz. Disc. 1996.

	$560	$475	$375				

Last MSR was $625.

Subtract $100 for percussion.
Add $200 for percussion cased pair.
Values also apply to smooth bore model (flintlock only).

❋ *Cased*

	$815	$685	$550				

Last MSR was $905.

❋ *Cased pair*

	$1,420	$1,195	$945				

Last MSR was $1,575.

❋ *1985 cased set* - custom order only, gold trim, consecutive serial number. Disc. 1994.

	$1,800	$1,200	$1,000				

Last MSR was $1,975.

JOHN MANTON MATCH PISTOL - .45 cal. perc., 10 in. white steel barrel and lock, brass trim, 2 lbs. 4 oz. Disc. 1994.

	$215	$185	$135				

Last MSR was $225.

MOORE AND PATRICK PISTOL - .45 cal. flintlock or perc., 10 in. octagon barrel, white steel hammer and lock, German silver trim, 2 lbs. Disc. 1987.

	$310	$270	$215				

Last MSR was $295.

MOUNTAIN PISTOL - .50 cal. flintlock or perc., 10 in. octagon barrel, color case hardened hammer and lock, brass furniture, 2 lbs. 4 oz. Disc. 1994.

	$220	$185	$140				

Last MSR was $215.

GRADING	100%	98%	95%	90%	80%	70%	60%

Add $10 for flintlock.

NAPOLEON LE PAGE PISTOL - .45 cal. perc., 10 in. octagon white steel barrel and lock, brass trim, adj. double set triggers, fluted grip, 2 lbs. 7 oz. Disc. 1994.

	$170	$145	$120

Last MSR was $175.

W. PARKER PISTOL - .45 cal. perc., 10 in. blue octagon barrel, German silver lock and trim, adj. double set triggers, 2 lbs. 8 oz. Disc. 1994.

	$270	$235	$190

Last MSR was $250.

QUEEN ANNE PISTOL - .50 cal. flintlock, 7.5 in. smooth bore, unique cannon style bronzed steel barrel, 2 lbs. 4 oz.

	$180	$155	$125

Last MSR was $200.

F. ROCHATTE PISTOL - .45 cal. perc., 10 in. round barrel with flat top, white steel lock and trim, adj. double set triggers, 2 lbs. 8 oz. Disc. 1994.

	$250	$210	$160

Last MSR was $250.

ELGIN CUTLASS KNIFE PISTOL - .44 cal. perc., combination knife pistol, white steel hammer and barrel, brass trim, 2 lbs. Disc. 1994.

	$75	$65	$50

Last MSR was $80.

PHILADELPHIA DERRINGER - .45 cal. perc., 3 in. barrel, color case hardened lock and hammer, German silver trim, checkered stock, .75 lb. Disc. 1994.

	$120	$100	$80

Last MSR was $130.

ENGRAVED (SNAKE EYES) DERRINGER - .36 cal. perc., 2.63 in. brass double barrel, double hammers, 1.5 lbs. Disc. 1994.

	$125	$105	$85

Subtract $75 if not engraved.

REVOLVERS: PERCUSSION

COLT PATERSON - .36 cal. perc., 7.5 in. octagon barrel, standard design, blue steel hardware, no loading lever, 2 lbs. 9 oz. Mfg. by Pietta. Disc. 2003.

	$305	$260	$215

Add $160 for hand engraved Paterson model.

Last MSR was $340.

1836 PATERSON - .36 cal. perc., 9 in. octagon barrel, standard design, blue steel hardware, no loading lever, 2.75 lbs. New 2003.

MSR	$350	$310	$260	$215

Add $165 for hand engraved Paterson model.

1847 WALKER DRAGOON - .44 cal. perc., 9 in. round barrel, color case hardened hammer, frame, and loading lever, brass trim, engraved barrel and cylinder, 4 lbs. 11 oz. Mfg. by Uberti.

MSR	$304	$275	$230	$185

Add $130 for cased set.
Add $265 for deluxe cased set.

GRADING	100%	98%	95%	90%	80%	70%	60%

1ST MODEL DRAGOON - .44 cal. perc., 7.5 in. barrel, color case hardened frame, brass trim, engraved cylinder, 4 lbs. 2 oz. Disc.

	$250	$210	$165				

Last MSR was $275.

3RD MODEL DRAGOON - .44 cal. perc., 7.5 in. barrel, color case hardened frame and loading lever, brass trim, engraved cylinder, adj. target sights, 4 lbs. 2 oz. Disc.

	$250	$210	$165				

Last MSR was $275.

Add $25 for Buntline model.
Add $10 for Texas Dragoon Model (Tucker and Sherrard and Co., Confederate States, Texas Star engraved on cylinder, square brass trigger guard).

1851 NAVY (YANK) - .36 or .44 cal. perc., 7.5 in. octagon barrel, color case hardened hammer, frame, and loading lever, brass trim. Mfg. by Pietta.

MSR	$170	$145	$120	$95			

* *Cased set*

		$250	$210	$170			

Last MSR was $290.

* *Double cased set*

		$410	$345	$275			

Last MSR was $470.

FRONTIERSMAN 1851 NAVY - .36 cal. perc., 5 in. charcoal blue octagon barrel and cylinder, color case hardened hammer, frame, and loading lever, German silver plated backstrap, and hand rubbed walnut grips. New 2003.

MSR	$200	$165	$135	$105			

AUGUSTA CONFEDERATE - .36 cal. perc., 5 or 7.5 in. barrel, brass frame (Confederate copy of 1851 Navy), walnut grips. Disc. 1994.

	$110	$95	$75				

Last MSR was $200.

1860 ARMY - .44 cal. perc., 8 in. round barrel, color case hardened hammer, frame, and loading lever, roll engraved or fluted cylinder, 2 lbs. 12 oz. Mfg. by Pietta.

MSR	$196	$165	$135	$100			

Add $100 for shoulder stock.
* *Cased set*

		$270	$230	$180			

Last MSR was $310.

* *Double cased set*

		$440	$375	$295			

Last MSR was $505.

1860 REB MODEL GRISWOLD AND GUNNISON - .36 or .44 cal. perc., 5.5 in. (Sheriff Model) or 7.5 in. round barrel, brass frame, color case hardened hammer and loading lever, 2 lbs. 12 oz. Mfg. by Pietta.

MSR	$124	$110	$95	$75			

Due to overstock, several 1860 Reb revolvers were factory deactivated and cannot be reactivated. These revolvers can be used only as props – values currently are in the $55 range.

GRADING	100%	98%	95%	90%	80%	70%	60%

❋ Cased set

	$205	$180	$150				

Last MSR was $245.

❋ Double cased set

	$310	$270	$220				

Last MSR was $380.

1861 NAVY - .36 cal. perc., 5.5 (Sheriff's Model) or 7.5 in. round barrel, cylinder engraved with navy scene, color case hardened hammer, frame, and loading lever, brass trim, 2.75 lbs. Disc. 1994.

	$145	$115	$90				

Last MSR was $140.

Add $60 for shoulder stock.

❋ Cased set - disc. 1994.

	$245	$215	$180				

Last MSR was $230.

❋ Double cased set. - disc. 1994.

	$400	$345	$290				

Last MSR was $385.

1862 (NEW MODEL) POLICE - .36 cal. perc., 5.5 in. round to octagon barrel, color case hardened hammer, frame, and loading lever, brass trim, 1 lb. 10 oz. Also available with nickel finish (new 2003). Mfg. by Uberti.

MSR	$325	$285	$245	$200			

Add $75 for cased Law and Order set (book style presentation case with accessories).
Subtract $15 for nickel finish.

LEECH and RIGDON - .36 cal. perc., 7.5 in. barrel, color case hardened hammer, frame, and loading lever, brass trim, 2 lbs. 10 oz. Disc. 1994.

❋ Non-Uberti Mfg.

	$120	$105	$80				

❋ Uberti Mfg.

	$210	$180	$135				

STARR DOUBLE/SINGLE ACTION - .44 cal. perc., 6 in. round barrel, 6-shot, two-piece blue steel frame. Available in original double action version, and later 1863 single action model with 8 in. barrel. Disc. 2001.

	$300	$255	$205				

Last MSR was $355.

LE MAT REVOLVERS - .44 cal. perc., 9 shot cylinder, .65 cal. center barrel, 7.63 in. octagon barrel, white steel frame, 3 lbs. 7 oz. Mfg. for Navy Arms by F.lli Pietta. Available in Cavalry (with spur trigger guard and lanyard ring), Navy (spur barrel selector), or Army version (cross-pin barrel selector).

MSR	$685	$615	$520	$430			

Add $405 for engraved Beauregard Model.
Add $200 for 18th Georgia engraved model.
Add $100 for single case.
Add $125 for double case (not including revolver).

1858 REMINGTON NEW ARMY - .44 cal. perc., 6.5 in. barrel, brass trigger guard. Mfg. by Pietta.

MSR	$185	$160	$140	$110			

Add $115 for stainless steel model.

GRADING	100%	98%	95%	90%	80%	70%	60%

Subtract $45 for brass frame.

* ✳ *Cased set*

	100%	98%	95%
	$260	$220	$175

Last MSR was $300.

* ✳ *Double cased set*

	100%	98%	95%
	$430	$365	$290

Last MSR was $495.

ROGERS & SPENCER - .44 cal. perc., 7.5 in. octagon barrel, blue trim, 3 lbs.

	MSR	$271	$240	$200	$155

SPILLER and BURR - .36 cal. perc., 7 in. barrel, brass frame, color case hardened hammer and loading lever, 2 lbs. 8 oz. Mfg. by Pietta.

	MSR	$160	$140	$120	$100

* ✳ *Cased set*

	100%	98%	95%
	$245	$205	$160

Last MSR was $270.

* ✳ *Double cased set*

	100%	98%	95%
	$390	$325	$260

Last MSR was $430.

REVOLVERS: CARTRIDGE CONVERSIONS & OPEN TOP

Since these are cartridge firing revolvers converted from black powder reproduction pistols, and require a FFL to transfer, these listings will be moved to the 25th Edition *Blue Book of Gun Values* by S.P. Fjestad after this edition.

1851 NAVY RICHARDS-TYPE CONVERSION - .38 Special or .38 Long Colt, 5.5 or 7.5 in. barrel, color case hardened frame and hammer, silver plated backstrap and trigger guard. Mfg. 2000-01.

	100%	98%	95%
	$310	$265	$215

Last MSR was $375.

1860 ARMY RICHARDS-TYPE CARTRIDGE CONVERSION - .38 Special or .38 Long Colt, 5.5 or 7.5 in. round barrel, color case hardened frame and hammer, steel backstrap, silver plated trigger guard. Mfg. 2000-01.

	100%	98%	95%
	$310	$265	$215

Last MSR was $375.

1861 NAVY RICHARDS-TYPE CARTRIDGE CONVERSION - .38 Special or .38 Long Colt, 5.5 or 7.5 in. round barrel, color case hardened frame and hammer, silver plated backstrap and trigger guard. Mfg. 2000-01.

	100%	98%	95%
	$310	$265	$215

Last MSR was $375.

1872 OPEN TOP - .38 Special, 5.5 or 7.5 in. round barrel, color case hardened frame and hammer, silver-plated backstrap and trigger guard. Mfg. 2000-01.

	100%	98%	95%
	$330	$280	$225

Last MSR was $400.

RIFLES: FLINTLOCK & PERCUSSION

BROWN BESS MUSKET - .75 cal. flintlock, 42 in. white steel barrel, hammer, and lock, brass trim, 9.5 lbs.

	MSR	$922	$785	$660	$545

GRADING	100%	98%	95%	90%	80%	70%	60%

Add $100 for Colonial Williamsburg seal.

BROWN BESS CARBINE - similar to Brown Bess Musket, except has 30 in. barrel.

MSR	$922	$785	$660	$545			

1763 CHARLEVILLE MUSKET - .69 cal. flintlock, 44.63 in. white steel barrel, hammer, and lock, brass trim, 8.75 lbs. Used prices are equal for 1777 Model, or 1816 Mt. Wickman Model with steel ramrod and brass flash pan. Mfg. by Pedersoli.

MSR	$1,030	$900	$785	$615			

BUFFALO HUNTER - .58 cal. perc., 26 in. round barrel, color case hardened hammer and lock, brass trim, 8 lbs. Disc. reintroduced 2003.

MSR	$529	$470	$400	$315			

COUNTRY BOY - .32, .36, .45, or .50 cal. perc., 26 in. octagon barrel, matte black metal finish on all parts, based on mule ear percussion lock, adj. sights, 6 lbs. Disc. 1994.

		$230	$200	$165			

Last MSR was $165.

Add $60 for extra barrel.

CUB RIFLE - .36 cal. perc., 26 in. octagon barrel, adj. sights, color case hardened lock, walnut stock, 5.75 lbs. Disc. 1994.

		$245	$200	$135			

Last MSR was $185.

Add $60 for extra barrel.
Add $115 for Deluxe Pedersoli Model.

1853 ENFIELD 3 BAND (PARKER-HALE) - .58 cal. perc., 39 in. round barrel, color case hardened hammer and lock, brass trim, blue bands, adj. rear sight, 9.5 lbs.

MSR	$659	$585	$500	$390			

1858 ENFIELD 2 BAND (PARKER-HALE) - .58 cal. perc., 33 in. round barrel, color case hardened hammer and lock, brass trim, blue bands, adj. rear sight, 10 lbs.

MSR	$618	$550	$475	$365			

1861 ENFIELD MUSKETOON (PARKER-HALE) - .58 cal. perc., 24 in. round barrel, color case hardened hammer and lock, brass trim, blue bands, adj. rear sight, 7 lbs.

MSR	$530	$470	$400	$315			

1803 HARPERS FERRY RIFLE - .54 cal. flintlock, 35 in. round barrel, color case hardened hammer and lock, brass trim, 8.5 lbs.

MSR	$695	$625	$535	$425			

✳ *1803 Lewis & Clark Edition Harpers Ferry Rifle* - .54 cal. flintlock, similar to 1803 Harpers Ferry Rifle, except authentic brown finish barrel, upgrade walnut finished stock, patchbox engraved "Lewis and Clark Journey of Discovery 1803-1806", and German Pewter replica Friendship Medalion attached to the trigger guard by a ribbon. New 2003.

MSR	$767	$685	N/A	N/A			

HAWKEN RIFLE - .50, .54, or .58 cal. flintlock or perc., 28 in. octagon barrel, double set triggers, brass trim, 8.5 lbs.

		$200	$170	$130			

Last MSR was $220.

Subtract $15 for percussion.

GRADING	100%	98%	95%	90%	80%	70%	60%

HAWKEN MARK 1 RIFLE - .50 or .54 cal. flintlock or perc. 26 in. octagon barrel, adj. double set triggers and sights, brass trim, 9 lbs. Disc. 1994.

$220 $190 $150

Last MSR was $260.

Add $15 for flintlock.
Add $140 for commemorative model.

HAWKEN HUNTER RIFLE/CARBINE - .50, .54, or .58 cal. perc., 28.5 in. octagon barrel, (22.5 in. carbine), color case hardened hammer and lock, double set triggers, 7 lbs. 12 oz. (6 lbs. 12 oz. carbine).

$220 $185 $145

Last MSR was $240.

ITHACA-NAVY HAWKEN - .50 or .54 cal. flintlock or perc., 26 in. octagon barrel, adj. double set triggers and sights, brass trim, 9 lbs. Disc. 1994, left-hand version disc. 1987.

$400 $340 $265

Last MSR was $445.

Add $65 for flintlock.

J.P. MURRAY ARTILLERY CARBINE - .58 cal. perc., 23.5 in. brown, round barrel, color case hardened hammer and lock, brass trim and bands, 7.5 lbs.

MSR $545 $495 $445 $370

KENTUCKY RIFLE - .45 or .50 cal. perc. or flintlock, 35 in. barrel, color case hardened hammer and lock, brass trim, adj. brass rear sight (windage only), 6 lbs. 14 oz.

$385 $320 $245

Last MSR was $425.

Add $10 for flintlock or .50 cal.
Add $125 for .45 cal. deluxe.

KODIAK DOUBLE RIFLE - .50, .54, or .58 cal. perc., 28 in. double barrel, white steel furniture. Mfg. 1989-98.

$695 $590 $465

Last MSR was $775.

1841 MISSISSIPPI RIFLE - .54 or .58 cal. perc., 33 in. brown round barrel, color case hardened hammer and lock, brass trim and bands, 9.5 lbs.

MSR $510 $460 $395 $310

MORSE RIFLE - .50 cal. perc., 26 in. octagon barrel, brass trim and action, blue barrel and hammer, adj. rear sight, (windage only), 6 lbs. Disc. 1987.

$260 $225 $185

MORTIMER RIFLE - .54 cal. flintlock, 36 in. brown barrel, color case hardened furniture, waterproof flash pan, chrome lined bore, 9 lbs. Disc. 1998.

$700 $595 $470

Last MSR was $780.

Add $300 for extra 12 ga. barrel.
Add $100 for flintlock match rifle.

MULE EAR MOUNTAIN MAN SQUIRREL RIFLE - .32, .36, or .45 cal. perc., 26 in. octagon barrel, brass trim, blue barrel, hammer, lock, and trigger, 5.5 lbs. Disc. 1994.

$230 $200 $165

Last MSR was $185.

GRADING	100%	98%	95%	90%	80%	70%	60%

PARKER HALE VOLUNTEER RIFLE (IMPORTED) - .451 cal. perc., 32 in. barrel, brass trim, blue band, color case hardened hammer and lock, adj. sights, 9.5 lbs.

MSR	$932	$835	$720	$570

PARKER HALE WHITWORTH VOLUNTEER RIFLE (IMPORTED) - .451 cal. perc., 36 in. barrel, brass trim, blue barrel and bands, color case hardened hammer and lock, adj. sights, detented lock hammer, long range accuracy app. 1,000 yds., comes with accessories, 9.25 lbs.

MSR	$958	$860	$735	$580

Pricing same for Parker-Hale 3 Band Volunteer rifle.

PENNSYLVANIA HALF STOCK HUNTER - .50 cal. perc., 30 in. octagon barrel, white steel hammer and lock, brass patchbox and trim, walnut stock, 6 lbs. 4 oz. Disc. 1994.

		$225	$190	$155

Last MSR was $220.

PENNSYLVANIA LONG RIFLE - .32 or .45 cal. flintlock or perc., 40.5 in. brown octagon barrel, adj. buckhorn rear sight, double set triggers, color case hardened hammer and lock, brass patch box and trim, walnut stock, 7 lbs. 8 oz.

		$445	$375	$295

Last MSR was $490.

Add $15 for flintlock.

PIONEER RIFLE - .45 or .50 cal. flintlock, 30 in. octagon barrel, color case hardened hammer and lock, walnut stock, 6 lbs. 4 oz. Disc. 1994.

		$225	$190	$155

Last MSR was $200.

1859 SHARPS RIFLE (BERDAN) MODEL - .54 cal. perc., 30 in. round blue barrel, color case hardened hammer, lock, patch box, trigger guard, and furniture, 3 barrel bands, double set triggers, walnut stock, 8 lbs. 8 oz. New 1994.

MSR	$1,200	$1,075	$925	$745

1859 SHARPS RIFLE/CARBINE - .45 or .54 cal. perc., 22, 28, 30 or 32 in. octagon or round barrel, color case hardened hammer, frame and buttplate, 7.75 lbs.

* *Rifle*

MSR	$1,133	$1,000	$850	$670

* *Carbine*

MSR	$1,030	$925	$780	$610

1861 SPRINGFIELD - .58 cal. 1858 Maynard priming perc., 40 in. barrel, all white steel, 3 barrel bands, 10.25 lbs.

MSR	$608	$550	$475	$370

1863 C.S. RICHMOND RIFLE - .58 cal. perc., 40 in. barrel, all white steel, 3 barrel bands, 10.25 lbs.

MSR	$608	$550	$475	$370

1863 SPRINGFIELD - .58 cal. perc., 40 in. barrel, all white steel, 3 barrel bands, 10.1 lbs.

MSR	$608	$550	$475	$370

SMITH ARTILLERY/CAVALRY CARBINE - .54 cal. perc., 20.5 in. octagon tapering to round barrel, color case hardened hammer and receiver. New in 1989. Mfg. by Pietta.

MSR	$664	$595	$505	$395

GRADING	100%	98%	95%	90%	80%	70%	60%

SWISS FEDERAL TARGET RIFLE - .45 cal. perc., 32 in. octagon barrel, color case hardened hammer, lock, and trim, double set triggers, classic Bristlen and Morges design, adj. sights, 13.25 lbs. Imported from West Germany by Neumann Co. Disc. 1994.

$1,510 $1,310 $975

Last MSR was $1,200.

Add $35 for palm rest.

TRYON RIFLE - .451 cal. perc., 34 in. octagon barrel, white steel hammer and engraved lock and patchbox, double set triggers, walnut stock, 9 lbs. 12 oz. Disc. 1996.

$415 $355 $265

Last MSR was $455.

Add $35 for target sights.

TRYON CREEDMOOR RIFLE - .451 cal. perc., Creedmoor target version of above. Disc. 1996.

$700 $590 $465

Last MSR was $780.

ZOUAVE RIFLE - .58 cal. perc., 32.5 in. round barrel, color case hardened hammer, lock, and trigger, brass trim, adj. rear sight, 9 lbs. Mfg. by Armi Sport and Euroarms.

MSR $510 $460 $390 $310

Add $115 for deluxe Range Model (mfg. by EuroSport).

RIFLES: IN-LINE IGNITION

COUNTRY BOY - .50 cal. perc., 24 in. round barrel, hard chrome breech plug, nipple and bolt, chrome lined barrel, Williams aperture sight, synthetic stock with storage compartment, 8 lbs. Disc. 1998.

$150 $125 $100

Last MSR was $165.

Add $10 for all chrome.

M98 IN-LINE - .50 cal. perc., 22 in. round barrel, hard chrome breech plug, nipple and bolt, chrome lined barrel, checkered synthetic stock, Williams aperture sight, modeled after the "M-98 Mauser", 8 lbs. Disc. 1998.

$350 $295 $235

Last MSR was $390.

Add $10 for all chrome.

SHOTGUNS: FLINTLOCK & PERCUSSION

MORSE MODEL - 12 ga. perc., 26 in. barrel, brass receiver and trim, blue hammer and buttplate, 5.75 lbs. Disc. 1987.

$300 $255 $200

Last MSR was $165.

MORTIMER MODEL - 12 ga. flintlock or perc., 36 in. brown barrel, color case hardened furniture, walnut stock, waterproof pan and chrome bore. New in 1989. Disc. 1998.

$660 $560 $440

Last MSR was $735.

STEEL SHOT MAGNUM SxS - 10 ga. perc., 28 in. barrels, engraved polished lock plates, chrome lined bores, checkered walnut stock, 7 lbs. 9oz.

$525 $450 $375

Last MSR was $605.

GRADING	100%	98%	95%	90%	80%	70%	60%

COUNTRY BOY IN-LINE MUZZLE LOADER - 12 ga. perc., 25 in. round smooth bore barrel with adj. rotary choke, bead front sight, hard chrome breech plug, nipple and bolt, chrome lined barrel, synthetic stock, 7 lbs. Disc. 1998.

	$150	$125	$100

Last MSR was $165.

TURKEY AND TRAP (T&T) SxS - 12 ga. perc., 28 in. blue barrels bored F/F, color case hardened locks and furniture, walnut stock. Mfg. by Pedersoli.

	$525	$450	$360

Last MSR was $580.

UPLAND MODEL SxS - 12 ga. perc., 28 in. blue barrels bored cyl./mod.

	$525	$450	$360

Last MSR was $580.

NEW ENGLAND FIREARMS

Current trademark established during 1987. New England Firearms is located and manufactured in Gardner, MA.

For more information and current pricing on New England Firearms firearms, please refer to the 24th Ed. *Blue Book of Gun Values* by S.P. Fjestad (now online also)

RIFLES: IN-LINE IGNITION

HUNTSMAN MODEL SMO-050 - .50 cal. (209 shotshell primer) perc., 24 in. 1:28 in. twist blue barrel, color case-hardened finish break-open side lever release action, American hardwood full PG stock and forearm w/ventilated recoil pad, adj. fiber-optic sights, tapped for scope base, 6.5 lbs.

MSR	$185	$150	$130	$110

HUNTSMAN MODEL SMS-050 - .50 cal. (209 shotshell primer) perc., 24 in. stainless steel barrel, 1:28 in. twist, matte nickel finish break-open side lever release action, matte black polymer full PG stock and forearm w/ventilated recoil pad, adj. fiber-optic sights, tapped for scope base, 6.5 lbs. New 2003.

MSR	$269	$220	$185	$160

NEW ULTRA LIGHT ARMS LLC

Current manufacturer located in Morgantown, WV. Dealer and consumer direct sales.

For more information and current pricing on both new and used New Ultra Light Arms LLC firearms, please refer to the 24th Ed. *Blue Book of Gun Values* by S.P. Fjestad (now online also).

RIFLES: IN-LINE IGNITION

MODEL 90 - .45 or .50 cal., 28 in. button rifled barrel, adj. Timney trigger, Kevlar/graphite stock with colors optional, Williams rear sight, 6 lbs., includes hard case. Disc. 1999.

	$875	$725	$575

Last MSR was $950.

NORTH AMERICAN ARMS, INC.

Current manufacturer located in Provo, UT. Dealer and consumer direct sales.

For more information and current pricing on both new and used North American Arms, Inc. firearms, please refer to the 24th Ed. *Blue Book of Gun Values* by S.P. Fjestad (now online also)

GRADING	100%	98%	95%	90%	80%	70%	60%

REVOLVERS: PERCUSSION

COMPANION MODEL - .22 cal. perc., 5 shot cylinder, 1.13 or 1.63 in. barrel, all stainless steel construction, .3-.4 lbs.

MSR	$156	$125	$100	$80

Add $18 for 1.13 barrel.

NORTH STAR WEST, INC.

Current manufacturer currently located in Frenchtown, MT, previously located in Glencoe, CA. Dealer and consumer direct sales.

PISTOLS: FLINTLOCK

TRADE PISTOL - 28, 24, or 20 ga. flintlock, 10 in. browned octagon to round barrel, steel trigger guard, serpent sideplate, walnut stock, 2.6 lbs. New 2002.

MSR	$540	$485	$425	$350

RIFLES: FLINTLOCK

OFFICER'S MODEL MUSKET - .66 cal., flintlock, 37.5 in. octagon to round barrel, brass furniture, steel trigger guard, serpent sideplate, walnut stock, 8 lbs.

MSR	$1,105	$995	$885	$715

SHOTGUNS: FLINTLOCK

BLANKET GUN - 24 or 20 ga., flintlock, 18 in. octagon to round barrel, brass furniture, steel trigger guard, steel lock and sideplate, walnut stock cut 4 in. past trigger guard.

MSR	$677	$610	$540	$440

BUFFALO RUNNER - 24 or 20 ga., flintlock, 12 in. octagon to round barrel, brass furniture, steel trigger guard, serpent sideplate, walnut stock cut at the end of the trigger guard.

MSR	$677	$610	$540	$440

CANOE GUN - 24 or 20 ga., flintlock, 18 in. octagon to round barrel, brass furniture, steel trigger guard, serpent sideplate, walnut stock 12 in. LOP. New 1994.

MSR	$685	$615	$545	$445

CHIEF'S GRADE - 28, 24, or 20 ga., flintlock, 30, 36, or 41 in. octagon to round barrel, brass furniture, steel trigger, brass trigger guard, serpent sideplate, full length walnut stock.

MSR	$923	$830	$740	$600

Add $25 for left-hand.

EARLY ENGLISH - 28, 24, or 20 ga., flintlock, 30, 36, or 41 in. octagon to round barrel, brass furniture, steel trigger, cast steel trigger guard, serpent sideplate, full length walnut stock.

MSR	$925	$830	$740	$600

Add $25 for left-hand.

NORTHWEST TRADE MODEL - 20 ga., flintlock, 36 in. octagon to round barrel, brass furniture, steel trigger guard, serpent sideplate, walnut stock, 6 lbs.

MSR	$870	$785	$695	$565

Add $25 for left-hand.

O SECTION

OCTOBER COUNTRY MUZZLELOADING, INC.

Current manufacturer/distributor specializing in the manufacturing of large bore muzzleloaders, and located in Hayden, ID.

All models are hand-made and custom finished, utilizing maple, walnut, or English walnut stocks. October Country Muzzleloading, Inc. also manufactures custom bullet molds, patches, and wads for large bore rifles.

GRADING	100%	98%	95%	90%	80%	70%	60%

RIFLES: PERCUSSION

GREAT AMERICAN SPORTING RIFLE - 12, 14, 16, or 20 bore perc., 28 in. octagon to round barrel, rifled 1 turn in 8 feet, 8 in., adj. rear sight, steel furniture, pewter nosecap, patented two piece breech, 10 lbs.

MSR	$1,695	$1,525	$1,350	$1,100

This model's design is based on theories of Lt. James Forsyth from his book *The Sporting Rifle and its Projectiles*.

LIGHT AMERICAN SPORTING RIFLE - .62 cal. perc., 28 in. barrel, fixed buckhorn rear sight, blue iron furniture, two piece breech, single trigger, iron trigger guard, walnut pistol grip stock, 8 lbs.

MSR	$1,595	$1,425	$1,275	$1,050

EIGHT BORE DOUBLE (SxS) HEAVY RIFLE - .85 cal. perc., 30 in. tapered round barrels, patented two-piece breech, steel furniture, bead front sight, 3 blade express rear sight, English walnut shotgun style stock, 14 lbs. 8 oz.

MSR	$4,995	$4,495	$3,820	$3,060

HEAVY RIFLE - .85 or 1.00 cal. perc., 30 in. tapered octagon barrel, patented two piece breech, steel furniture, 3 blade express rear sight, steel bead front sight, English walnut pistol grip stock, checkered at the forestock and pistol grip, 18 lbs.

MSR	$2,995	$2,695	$2,290	$1,850

OLD-WEST GUN CO.

Previous importer and distributor that took over the inventory of Allen Firearms after they went out of business in early 1987. Old-West Gun Co. became Cimarron F.A. Co. in 1987.

Older variations marked Old-West have approx. the same values as those of Cimarron Arms Co. (please refer to the Cimarron heading in this text).

NOTES

P SECTION

PACIFIC RIFLE COMPANY

Current manufacturer located in Lake Oswego, OR. Pacific Rifle Company specializes in underhammer rifles utilizing the James Forsyth rifling technique developed in the 19th century. Consumer direct sales.

Christened "The Zephyr" by gunmaker Roger Renner of Pacific Rifle Co., this unique long rifle utilizes a advanced underhammer mechanism providing the fewest number of moving parts in any percussion rifle. The trigger guard serves as the mainspring. The Zephyr uses the Forsyth rifling technique for superior long range accuracy. Each rifle is hand crafted to order.

GRADING	100%	98%	95%	90%	80%	70%	60%

RIFLES: PERCUSSION, UNDERHAMMER

1837 ZEPHYR MODEL - 12 or 20 bore perc., underhammer lock, 30 in. tapered octagon barrel, color case hardened (disc.) or slow-rust browned finish, fire-blue hammer, trigger and screws, oil finish black walnut stock and forend, semi-buckhorn rear and german silver blade front sight, 7.75 lbs.

MSR	$1,500	$1,500	$1,250	$995

Add $100 for Peephorn rear sight.
Add $100 for upgrade walnut.
Add $100 for Damascus Bronze receiver and buttplate.

AFRICAN ZEPHYR 12 BORE - .72 cal. perc., underhammer lock, dual cap ignition, 26 in. tapered octagon barrel, cast steel, color case hardened receiver with "B" engraving, nitrite-blue hammer, trigger, screws and mainspring, English walnut stock and forend, smooth shotgun color case hardened plate on buttstock, short caterpillar of .090 in. diameter at the front of integral full-length sighting rib, U notched rear blade sight, rust brown finish on barrel, 9 lbs. Disc. 2001.

	$2,000	$1,500	$1,100

Last MSR was $2,000.

AFRICAN ZEPHYR 8 BORE - .83 cal. perc., underhammer lock, dual cap ignition, 26 in. tapered octagon barrel, cast steel, color case hardened receiver with "B" engraving, nitrite-blue hammer, trigger, screws and mainspring, English walnut stock and forend, smooth shotgun color case hardened plate on buttstock, short caterpillar of .090 in. diameter at the front of integral full-length sighting rib, U notched rear blade sight, rust brown finish on barrel, 12 lbs. Disc. 2001.

	$2,500	$1,750	$1,350

Last MSR was $2,500.

PEDERSOLI, DAVIDE & C. Snc.

Current manufacturer located in Gardone, Italy. Currently imported by Cabela's, located in Sidney, NE, Cape Outfitters, located in Cape Girardeau, MO, Cimarron F.A., located in Fredricksburg, TX, E.M.F., located in Santa Ana, CA, Flintlocks, Etc located in Richmond, MA, and Navy Arms located in Union City, WV. Current full line distributors include and Cherry's Fine Guns, located in Greensboro, NC, Dixie Gun Works, located in Union City, TN, and Flintlocks, Etc. located in Richmond, MA.

Davide Pedersoli & C. is a family company, founded in 1957 by Davide Pedersoli (1924-1996). In 1960, it started production of muzzle loading guns, and from 1970-73, several models of O/U shotguns were produced. Flasks became the first accessory in 1973, starting a wide range of accessories for muzzle loading shooting.

In 1975, Pierangelo, Davide's son, joined the company. Dr. Pierangelo Pedersoli directs and manages the company together with his brother-in-law, production manager Giovanni Gottardi. Currently the company has 40 people on staff, divided into 3 departments. Since 1982, the production stocks, barrels, and small parts has been "in-house," as well as final assembly. Since 1990, the company has undergone a constant technology change, replacing much of the older equipment with modern CNC technology and designs utilizing CAD-CAM systems.

Pedersoli actively sponsors important shooting competitions for muzzle loading, Western target shooting, as well as long distance target shooting competitions with metallic cartridge rifles. Pedersoli's wide range of

GRADING	100%	98%	95%	90%	80%	70%	60%

muzzle loading reproductions and replicas have won all the major international shooting competitions, and continue to capture many gold, silver, and bronze medals annually.

For more information and current pricing on both new and used Pedersoli firearms, please refer to the 24th Ed. *Blue Book of Gun Values* by S.P. Fjestad (now online also).

PISTOLS: FLINTLOCK & PERCUSSION

CHARLES MOORE PISTOL - .36, .44 smoth bore, or .45 cal., flintlock (.44 or .45 cal.) or perc. (.36 or .45 cal.), 11 in. blue octagon barrel, color case hardened hammer and lock, brass furniture, adj. trigger, hand checkered walnut stock, 2.5 lbs.

MSR	$410	$355	$300	$240

Add $60 for flintlock.

✳ *Charles Moore Target Pistol* - .36, .44, or .45 cal., similar to Charles Moore Pistol, except polished steel German silver color barrel and all parts.

MSR	$485	$395	$300	$240

Add $45 for flintlock.

DERRINGER RIDER - 4.3mm cal., perc., 2 .07 in. round barrel. Reproduction of the rare Remington Rider single shot "Parlor Pistol" of which only about 200 were produced. Fires a small 4.3mm ball using only a percussion cap for propellant. No powder is required. Available in the white and color case hardened. Imported. 2002 only.

	$135	$115	$90

Last MSR was $150.

ENGLISH DUELING PISTOL - .45 cal. perc., 11 in. octagon barrel, silver thimble and endcap.

	$240	$210	$165

1806 HARPERS FERRY - .58 cal. flintlock, 10 in. barrel, color case hardened lock, brass furniture, and inlaid buttcap, 2.5 lbs.

MSR	$350	$315	$265	$215

Add $165 for commemorative model with silver plated hardware and white steel barrel stamped "U.S. Army Commemorative".

KENTUCKY PISTOL - .45, .50 & .54 cal. flintlock or perc., 10.25 octagon barrel (steel or brass), walnut stock, brass furniture and trigger guard, 2.25 lbs. Available in deluxe versions and Silver Star model.

MSR	$245	$220	$190	$150

Add $15 for .50 and .54 cal. "Big Bore" Models.
Add $40 for maple stock.
Add $130 for deluxe model.
Add $215 for Silver Star flintlock model with engraved white steel hammer and lock, German silver furniture, inlaid stock (star on forearm) and brown barrel.
Subtract $15 for percussion model.

✳ *Kentucky Bounty* - .44 or .50 cal. flintlock or perc., 16.5 in. octagon barrel, white steel hammer and lock, brass furniture and trigger guard, walnut stock, 3 lbs.

MSR	$310	$265	$225	$180

Add $15 for flintlock.

KUCHENREUTER - .38, .40, or .44 cal., 11.25 in. octagon brown barrel, color case hardened, hammer lock, trigger guard, and furniture, walnut stock, 2 lbs. 10 oz. New 1994.

MSR	$1,350	$1,125	$955	$760

Add $1,025 for deluxe engraved and cased model. Special Order only.

LE PAGE INTERNATIONAL PISTOL - .31 (disc.), .36, .38, and .44 cal. flintlock or perc., 10.5 in. brown or white octagon barrel, white steel or color case hardened hammer and lock, adj. triggers, 2 lbs. (cased set, gold trim, consecutive serial number).

MSR	$675	$565	$480	$385

Add $105 for flintlock model.

GRADING	100%	98%	95%	90%	80%	70%	60%

Add $105 for deluxe maple stock.

Add $1,020 for engraved Target International model with presentation case.

Add $1,220 for engraved Target International flintlock with wood case.

Subtract $50 for white barrel.

LIEGI DERRINGER/LIEGE POCKET DERRINGER - .36 (Pocket) or .44 cal. perc., 2.37 or 4 in. round barrel, color case hardened frame, screw-on barrel, folding trigger, .5 lb.

	100%	98%	95%	90%
MSR	$130	$110	$90	$75

Add $20 for .36 cal. Pocket Model new 2003.

Add $35 for gold finish w/simulated ivory grip new 2003.

Add $45 for engraved white steel.

MANG IN GRÄZ PISTOL - .38 or .44 cal. perc., 11.5 in. octagon brown barrel, color case hardened or white hammer and lock, fluted walnut stock, 2.5 lbs.

	100%	98%	95%	90%
MSR	$1,095	$920	$785	$625

Add $2,980 for deluxe engraved model with presentation case.

MORTIMER "SAW HANDLE" PISTOL - .36, .44 (smooth bore), or .45 (new 2003) cal. flintlock or perc., brown 10.07 in. octagon barrel, color case hardened hammer and lock, hand checkered walnut "saw grip." Authentic reproduction of the historic Mortimer target pistol. New 2001.

	100%	98%	95%	90%
MSR	$725	$625	$530	$425

Add $15 for flintlock model.

Add $55 for flintlock "Match" pistol. Imported 2002 only.

Add $30 for percussion "Match" pistol. Imported 2002 only.

Add $755 for Deluxe engraved, silver plated, flintlock model with gold barrel inlays by master engraver Renato Sanzogni.

Add $700 for percussion model. Imported 2002 only.

MOUNTAIN KENTUCKY PISTOL - .44 or .50 cal. flintlock or perc., 14.5 in. octagon barrel, color case hardened hammer and lock, brass furniture and trigger guard, hand checkered walnut stock, 2.25 lbs.

95%	90%	80%
$225	$190	$140

Last MSR was $255.

Add $10 for flintlock.

PENNSYLVANIA PISTOL - .44 cal. flintlock or perc., 10 in. octagon barrel, brass furniture, locks left in white.

95%	90%	80%
$150	$130	$95

QUEEN ANNE PISTOL - .50 cal. flintlock, 7.5 in. cannon shaped brass or white steel barrel (smooth bore), white steel hammer and lock, grotesque mask under buttstock, 2.25 lbs.

	100%	98%	95%	90%
MSR	$250	$225	$190	$155

Add $70 for silver plated or deluxe model.

Add $45 for Queen Anne "Gold" w/brass barrel, simulated ivory grip, and silver color lock new 2003.

SALOON PISTOL - .36 cal. perc., straight through ignition, 8 in. rounded barrel, color case hardened hammer and frame, walnut stock, 1.75 lbs.

	100%	98%	95%	90%
MSR	$225	$190	$160	$130

CARLESTON UNDERHAMMER PISTOL - .36 cal. perc., 8.5 in. octagon to round brown barrel, metal fittings are color case hardened, walnut stock, 2 lbs.

	100%	98%	95%	90%
MSR	$595	$520	$445	$355

ZIMMER PISTOL - .36 cal. perc., 8 in. octagon blue barrel, white steel hammer and frame, fluted walnut stock.

	100%	98%	95%	90%
MSR	$315	$270	$235	$190

Add $45 for deluxe model.

REVOLVERS: PERCUSSION

Add approximately 25% for engraving, and 200% for extra luxury engraving.

GRADING	100%	98%	95%	90%	80%	70%	60%

PATERSON - .36 cal. perc., 5 shot, 9 in. octagon barrel, no loading lever, walnut stock, 2.5 lbs. Mfg. for Pedersoli. Disc. 1997.

	$300	$260	$200

Last MSR was $310.

REMINGTON PATTERN - .44 cal. perc. Mfg. by Pedersoli.

MSR	$640	$560	$480	$380

ROGERS & SPENCER (FEINWERKBAU MFG.) - .44 cal. perc., 6 shot, 7.5 in. octagon barrel, walnut grips, 3 lbs. Disc. 1997.

	$1,600	$1,380	$1,100

Last MSR was $1,850.

Manufactured by Feinwerkbau using the latest technology, molybdenum chrome steel frame, etc. Weight balanced for accurate firing.

ROGERS & SPENCER - similar to the model above. Mfg. by Pedersoli.

MSR	$940	$810	$690	$550

RIFLES: FLINTLOCK & PERCUSSION

1766 CHARLEVILLE MUSKET - .69 cal. flintlock or perc., 44.62 in. white steel barrel, hammer, lock, and trim, 9.75 lbs. New 2003.

MSR	$1,040	$950	$850	$595

1777 CHARLEVILLE MUSKET - .69 cal. flintlock or perc., 44.62 in. white steel barrel, hammer, lock, and trim, 9.75 lbs. Imported 1989-2002.

	$875	$740	$595

Last MSR was $970.

1777 REVOLUTIONNAIRE - .69 cal. flintlock, 44 7/8 in. white steel barrel, hammer, lock, and trim. Predecessor of the 1777 Corrigé An IX. Issue arm of the infantry during the French Revolution., 9.69 lbs.

MSR	$995	$895	$750	$595

1777 CORRIGÉ ANNO IX MUSKET - .69 cal. flintlock., 44 7/8 in. white steel barrel, hammer, lock, and trim. Exact copy of the 1777 Corrigé employed during the ninth year of the French Revolution, 9.69 lbs.

MSR	$995	$895	$750	$595

1777 CORRIGÉ ANNO IX DRAGOONS MUSKET - .69 cal. flintlock., 40.5 in. white steel barrel, hammer, lock, and trim., 9.47 lbs.

MSR	$1,040	$950	$850	$595

1798 AUSTRIAN INFANTRY MUSKET - .69 cal. flintlock., 44 5/16 in. white steel barrel, hammer, lock, and trim. Exact copy of the 1798 based on the French 1777 French Corrigé but incorporating characteristics of Austrian design, 10 lbs.

MSR	$1,075	$975	$875	$630

1809 PRUSSIAN - .75 cal. flintlock, 41 1/8 in. round white steel barrel, white steel hammer and lock, brass furniture, walnut stock, lock marked "Potsdam", 9.25 lbs.

MSR	$1,025	$935	$825	$595

1816 MT. WICKHAM RIFLE - similar to 1777 Charleville musket, except has shorter barrel. Disc. 1997.

	$625	$550	$455

Last MSR was $840.

1816 SPRINGFIELD/HARPERS FERRY - .69 cal. flintlock, 40 in. white steel round barrel, all white steel hardware, sling swivels, walnut stock, 9.75 lbs.

MSR	$995	$895	$750	$595

GRADING	100%	98%	95%	90%	80%	70%	60%

1848 SPRINGFIELD - .69 cal. perc., 40 in. white steel barrel, white steel or color case hardened hammer and lock, white steel furniture, walnut full stock, lock stamped "U.S. Springfield". Accurate reproduction of the "Colt conversion style" from flintlock to percussion lock done by Harper's Ferry and Springfield arsenals between 1848-1860, 9.75 lbs.

	MSR	$995	$895	$750	$595			

1857 WÜRTTEMBERGISCHEN MAUSER - .54 cal. perc., 38.37 in. white steel barrel, adj. sights, color case hardened hammer and lock, walnut full stock, 9.47 lbs. New 2003.

	MSR	$1,095	$985	$885	$650			

1859 SHARPS - .54 cal. perc., 22, 28, or 30 in. round barrel, color case hardened hammer, frame and buttplate, 7.75 lbs. average. Base price for Cavalry Carbine.

	MSR	$985	$875	$750	$585			

Add $165 for 1859 Infantry model with single trigger, 30 in. barrel.
Add $240 for 1859 Infantry model with set triggers, 30 in. barrel.

1861 SPRINGFIELD RIFLE - .58 cal. perc., 40 in. white steel barrel, white steel or color case hardened hammer and lock, white steel furniture, walnut full stock, lock stamped "U.S. Springfield", 9.75 lbs. Disc. 1997.

			$715	$625	$500			

Last MSR was $870.

1863 SHARPS SPORTING RIFLE - .45 or .54 cal. perc., 32 in. octagon barrel, color case hardened hammer, frame and buttplate, 10.15 lbs.

	MSR	$1,080	$975	$850	$700			

Add $1,125 for engraved Sporting Rifle.
Add $1,700 for engraved and gold inlay Sporting Rifle.
Add $175 for Sporting Rifle with patch box.

ALAMO - .32, .45., or .50 cal. perc. or flintlock, 36 in. octagon barrel with double set triggers, white steel hammer and lock, brass furniture, patchbox engraved with scenes of the period, walnut stock, 6.5 lbs.

	MSR	$560	$480	$405	$325			

Add $15 for flintlock.

BRISTLEN MORGES - .44 cal. perc., 29.5 in. octagon barrel, color case hardened hammer and lock, walnut half stock, palm rest professional target rifle, 16.75 lbs.

	MSR	$1,940	$1,725	$1,435	$1,1450			

Add $910 for deluxe version with engraved white steel hammer and lock.

BROWN BESS MUSKET/CARBINE - .75 cal. flintlock, 31.5 (carbine) or 42 (musket) in. smooth bore barrel, white steel hammer and lock, brass furniture, three quarter stock (walnut), 8.75 lbs. (7.75 lbs. carbine).

	MSR	$895	$795	$650	$520			

Add $30 for Musket Model.

COUNTRY BOY - .32, .36, .45, or .50 cal. perc., 26 in. octagon barrel, color case hardened hammer and lock, unique mule ear hammer, blue furniture, adj. sights, walnut half stock, 5.5 lbs. Disc. 1994.

			$230	$200	$165			

Last MSR was $240.

COUNTRY HUNTER - .36, .45, and .50 cal. flintlock or perc., 28.25 in. octagon barrel, blue hardware, color case hardened hammer and lock, walnut half stock, 6 lbs.

	MSR	$325	$295	$250	$200			

Add $25 for flintlock.

DELUXE CUB RIFLE - .40 cal. flintlock or perc., 28 in. octagon barrel, color case hardened hammer, plate and triggers, brass trim and patch box, double set triggers.

			$345	$300	$240			

Last MSR was $385.

GRADING	100%	98%	95%	90%	80%	70%	60%

FREDERICKSBURG MUSKET - .75 cal. flintlock. Disc.

	$610	$555	$470

FRONTIER RIFLE/CARBINE - .32, .36, .45, .50, or .54 cal. flintlock (.54 cal. carbine only) perc., 39 in. octagon brown barrel, color case hardened hammer and lock, brass furniture, walnut or bird's eye maple full stock, 7.75 lbs. (7.25 lbs. .45 and .50 cal.).

MSR	$560	$495	$420	$335

Add $15 for flintlock.
Subtract $35 for Carbine Model.
Add $450 for Grade 5 maple.
Add $575 for Grade 7 with bird's-eye maple stock and patchbox.
This model is also sold as the Blue Ridge Rifle by Cabela's with walnut stock.

GIBBS RIFLE WITH TARGET SIGHTS - .451 .cal. perc. 35.25 in. octagonal to round barrel, color case hardened hammer and lock, European walnut stock with fine hand checkering on the wrist and forend, Creedmoor sight, adjustable spirit level tunnel front sight with 18 interchangable inserts. Reproduction of the 1865 target model produced by English gunsmith George Gibbs. Designed for 100 meter target shooting, 10.79 lbs. Imported 2002 only.

	$1,015	$860	$690

Last MSR was $1,125.

HAWKEN RIFLE - .54 cal. perc., 32.25 in. octagon brown barrel, color case hardened hammer, lock, and furniture, double set triggers, walnut or bird's eye maple .5 stock, 8.75 lbs. Disc. 1994.

	$425	$375	$300

Last MSR was $450.

Add $115 for bird's-eye maple stock.

JAPANESE RIFLE - .492 cal., matchlock, 41.5 in. octagon brown barrel, brass matchlock and furniture, authentic reproduction of 16th century Tomonobu rifle.

	$1,040	$880	$695

Last MSR was $1,155.

KENTUCKY - .32, .45, or .50 cal. perc. or flintlock, 35 in. barrel, color case hardened hammer and lock, brass furniture and patchbox, walnut full stock, 6.5 lbs.

MSR	$460	$395	$345	$285

Add $20 for flintlock.
Add $425 for Silver Star model with engraved silver plated hammer, lock, trigger guard and patchbox, also has silver stars inlaid in stock.

KODIAK EXPRESS SxS DOUBLE RIFLE - .50, .54, .58 .72 (new 2003) cal. or 12 ga. (slug) perc., 25.62 (.72 cal. or 12 ga.) or 28 in. SxS blue barrels, adj. sights, blue or silver finish hammers and locks, pistol or streight grip walnut stock, 9.25-10.79 lbs.

MSR	$895	$805	$685	$545

Add $25 for .72 cal. New 2003.
Subtract $225 for 12 ga. New 2003.

MORTIMER STANDARD/TARGET/VETTERLI/WHITWORTH RIFLE - .45, .541 or .54 (new 2003) cal. flintlock or perc., 36.25 in. octagon to round brown barrel, color case hardened hammer, lock and trigger guard, waterproof pan, 8.87 lbs.

MSR	$875	$795	$695	$595

Add $50 for .54 cal. flintlock model.
Add $150 for .54 cal. flintlock Target Model.
Add $2,050 for deluxe engraved .54 cal. flintlock Target Model.
Add $1,850 for .45 cal. engraved "Vetterli" Model.
Add $100 for .451 cal. Whitworth Model (disc. 1994) reintroduced 2003.
Add $1,875 for engraved .451cal. Mortimer Whitworth.

GRADING	100%	98%	95%	90%	80%	70%	60%

PENNSYLVANIA CHAMBERSBURG/DIXIE RIFLE - .32 or .45 cal. flintlock or perc., 41.5 in. barrel, brass trim, color case hardened or white steel lock, hammer, and double set trigger, walnut full stock, 8.25 lbs. New 1989.

	MSR	$555	$475	$400	$320			

Add $20 for flintlock.
Add $205 for Chambersburg Pennsylvania Rifle.

PLAINSMAN RIFLE - .38, .45, or .50 cal. flintlock or perc., 37 in. octagon barrel, white steel hammer and lock, brass furniture and patch box, adj. sights and double set triggers, 6.5 lbs. Disc. 1994.

		$400	$345	$240			

Last MSR was $435.

Add $20 for flintlock.
Add $65 for engraved model.

ROLLING BLOCK MUZZLELOADER RIFLE/CARBINE - .50 or .54 cal. perc., 22.25 (carbine) or 26.25 in. octagon barrel color case hardened hammer, block & buttplate, brass trigger guard. Based on Remington rolling block frame, adj. sights, 8.5 lbs. (7.75 lbs carbine).

		$350	$310	$250			

Last MSR was $300.

SANFTL - .45 cal. perc., 32.25 in. octagon white steel barrel, white steel hammer and lock, brass trigger guard and buttplate (copy of Tyrolese Target Rifle), walnut stock, 10 lbs. New 1994.

	MSR	$1,995	$1,750	$1,450	$1,160			

SCOUT RIFLE - .32, .45, or .50 cal. flintlock or perc., carbine version of Pennsylvania rifle listed above with 28.25 in. barrel, 6 lbs.

	MSR	$475	$415	$350	$280			

Add $20 for flintlock.

SWIVEL BARREL RIFLE/SHOTGUN/COMBINATION O/U - 20 ga.x 20 ga. or 20 ga. x 50 cal., .50 x .50 cal., .54 x .54 cal. perc., 23.62 in. double (O/U) octagon barrel, blue barrel, hammer, lock and furniture (after 1st shot barrel simply needs to be rotated 180 degrees for second shot), checkered walnut stock, 9.5 lbs. (9.75 lbs. on .54 cal.). New 1994.

		$445	$375	$295			

Last MSR was $495.

TRYON RIFLE - .45, .50, or .54 cal. perc., 32.25 in. octagon barrel, color case hardened hammer, lock, patchbox, and furniture, double set triggers, walnut half stock, 9.5 lbs.

	MSR	$650	$585	$495	$395			

Add $390 for maple stock.
Add $200 for engraved model.

TRYON CREEDMOOR - .451 cal. perc., 32.75 in. oct. barrel, all blue hardware, target version of the Tryon Rifle, double set triggers, walnut half stock, 9.5 lbs.

	MSR	$960	$850	$725	$600			

WAADTLANDER RIFLE - .45 cal. perc., 31 in. octagon brown barrel, target sights, 14.37 lbs. Target version of Bristlen Morges Model.

	MSR	$1,940	$1,725	$1,435	$1,1450			

Add $985 for deluxe engraved model with white steel hardware and silver inlays.

RIFLES: IN-LINE IGNITION

GAMMA 901 - .50 or .54 cal. perc., 28 in. round barrel, all salt blue except bolt (hammer), automatic safety, walnut stock, 6.5 lbs. (.54 cal.) or 7.25 lbs. (.50 cal.).

		$335	$280	$225			

Last MSR was $370.

GRADING	100%	98%	95%	90%	80%	70%	60%

GAMMA 900 - similar to Gamma 901, except with sight upgrade, recoil pad, blue aluminum ramrod and better wood.

$395 $335 $265

Last MSR was $440.

GAMMA 9000 - similar to Gamma 900, except 32 in. barrel, sight upgrade, and checkered walnut stock.

$475 $400 $345

Last MSR was $530.

SHOTGUNS: PERCUSSION

CLASSIC TURKEY SxS - 12 ga., perc., 28 in. round double barrels, color case hardened lock, stainless steel nipple, recoil pad, 9 lbs.

$420 $355 $300

KODIAK SxS SHOTGUN/EXPRESS/COMBO - 12 ga. x .50, or .58 cal., or .50 x .50, .54 x .54, and .58 x .58 cal. perc., 28 in. double barrels, engraved white steel hammer and lock, blue furniture, checkered walnut .5 stock, 9 lbs.

MSR $895 $805 $685 $550

Add $540 for rifle or comb. barrels (extra set).

SxS MODEL - 10, 12, or 20 ga., perc., 28 in. barrels, chrome bore, color case hardened hammer and lock, (engraved white steel on 10 ga.), checkered walnut stock, double triggers, 7.5 lbs. Deluxe hand engraved models available on special order.

MSR $625 $560 $480 $380

Add $70 for 10 ga.
Add $265 for extra 12 ga. barrels, and $290 for extra 10 ga. barrels.
Add $1,070 for engraved model.
Add $2,500 for extra deluxe engraved model with gold inlays.
Add $4,570 for super deluxe engraved model with gold inlays.

MORTIMER SHOTGUN - 12 ga., flintlock or perc., version of Mortimer Rifle.

MSR $840 $725 $600 $475

Add $60 for flintlock.
Add $1,795 for deluxe engraving with gold inlays.

INDIAN TRADE MUSKET - 12 ga. flintlock, 36.25 in. octagonal to round barrel, large trigger guard and trigger (for gloved hand). A faithful reproduction of the late 18th century fowler used by well known trade companies such as Hudson Bay Co., and American Fur Co., and produced with period fit and finish, including engraved brass snake decoration on the left side of the stock, 6.60 lbs. Imported 2002 only.

$875 $745 $595

Last MSR was $975.

PEIFER RIFLE CO.
Current manufacturer located in Nokomis, IL. Consumer direct sales.

RIFLES: PERCUSSION

TS-93 RIFLE - .45 or .50 cal. perc., uses #209 primer instead of percussion cap for ignition, 24 in. blue chrommoly or stainless steel barrel, cocking action provided by moving trigger guard to right or left, primer holder rotates 90 degrees for added safety, tang safety, synthetic stock with recoil pad, 7 lbs.

MSR $730 $625 $550 $440

Add $50 for wood look synthetic stock.
Add $50 for stainless steel.

GRADING	100%	98%	95%	90%	80%	70%	60%

PIETTA, F.LLI

Current manufacturer established in 1960, and located in Brescia, Italy. Distributor sales only.

Fratelli Pietta is one of Italy's premier black powder makers utilizing modern, high-tech facilities. Quality ranges from very good to excellent, depending upon the model. Pietta is the only manufacturer of the LeMat, Starr, and John Henry Dance & Bros. percussion revolvers, all of which have exceptional construction, fit, and finish. Pietta models can be special ordered with period engraving (Young, Nimschke, Helfricht-style scrollwork) handcrafted in Gardone and Brescia Italy, through Navy Arms, Taylor's & Co, Dixie Gun Works, Cabela's, Traditions Inc., & E.M.F., Inc.

Well known and appreciated in international circles for the quality and the reliability of their products, the arms factory F.lli Pietta plays an important part in the world production of replicas. The company history began in 1960 with the production of hunting guns. During 1964, following a large increase in demand for American Civil War arms reproductions, the company began making muzzleloading revolvers. The first model, the Colt 1851 Navy, enjoyed immediate success, and was followed by some other popular variations. Other models quickly followed, including the Colt 1860 Army, the 1858 Remington New Model Army, the Spiller & Burr, the LeMat, which was awarded the prestigious prize in 1985 as "the best gun of the year" by the American National Association of Federally Licensed Firearms Dealers, and finally the Starr.

Each piece is produced with exacting quality control standards in order to guarantee parts interchangeability. Skilled and highly specialized personnel perform fitting, polishing, and assembly by hand. As a result, Pietta has achieved both success and industry respect worldwide.

Please refer to *Colt Blackpowder Reproductions & Replicas—A Collector's & Shooter's Guide* for color pictures of the Pietta makes and models listed below. Pietta revolvers can be found on pages 43, 44, 46, 47, 48, 49, 50, 69, 70, and 102.

Note that MSR prices are generally not shown for revolvers that have been in production for many years, as their prices vary with different distributors. F.lli Pietta arms are sold by Navy Arms, Taylor's & Co., Dixie Gun Works, Cabela's, Traditions Inc., and E.M.F., Inc., as well as in retail gun stores. Please refer to individual listings for the latest retail pricing.

REVOLVERS: PERCUSSION

1851 NAVY - .36 or .44 cal. perc., 7.5 in. octagon barrel, many styles, 6 shot engraved cylinder, 2 lbs. 12 oz.

$150	$130	$110

Add $30 for steel frame.

Prices are similar for Sheriff's Model & Confederate Model with round barrel.

1860 ARMY - .44 cal. perc., 7.5 in. barrel, 6 shot rebated cylinder, color case hardened or brass frame, hammer and loading lever, steel backstrap and brass trigger guard, 2 lbs. 9 oz.

$200	$170	$145

1861 NAVY - .36 or .44 (disc.) cal. perc., 7.5 in. barrel, brass backstrap and trigger guard, color case hardened frame, hammer, and loading lever, 2 lbs. 8 oz.

$153	$130	$105

1862 POLICE - .36 cal. perc., 5.5 in. round to octagon barrel, color case hardened hammer, frame, and loading lever, brass trim, 1 lb. 10 oz.

$166	$140	$110

COLT PATERSON - .36 cal. perc., 7.5 in. octagon barrel, standard "hidden trigger" design, blue steel hardware, no loading lever, 2 lbs. 9 oz.

$340	$305	$260

Add $160 for engraved version.

LEMAT REVOLVER - .44 cal. perc., 9 shot cylinder plus 1 shot center barrel (maximum fire power for its day), 7.62 in. octagon barrel, blue steel frame, 3 lbs. 7 oz.

$655	$555	$445

Add $375 for engraved Beauregard model.
Add $175 for 18th Georgia engraved model.
Add $1,145 for fully engraved models in the white or blue. Special order only.

GRADING	100%	98%	95%	90%	80%	70%	60%

1858 REMINGTON (BRASS FRAME) - .36 or .44 cal. perc., 8 or 12 (Buffalo Model) in. octagon barrel, 6 shot, brass frame and trigger guard.

	$110	$95	$80				

Add $20 for Buffalo Model with 12 in. barrel.

1858 REMINGTON (STEEL FRAME) - similar to 1858 Remington, except has steel frame with brass backstrap and trigger guard.

	$135	$115	$100				

Add $70 for stainless steel.
Add $30 for Target Model.
Add $125 for stainless steel Buffalo model with 12 in. barrel.

SPILLER and BURR - .36 cal. perc., 7.5 in. barrel, brass frame, color case hardened hammer and loading lever, 2 lbs. 8 oz.

	$150	$140	$115				

STARR DOUBLE/SINGLE ACTION - .44 cal. perc., 6 in. round barrel, 6-shot, two-piece blue steel frame. Available in original double action version, and later single action model with 8 in. barrel. Available through Taylor's & Co., Traditions, Cabela's, and Navy Arms. Available in nickel finish 2002.

MSR	$330	$300	$250	$200			

1861 J.H. DANCE NAVY - .36 cal. perc., 7.5 in. round barrel, 6 shot smooth cylinder, color case hardened frame without recoil shield, brass backstrap and squareback trigger guard, 2 lbs. 12 oz.

MSR	$248	$210	$180	$140			

This model is available through Dixie Gun Works.

RIFLES: PERCUSSION

SMITH ARTILLERY/CAVALRY CARBINE - .54 cal. perc., 20.5 in. octagon tapering to round barrel, color case hardened hammer and receiver.

MSR	$650	$555	$475	$385			

SHOTGUNS: PERCUSSION

FOWLER SxS - 10 or 12 ga., 28 in. barrels, color case hardened hammer and lock, 7 lbs. 6 oz.

MSR	$475	$445	$415	$325			

Add $25 for 10 ga.

PRAIRIE RIVER ARMS

Current manufacturer located in Princeton, IL. Consumer direct and dealer sales.

Prairie River Arms has developed a new percussion ignition system that contains the firing mechanism entirely within the stock. Advantages include more weather resistance, protection from percussion cap fragmentation, and better balance.

RIFLES: PERCUSSION

BULLPUP - .50 or .54 cal. perc., 28 in round barrel (alloy or stainless steel), unique Bullpup design, hardwood or synthetic all weather thumbhole stock, 7.5 lbs.

MSR	$375	$340	$290	$235			

Add $50 for stainless steel.
Add $50 for carry handle and rear sight assembly.
Add $15 for all weather synthetic stock.

CLASSIC - .50 or .54 cal. perc., 28 in. round barrel (alloy or stainless), hardwood or synthetic all weather stock.

	$340	$290	$230				

Last MSR was $375.

Add $15 for all weather stock.
Add $50 for stainless steel.

R SECTION

REMINGTON ARMS CO., INC.

Current manufacturer established in 1816, with the factory located in Ilion, NY.

Originally founded by E. Remington, and previously located in Litchfield, Herkimer County, NY, circa 1816-1828. Remington moved to Ilion, NY, in 1828, where they continue to manufacture a wide variety of products. Corporate offices were moved to Madison, NC, in 1996. Distributor and dealer sales.

For more information and current pricing on both new and used Remington Arms Co., Inc. firearms, please refer to the 24th Ed. *Blue Book of Gun Values* by S.P. Fjestad (now online also).

GRADING	100%	98%	95%	90%	80%	70%	60%

RIFLES: FLINTLOCK

1816 COMMEMORATIVE FLINTLOCK RIFLE - .50 cal. flintlock, 39 in. barrel, extra fancy curly maple stock, manufactured by Remington Custom Shop. Mfg. 1995.

	$1,759	$1,650	$1,500

Last MSR was $1,899.

RIFLES: IN-LINE IGNITION

MODEL 700 ML/MLS MAGNUM - .45 (Model 700 MLS) or .50 cal. perc., 24 in. barrel 700 ML, 26 in. barrel 700 MLS Magnum, in-line ignition, short throw bolt action, 3.0 millisecond lock time, synthetic stock with recoil pad, 7¾ lbs. 700 ML new 1996. 700 MLS Magnum new 2002. Improved 3-way ignition system for No. 11 percussion caps, musket caps, or 209 shotshell primers. New 2002.

* *Model 700 ML Blued Steel* - .50 cal. perc., available with black synthetic or Mossy Oak Break-Up (1999-2002) camo finish.

MSR	$415	$365	$300	$255

Add $45 for camo finish on models produced in 1999-2002.

* *Model 700 MLS Magnum (Stainless)* - .45 or .50 cal. perc., available with black synthetic or Mossy Oak Break-Up camo finish. New 2002.

MSR	$533	$469	$385	$325

Add $36 for MLS Magnum Camo.

MODEL 700 ML/MLS CUSTOM - .50 cal. perc., similar to 700 ML/MLS, except has gray laminated thumbhole stock. New 2000. Disc. 2001.

* *700 ML Custom*

	$705	$625	$495

Last MSR was $799.

* *700 MLS Custom*

	$790	$695	$525

Last MSR was $896.

RICHLAND ARMS

Previous importer/distributor located in Blissfield, MI.

PISTOLS: PERCUSSION

ANDREW TARGET - .32, .36 or .45 cal. perc., 10 in. octagon barrel, white steel hammer, barrel, frame, and sights, brass trigger guard, adj. trigger and sights, blue and engraved, 2 lbs. 10 oz. Disc. 1994.

	$195	$170	$135

Last MSR was $150.

Add $55 for deluxe grade.

GRADING	100%	98%	95%	90%	80%	70%	60%

REVOLVERS: PERCUSSION

WALKER - .44 cal. perc., 9 in. round barrel, color case hardened hammer, frame, trigger and loading lever, engraved cylinder, brass trigger guard, 73 oz. Disc. 1994.

	$275	$240	$165

Last MSR was $185.

3rd MODEL DRAGOON - .44 cal. perc., 7.5 in. barrel, color case hardened hammer, frame, trigger and loading lever, engraved cylinder, 66 oz. Disc. 1994.

	$265	$235	$180

Last MSR was $165.

1851 NAVY - .36 cal. perc., 7.5 in. octagon barrel, color case hardened loading lever and hammer, brass or steel frame and trigger guard, 44 oz. Disc. 1994.

	$110	$95	$75

Last MSR was $100.

Add $25 for steel frame.

1860 ARMY - .44 cal. perc., 8 in. barrel, color case hardened hammer, steel or brass frame and trigger, loading lever, engraved cylinder. Disc. 1994.

	$175	$160	$130

Last MSR was $160.

Subtract $35 for brass frame.

1858 REMINGTON ARMY - .44 cal. perc., 8 in. octagon barrel, brass frame and trigger guard, 44 oz. Disc. 1994.

	$135	$120	$95

Last MSR was $125.

Add $35 for steel frame.

1858 REMINGTON NAVY BUFFALO TARGET - .44 cal. perc., 12 in. octagon barrel, brass frame and trigger guard, adj. sights, based on 1858 Navy frame, 38 oz. Disc. 1994.

	$200	$185	$165

Last MSR was $150.

RIFLES: PERCUSSION

BRISTOL HUNTER - .50 or .54 cal. perc., 28 in. octagon barrel, color case hardened hammer and lock, rubber recoil pad, adj. rear sights, chrome plated bore, double set triggers. Disc. 1994.

	$220	$190	$150

Last MSR was $240.

HAWKEN RIFLE - .50 cal. perc., 28 in. octagon barrel, color case hardened hammer and lock, brass trim, adj. sights, double set triggers. Disc. 1994.

	$185	$160	$125

Last MSR was $225.

KODIAK SxS RIFLE - .50 or .58 cal. perc., 28 in. octagon barrels. Disc. 1994.

	$660	$570	$440

Last MSR was $560.

Add $280 for extra 12 ga. shotgun barrels.

GRADING	100%	98%	95%	90%	80%	70%	60%

SHOTGUNS: PERCUSSION

MUZZLE LOADING MODEL - 10 or 12 ga., perc. Disc. 1994.

	$315	$275	$220

Last MSR was $320.

Add $20 for 10 ga.

ROSSI

Current trademark manufactured by Amadeo Rossi, S.A. located in Sao Leopoldp, Brazil. Currently imported exclusively by BrazTech, International located in Miami, FL.

For more information and current pricing on both new and used Rossi firearms, please refer to the 24th Ed. *Blue Book of Gun Values* by S.P. Fjestad (now online also).

RIFLES: IN-LINE IGNITION

MODEL S50BM/S50SM - .50 cal. perc., 209 primer ignition, top button break open action, 23 in. barrel, matte blue or matte stainless steel (Model S50SM) finish, adj. Tru-Glo sights, drilled and tapped for scope base, wood stock and forearm, ventilated recoil pad, 6.3 lbs. New 2003.

MSR	$166	$150	$125	$100

Add $35 for stainless steel Model S50SM.

NOTES

S SECTION

SAVAGE ARMS, INC.

Current manufacturer located in Westfield, MA.

Originally established in 1895 in Utica, NY. In addition to cartridge rifles, Savage now produces a line of bolt-action, in-line muzzleloaders, first introduced in 2001.

For more information and current pricing on both new and used Savage Arms, Inc. firearms, please refer to the 24th Ed. *Blue Book of Gun Values* by S.P. Fjestad (now online also).

GRADING	100%	98%	95%	90%	80%	70%	60%

RIFLES: IN-LINE IGNITION

MODEL 10ML-II/10MLSS-II - .50 cal. perc., 24 in. barrel, in-line 209 primer ignition, bolt action, black synthetic, brown laminate, or Realtree Hardwoods camo stock with recoil pad, 7.5 lbs.

* *Model 10ML-II Blue Steel* - black synthetic stock. New 2001.

MSR	$496	$430	$365	$295

* *Model 10ML-II Blue Steel Camo* - Realtree Hardwoods camouflage synthetic stock, blue steel barrel. New 2002.

MSR	$533	$460	$390	$310

* *Model 10MLSS-II Stainless* - black synthetic stock. New 2001.

MSR	$554	$469	$385	$325

* *Model 10MLSS-II Stainless Camo* - black synthetic stock. New 2002.

MSR	$589	$469	$385	$325

* *Model 10MLBSS-II (Stainless)* - brown laminate stock, stainless steel barrel, adjustable fiber optic hunting sights. New 2002.

MSR	$626	$540	$460	$370

* *Model 10ML-IIXP* - similar to Model 10ML-II, except, 3-9x40mm matte finish scope mounted and bore sighted. Available with blue or stainless barrel. Black synthetic stock w/nylon sling and swivel studs. New 2002.

MSR	$533	$460	$390	$310

Add $56 for stainless steel barrel.

SHILOH RIFLE MFG. CO.

Current manufacturer located in Big Timber, MT since 1983.

RIFLES: PERCUSSION

SHARPS MODEL 1863 CARBINE - .50 or .54 cal. perc., 22 in. round blue barrel, color case hardened reciever and hammer, single trigger, adj. sights, walnut stock and forearm, barrel band, steel military buttplate, approx. 7.5 lbs.

MSR	$1,504	$1,335	$1,200	$975

SHARPS MODEL 1863 MILITARY RIFLE -.50 or .54 cal. perc., 30 in. round blue barrel, color case hardened reciever and hammer, single trigger, adj. sights, walnut stock and long forearm w/cap, three barrel bands, military buttplate, sling swivels.

MSR	$1,750	$1,575	$1,400	$1,135

SHARPS MODEL 1863 SPORTING RIFLE -.50 or .54 cal. perc., 30 in. octagon blue barrel, color case hardened reciever and hammer, double triggers, adj. sights, walnut stock and forearm, steel military buttplate.

MSR	$1,504	$1,335	$1,200	$975

SILE DISTRIBUTORS

Previous importer and distributor of Invest Arms brand and D. Pedersoli brand, located in New York, NY until 1999.

GRADING	100%	98%	95%	90%	80%	70%	60%

REVOLVERS: PERCUSSION

1860 COLT ARMY - .44 cal. perc., 8 in. blue round barrel, brass or color case hardened steel frame, brass trigger guard and back strap, color case hardened hammer, trigger, and loading lever, 2 lbs. 11 oz. Disc.

	$100	$80	$50

Add $35 for steel frame.

1858 REMINGTON ARMY - .44 cal. perc., 8 in. white octagon barrel, white steel frame, brass trigger guard, 2 lbs. 9 oz. Disc.

	$135	$115	$100

Add $70 for stainless steel.
Add $30 for Target Model.

RIFLES: FLINTLOCK & PERCUSSION

BROWN BESS MUSKET - .75 cal. flintlock, 41¾ in. smooth bore barrel, brass furniture, white steel barrel, hammer, and lock, engraved lock, 9 lbs. Disc. 1994.

	$480	$425	$340

Last MSR was $565.

HAWKEN RIFLE - .45, .50, or .54 cal. flintlock or perc. (.50 cal. only in flintlock), 29 in. octagon barrel, solid brass furniture, color case hardened engraved lock, coil spring mechanism with adj. set triggers, stainless steel nipple, chrome bore, brass patch box, adj. sights, 8 lbs. 10 oz. Disc. 1994.

	$200	$175	$140

Last MSR was $230.

Add $35 for flintlock.

HAWKEN RIFLE CARBINE - .45, .50, or .54 cal. flintlock or perc. (.50 cal. only in flintlock), 22 in. octagon barrel, solid brass furniture, color case hardened engraved lock, coil spring mechanism with adj. set triggers, stainless steel nipple, chrome bore, brass patch box, adj. sights, 7 lbs. Disc. 1994.

	$185	$160	$130

Last MSR was $250.

Add $10 for flintlock.

HAWKEN HUNTER CARBINE - .45, .50, or .54 cal. flintlock or perc. (.50 cal. only in flintlock), 22 in. octagon barrel, solid brass furniture, color case hardened engraved lock, coil spring mechanism with adj. set triggers, stainless steel nipple, chrome bore, brass patch box, adj. sights, 7 lbs. Disc. 1994.

	$185	$160	$130

Last MSR was $225.

Add $10 for flintlock.

KENTUCKY RIFLE - .45 or .50 cal. flintlock or perc., 32 in. blue octagon barrel, solid brass furniture, color case hardened hammer and engraved lock, brass patch box, adj. rear sight, 7 lbs. 2 oz. Disc. 1994.

	$300	$255	$200

Add $10 for flintlock.

PENNSYLVANIAN SQUIRREL RIFLE - .32 cal. flintlock, 40.5 in. brown octagon barrel, adj. double set triggers, polished white steel hammer and lock, 9 lbs. Disc.

	$410	$360	$290

SHOTGUNS: PERCUSSION

SxS MODEL - 10 or 12 ga., perc., 28 in. blue barrels, engraved furniture, color case hardened hammer and engraved lock, chrome lined bores, 7 lbs. 12 oz. (8 lbs. 12 oz. for 10 ga.). Disc.

	$420	$380	$300

Add $20 for 10 ga.

GRADING	100%	98%	95%	90%	80%	70%	60%

SOUTHWEST MUZZLE LOADERS SUPPLY

Previous importer/distributor located in Angleton, TX until 1994.

Southwest Muzzle Loaders Supply imported many Uberti models.

REVOLVERS: PERCUSSION

DANCE MODEL - .36 or .44 cal., exact reproduction of the original J.H. Dance and Brothers revolver manufactured in Columbia, Texas, advertising listed 500 as total production, less than 50 were actually assembled and delivered. Mfg. by Aldo Uberti and Co. from Gardone, Italy, cased. Mfg. 1985-1994. Scarce.

$800	$675	$540

Last MSR was $1,500.

SPLIT FIRE SPORTING GOODS, LLC

Previous distributor of White Rifles, located in Orem, UT. During 2001 the name was changed to White Rifles LLC. Split Fire was the exclusive distributor for all White models manufactured by Muzzleloading Technologies, Inc.

For current information refer to White Rifles LLC, and for White models produced through 1997, refer to the White Muzzleloading Systems section.

STONE MOUNTAIN ARMS, INC.

Current manufacturer located in Norcross, GA. Currently marketed exclusively by Connecticut Valley Arms. Colt and Remington reproductions are imported from Italy. Dealer and consumer direct sales.

REVOLVERS: PERCUSSION

1848 BABY DRAGOON - .31 cal. perc., 5 shot, 4 in. octagon barrel, color case hardened steel frame, 1.4 lbs.

$200	$180	$140

Last MSR was $240.

3RD MODEL DRAGOON - .44 cal. perc., 6 shot, 7.5 in. barrel, roll engraved cylinder, color case hardened steel frame, 3.9 lbs.

$220	$190	$155

Last MSR was $250.

1851 NAVY - .36 cal. perc., 6 shot, 7.5 in. barrel, (5.5 in. on Sheriff's model), color case hardened steel frame, brass backstrap and trigger guard, 2.8 lbs.

$130	$115	$85

Last MSR was $180.

1858 REMINGTON - .31 (Pocket Model) or .44 cal. perc., 6 shot, 8 in. barrel, adj. rear sight, fixed sights with color case hardened frame.

$140	$120	$95

Last MSR was $243.

Subtract $15 for .31 cal. Pocket Model.

ROGERS & SPENCER - .44 cal. perc., 6 shot, 7.5 in. octagon barrel, 3 lbs.

$200	$170	$135

Last MSR was $290.

RIFLES: FLINTLOCK & PERCUSSION

1803 HARPERS FERRY - .54 cal. flintlock, 32.5 in. brown barrel, brass furniture, walnut stock, 9 lbs.

$585	$510	$400

Last MSR was $730.

GRADING	100%	98%	95%	90%	80%	70%	60%

1841 MISSISSIPPI RIFLE - .54 cal. perc., 33.5 in. barrel, brass furniture, walnut stock, 9.5 lbs.

	$450	$390	$300				

Last MSR was $575.

1853 ENFIELD (3 BAND) - .58 cal. perc., 39 in. barrel, color case hardened hammer and lock, blue barrel bands, brass furniture, walnut stock, 9.5 lbs.

	$460	$400	$300				

Last MSR was $550.

SILVER EAGLE RIFLE/HUNTER - .50 cal. perc., 26 in. octagon barrel, matte Weatherguard nickel finish, synthetic stock.

	$120	$100	$80				

Last MSR was $140.

Add $20 for Hunter model w/adj. hunting sights and sling swivels.

1861 SPRINGFIELD - .58 cal. perc., 40 in. barrel, all white steel, walnut stock.

	$480	$420	$340				

Last MSR was $600.

RIFLES: IN-LINE IGNITION

PRO I - .50 cal. perc., 24 in. round barrel with Weatherguard nickel finish, std. trigger, blade front sight, duragrip synthetic stock, chrome plated bolt, 6.5 lbs.

	$170	$150	$120				

Last MSR was $200.

PRO II RIFLE - .50 cal. perc., similar to Pro I, except adj. sights and trigger, and stainless steel bolt, 6.5 lbs.

	$180	$155	$125				

Last MSR was $220.

STURM, RUGER, AND COMPANY, INC.

Current manufacturer located in Newport, NH and Prescott, AZ. Distributor and dealer sales.

The first series of Ruger Old Army revolvers were blue and had adj. sights. Current models are available in blue, stainless steel, and polished stainless steel finishes. Based on the 1858 Remington New Army design, the Ruger Old Army incorporates significant advances in design and operation. Old Army revolvers are constructed using the latest investment casting and precision CNC machining techniques.

For more information and current pricing on both new and used Sturm, Ruger, And Co., Inc. firearms, please refer to the 24th Ed. *Blue Book of Gun Values* by S.P. Fjestad (now online also).

Please refer to *Colt Blackpowder Reproductions & Replicas—A Collector's & Shooter's Guide* for color pictures of all Ruger Old Army models listed below. Ruger Old Army pistols can be found on pages 52 through 57.

REVOLVERS: PERCUSSION

Current models offer both fixed and adj. sights, blue alloy, satin or gloss stainless steel finishes.

OLD ARMY - .44 cal. perc., 6 shot, 5.5 (new 2003) or 7.5 in. barrel, fixed or adj. rear sight, blue finish, 2.5 (5.5 in. barrel) lbs.

MSR	$499	$399	$320	$239			

Add $40 for simulated ivory grips (new 1997).

STAINLESS OLD ARMY - stainless steel variation of current Old Army model with adj. rear sight, 2.87 (7.5 in. barrel) lbs.

MSR	$535	$430	$340	$255			

Add $40 for simulated ivory grips (new 1997).

GRADING	100%	98%	95%	90%	80%	70%	60%

NATIONAL MUZZLE LOADING RIFLE ASSOCIATION SPECIAL EDITION - serial no. range 140-14000 to 140-14100. Identified by N.M.L.R.A. logo on the grip panel.

$820   **$600**   **$465**

RUGER COLLECTORS ASSOCIATION FIRST SERIES - serial no. range 1500–1599, "RCA" marked on the topstrap and a star motif preceding the serial number.

$820   **$600**   **$465**

RUGER COLLECTORS ASSOCIATION SECOND SERIES 1976 - serial no. range 145-01401 through 145-01600. Total of 201. Engraved RCA logo and intertwined RCA monogram on topstrap, eagle marked before serial number. Last Rugers with barrel inscription "MADE IN THE 200th YEAR OF AMERICAN LIBERTY".

$820   **$600**   **$465**

RUGER COLLECTORS ASSOCIATION THIRD SERIES 1997 - commemorates the 25th anniversary of the Ruger Old Army. Limited to 2000 pistols serial numbered 1-2000. Floral engraving on top strap and frame, bottom of trigger guard with RCA logo, Ruger Collectors Association bordered with scrollwork along both sides of the barrel, 24Kt. gold plated cylinder with engraved Ruger emblem and scrollwork, 24Kt. gold plated front sight, white Micarta grips with RCA logo.

MSR $700   **$600**   **$475**   **$375**

This model was sold through Sportsman's Guide.

RIFLES: IN-LINE IGNITION

SPORTER MODEL 77/50RS - .50 cal. perc., bolt-action, 22 in. barrel with one band, 3 position safety, hardwood or synthetic stock, black rubber recoil pad, sling swivel studs, 6.5 lbs. New 1997.

MSR $434   **$380**   **$320**   **$260**

Add $121 for Model 77/50RSO Officer's Model with checkered walnut stock, new 1998.
Add $146 for Model K77/50RSP with synthetic stock and stainless steel, new 1999.
Add $165 for Model K77/50RSBBZ with black laminate stock and stainless steel, new 1998.

NOTES

T SECTION

TAYLOR'S & COMPANY, INC.

Current importer/distributor located in Winchester, VA. Taylor's imports pistols and longarms produced by Armi Sport, Pietta, and Uberti. Dealer or consumer direct sales.

For more information and current pricing on Taylor's & Company, Inc. firearms, please refer to the 24th Ed. *Blue Book of Gun Values* by S.P. Fjestad (now online also).

GRADING	100%	98%	95%	90%	80%	70%	60%

PISTOLS: PERCUSSION

KENTUCKY PISTOL - .45 cal. flintlock or perc., 10 in. octagon barrel, brass blade front sight, brass nose cap, color case hardened sidelock, one piece stock with bird's head grip, 2.5 lbs. Mfg. by Armi Sport.

MSR	$239	$205	$175	$145

Add $16 for flintlock model.

NAPOLEON LE PAGE PISTOL - .45 cal. perc., 10 in. barrel, white steel barrel and lock, fixed sights with single barrel wedge, fluted grip, silver plated butt cap and trigger guard with spur, double set triggers, 2 lbs. 7 oz.

MSR	$360	$305	$270	$235

F. ROCHATTE DUELING PISTOL - .45 cal. perc., 10 in. round barrel with flat top, white steel lock and trim, adj. double set triggers, 2.5 lbs. Disc. 1994.

	$250	$210	$160

Last MSR was $395.

REVOLVERS: PERCUSSION

1847 WALKER - .44 cal. perc., 9 in. blue barrel, color case hardened frame, hammer, and loading lever, brass trigger guard and steel backstrap, 4 lbs. 6 oz. Mfg. by Uberti.

MSR	$269	$230	$200	$170

DRAGOON (1st, 2nd, and 3rd MODELS) - .44 cal. perc., 7.5 in. barrel, roll engraved cylinder, brass backstrap. Round trigger guard on 3rd Model. Mfg. by Uberti.

MSR	$255	$220	$190	$160

Add $7 for 3rd Model Dragoon.

1848 BABY DRAGOON - .31 cal. perc., 4 in. octagon barrel, 5 shot, color case hardened frame, hammer, no loading lever, roll engraved cylinder, brass backstrap and trigger guard, also available in white steel, 1.4 lbs. Mfg. by Uberti.

MSR	$205	$175	$150	$125

Add $32 for model in the white.

1849 POCKET - .31 cal. perc., 4 in. octagon barrel, 5 shot, color case hardened frame, hammer, loading lever, roll engraved cylinder, brass backstrap and round trigger guard, 1.4 lbs. Mfg. by Uberti.

MSR	$205	$175	$150	$125

1851 NAVY - .36 or .44 (new 2003) cal. perc., 7.5 in. octagon barrel, rolled cylinder scene, color case hardened frame, hammer, and loading lever, brass backstrap and trigger guard. Mfg. by Uberti & Pietta.

MSR	$200	$170	$145	$120

Subtract $30 for Pietta model.

1851 NAVY BRASS - .36 or .44 (new 2003) cal. perc., 7.5 in. octagon barrel, rolled cylinder scene, brass frame, backstrap and trigger guard. Referred to as a Confederate version of the Colt 1851 Navy. Mfg. by Uberti & Pietta.

MSR	$140	$120	$105	$90

GRADING	100%	98%	95%	90%	80%	70%	60%

Add $25 for engraved barrel and frame.

1851 NAVY SHERIFF'S MODEL - .36 (brass) or .44 cal. (steel) perc., 5.5 in. octagon barrel, rolled cylinder scene, brass or steel frame, color case hardened frame, hammer, and loading lever, brass backstrap and trigger guard. Mfg. by Uberti & Pietta.

MSR	$170	$145	$125	$105

Subtract $30 for .36 cal. brass frame model (Pietta mfg).

1860 ARMY - .44 cal. perc., 8 in. round barrel, brass or steel frame and backstrap, brass trigger guard, color case hardened frame, hammer, and loading lever, 2.75 lbs. Mfg. by Pietta & Uberti.

MSR	$210	$180	$155	$135

Subtract $56 for brass frame model.
Subtract $12 for Pietta model.

1860 ARMY SHERIFF'S MODEL - .44 cal. perc., 5.5 in. round barrel, rolled cylinder scene, color case hardened frame, hammer, and loading lever, steel backstrap, brass trigger guard, walnut grips. Mfg. by Pietta.

MSR	$198	$178	$151	$119

Add $7 for semi-fluted cylinder.

1861 NAVY - .36 cal. perc., 7.5 in. barrel, brass or steel backstrap and trigger guard, color case hardened frame, hammer and loading lever, 2.5 lbs. Mfg. by Uberti and Pietta.

MSR	$205	$175	$150	$125

Subtract $8 for Pietta mfg.

1862 POCKET NAVY - .36 cal. perc., 6.5 in. barrel, half fluted cylinder, brass backstrap and trigger guard, color case hardened frame, hammer and loading lever. Mfg. by Uberti.

MSR	$210	$180	$155	$135

1862 POLICE - .36 cal. perc., 5.5 (new 2003) or 6.5 in. barrel, brass backstrap and trigger guard, color case hardened frame, hammer and loading lever. Mfg. by Uberti and Pietta.

MSR	$210	$180	$155	$135

1858 REMINGTON ARMY - .44 cal. perc., 5.5 (Short Model new 2003) or 8 in. octagon barrel, color case hardened hammer, steel frame, backstrap, and trigger gaurd, blue finish, 2 lbs. 6 oz. Mfg. by Uberti & Pietta.

MSR	$198	$178	$151	$119

Subtract $18 for Pietta model.
Add $7 for white finish 5.5 in. barrel Short Model.
Add $122 for "Old Silver" silver plated frame.

1858 REMINGTON BRASS - .44 cal. perc., 8 in. octagon barrel, color case hardened hammer, brass frame, backstrap, and trigger guard, blue finish, 2 lbs. 6 oz. Mfg. by Uberti & Pietta.

MSR	$147	$125	$110	$95

1858 REMINGTON NAVY - .36 cal. perc., 7.37 in. octagon barrel, color case hardened hammer, steel frame and back strap, brass trigger guard, 2 lbs. 6 oz. Mfg. by Uberti & Pietta.

MSR	$198	$178	$151	$119

Subtract $18 for Pietta model.

1858 REMINGTON STAINLESS STEEL - .44 cal. perc., 8 in. octagon barrel, stainless steel hammer and frame, groove or adj. (Target Model) rear sight, walnut grips. Mfg. by Uberti.

MSR	$275	$235	$205	$175

Add $25 for adj. rear sight (Target Model).

GRADING	100%	98%	95%	90%	80%	70%	60%

1858 ARMY STARR SINGLE/DOUBLE ACTION - .44 cal. perc., 6 in. tapered round barrel, all blue steel frame, backstrap and trigger guard. Mfg. by Pietta.

MSR	$378	$320	$280	$245

Add $12 for Double Action Model.

1863 REMINGTON POCKET - .31 cal. perc., 3.5 in. 5 shot, octagon barrel, brass frame, walnut grips. Mfg. by Armi San Marco.

MSR	$165	$140	$120	$105

Add $20 for Nickel finish.

1873 CATTLEMAN SINGLE ACTION REVOLVER - .44 cal. perc., 4.75, 5.5, or 7.5 in. blue barrel, color case hardened hammer and frame, blue backstrap and trigger guard, walnut grips. New 2003.

MSR	$320	$275	$240	$205

RIFLES: FLINTLOCK & PERCUSSION

1777 CHARLEVILLE MUSKET - .69 cal. flintlock, 44.75 in. smooth bore barrel, white steel lockplate, hammer, and ramrod, brass barrel bands, trigger guard, and buttplate, walnut stock. Disc. 1993.

	$500	$430	$340

Last MSR was $595.

1842 SPRINGFIELD U.S. MUSKET - .69 cal. perc., 42 in. round smooth bore white steel barrel, hammer, lock trigger guard and trigger, marked "SPRING–FIELD" in two lines behind the hammer, lock and tang dated 1847, barrel stamped with the correct style V.P. and eagle head proof marks on the breech, one-piece American Walnut stock, 9.75 lbs. Mfg. by Armi Sport. N-S.S.A. approved.

MSR	$620	$535	$465	$400

Add $55 for 1842 Musket with rifled barrel and adj. rear sight. N-S.S.A. approved.

1853 ENFIELD 1853 (3 BAND) - .58 cal. perc., 39 in. round barrel, color case hardened hammer and lock, brass furniture, blue barrel bands, 9.5 lbs. Mfg. by Armi Sport.

MSR	$520	$445	$390	$335

1855 U.S. RIFLE - .58 cal. perc., 40 in. round barrel, white steel barrel, hammer, lock, trigger, and trim, one-piece American walnut stock, white satin furniture, brass endcap. 9.75 lbs. New 1998. Mfg. by Armi Sport.

MSR	$659	$560	$495	$425

1858 ENFIELD (2 BAND) - .58 cal. perc., 33 in. round barrel, color case hardened hammer and lock, brass furniture, blue barrel bands, adj. rear sight, 9.5 lbs. Mfg. by Armi Sport.

MSR	$499	$425	$375	$320

1858 REMINGTON REVOLVING CARBINE - .44 cal. perc., 18 in. octagon barrel, color case hardened hammer, steel frame, brass trigger guard, blue finish, adj. rear sight, walnut stock w/brass buttplate. Mfg. by Uberti. New 2003.

MSR	$299	$255	$220	$185

1859 INFANTRY SHARPS RIFLE - .54 cal. perc., 30 in. round barrel, 3 metal band stock, color case hardened hammer and receiver. Mfg. by Armi Sport.

MSR	$1,010	$860	$750	$650

1859 BERDAN MILITARY SHARPS RIFLE - .54 cal. perc., 30 in. round barrel, 3 metal band stock, color case hardened hammer and receiver, double set triggers. Mfg. by Armi Sport.

MSR	$1,075	$915	$805	$695

GRADING	100%	98%	95%	90%	80%	70%	60%

1859 CAVALRY SHARPS CARBINE - .54 cal. perc., 22 in. round barrel, 1 metal band, color case hardened hammer and receiver. Mfg. by Armi Sport.

| MSR | $895 | $760 | $670 | $575 |

1861 SPRINGFIELD MUSKET - .58 cal. perc., 40 in. round barrel, white steel barrel, hammer, lock, trigger, and trim, 10.25 lbs. Mfg. by Armi Sport.

| MSR | $545 | $465 | $405 | $350 |

1862 C.S. RICHMOND MUSKET - .58 cal. perc., 40 in. barrel, white satin finish, brass nosecap, similar to 1861 Springfield, 9 lbs. Mfg. by Armi Sport.

| MSR | $575 | $490 | $430 | $370 |

1863 CAVALRY SHARPS CARBINE - .54 cal. perc., 22 in. round barrel 1 metal band, color case hardened hammer and receiver. Mfg. by Armi Sport.

| MSR | $855 | $730 | $640 | $550 |

1863 SHARPS SPORTING RIFLE - .54 cal. perc., 30 or 32 in. octagon barrel, color case hardened hammer and receiver, single or double set triggers, adj. rear sight, walnut stock and forearm. New 2003.

| MSR | $895 | $760 | $670 | $575 |

Add $15 for double set triggers.

1863 ZOUAVE RIFLE - .58 cal. perc., 32.5 in. round barrel, color case hardened hammer, lock, and trigger, brass patchbox, trigger guard, and barrel bands, 9 lbs. Mfg. by Armi Sport.

| MSR | $470 | $395 | $350 | $300 |

BROWN BESS MUSKET - .75 cal. flintlock, 31.5 in. or 42 in. smooth bore barrel, white steel barrel, hammer, lock and furniture, 8.5 lbs. Disc. 1993.

| | | $610 | $555 | $470 |

Last MSR was $675.

DELUXE HAWKEN RIFLE - .50 cal. perc., 30 in. octagon chrome lined barrel, brass patchbox, target sights, double set triggers, 8 lbs. Mfg. by Invest Arms.

| | | $200 | $175 | $140 |

Last MSR was $260.

Subtract $40 for Trailsman Model.

HAWKEN HUNTER CARBINE - .50 cal. perc., 24 in. octagon chrome lined barrel, rubber recoil pad, sling swivels, double set triggers. Mfg. by Invest Arms.

| | | $185 | $160 | $130 |

Last MSR was $285.

KENTUCKY RIFLE - .45 or .50 cal. perc. or flintlock, 35 in. octagon barrel, color case hardened lock, brass buttplate, trigger guard, patchbox, sideplates, thimbles and nosecap, walnut stock with large or small patchbox, rifle weighs 7.5 lbs., carbine is 6 lbs. Mfg. by Armi Sport.

| MSR | $465 | $390 | $345 | $295 |

Add $30 for flintlock version.

✷ *Carbine Model* - .50 cal. perc., chrome lined barrel. Disc. 1993.

| | | $255 | $220 | $180 |

Last MSR was $325.

Add $10 for large patch box.

GRADING	100%	98%	95%	90%	80%	70%	60%

MORTIMER HUNTER RIFLE - .50 or .54 cal. perc., 25 in. blue (matte finish) .5 octagon, .5 round barrel, adj. sights (rear), 8 7/8 lbs. Disc. 1993. Mfg. by Pedersoli.

$450 $375 $300

Last MSR was $485.

PENNSYLVANIA RIFLE -.45 cal. perc., octagon barrel, color case hardened hammer and lock, small brass patchbox, approx. 7 lbs.

$200 $175 $140

Last MSR was $215.

Add $185 for new Pedersoli model.

ST. LOUIS HAWKEN RIFLE - .50 cal. perc., 30 in. octagon barrel, all black steel furniture, adj. rear sight, double set triggers, approx. 8 lbs. Disc. 1994.

$245 $215 $160

Last MSR was $260.

TRYON RIFLE - .50 or .54 cal. perc., 32.25 in. octagon barrel, all white steel, engraved lock and hammer, 9.5 lbs. Disc. 1994.

$415 $355 $265

Last MSR was $595.

THOMPSON/CENTER ARMS CO.

Current manufacturer located in Rochester, NH. Distributor and dealer sales.

PISTOLS: PERCUSSION

PATRIOT - .36 or .45 cal. perc., 9 in. barrel, double set triggers, target stock, walnut, color case hardened hammer and lock. Disc. 1987.

$240 $200 $145

Last MSR was $235.

PISTOLS: IN-LINE IGNITION

SCOUT PISTOL - .45, .50, or .54 cal. perc., 12 in. barrel, walnut grips, 4 lbs. 6 oz. Disc.

$280 $250 $200

Last MSR was $350.

Add $125 for extra barrel.
This model is similar in design to the old style single shot Remington Target Model.

ENCORE 209X50 MODEL - .50 cal. perc., uses #209 primer for ignition, Thompson Contender style, 15 in. blue barrel, walnut grip and forend.

MSR $611 $520 $435 $350

RIFLES: FLINTLOCK & PERCUSSION

BLACK MOUNTAIN MAGNUM - .50 or .54 cal. perc., musket cap ignition, cap lock, 26 in. round barrel, blue finish, composite stock. Disc. 2002.

$317 $270 $216

Last MSR was $353.

Add $34 for walnut stock.
Add $34 for .54 cal. Westerner model with walnut stock.

GRADING	100%	98%	95%	90%	80%	70%	60%

BIG BOAR - .58 cal. perc., 26 in. octagon barrel, color case hardened hammer and lock, single hunting style trigger, American walnut stock, recoil pad and swivels, 7 lbs. 12 oz. Disc.

$300 $250 $200

Last MSR was $355.

CHEROKEE - .32, .36, or .45 cal. perc., 24 in. octagon barrel, double set triggers, color case hardened hammer and lock, brass trim, American walnut. Disc. 1994.

$300 $255 $200

Last MSR was $320.

Add $105 for extra barrel.

FIRESTORM (FLINTLOCK) - .50 cal. flintlock, 26 in. round barrel, blue or stainless steel finish, composite stock, fiber optic sights. New 2000.

MSR $415 $370 $325 $265

Add $50 for stainless steel.

FIRESTORM (PERCUSSION) - .50 cal. perc., percussion lock, #209 primer ignition, 26 in. round barrel, blue finish, composite stock, fiber optic sights. Mfg. 2000-02.

$352 $300 $240

Last MSR was $391.

GREY HAWK - .50 cal. perc., 24 in. round barrel, all stainless steel construction, Rynite stock, 7 lbs. Mfg. 1993-disc.

$260 $220 $175

Last MSR was $330.

HAWKEN - .50 or .54 cal. perc. or flintlock, 28 in. octagon barrel, color case hardened hammer and lock, double set triggers, 8.5 lbs.

MSR $545 $485 $440 $355

Add $24 for flintlock model.

HAWKEN SILVER ELITE - .50 cal. perc., 28 in. stainless steel octagon barrel and lock, double set triggers, semi fancy wood stock.

$480 $405 $320

Last MSR was $535.

HAWKEN COUGAR - .45 or .50 cal. perc., stainless steel version of Hawken, select hardwood stock.

$360 $295 $235

HIGH PLAINS SPORTER - .50 cal. perc., 24 in. round blue barrel, blue furniture, sling swivels, walnut stock w/recoil pad, 7 lbs. Mfg. 1992-94.

$310 $260 $205

Last MSR was $340.

NEW ENGLANDER RIFLE - .50 or .54 cal. perc., 24 and 28 in. barrel, brass furniture, walnut or Rynite (new 1991) stock, 5 lbs. 2 oz. Disc. 2002.

$300 $250 $200

Last MSR was $335.

Add $105 for extra .50 cal. barrel, and $15 for left-hand.
Subtract $15 for Rynite stock.

GRADING	100%	98%	95%	90%	80%	70%	60%

PENNSYLVANIA HUNTER RIFLE/CARBINE - .50 cal. flintlock, 21 (carbine) or 31 (rifle) in. octagon to round barrel, color case hardened hammer and lock, 7 lbs. 9 oz. Disc. 2002.

		$398	**$335**	**$270**			

Last MSR was $438.

Add $15 for left-hand.
Add $135 for 21 in. extra carbine barrel.
Add $20 for Match Rifle (Percussion Model Disc.)

RENEGADE -.50, .54, or .56 (smooth bore) cal. perc. or flintlock, 26 in. octagon barrel, color case hardened hammer and lock, double set triggers, 8 lbs. Disc.

		$290	**$245**	**$195**			

Last MSR was $360.

Add $10 for flintlock.
Add $105 for 12 ga. barrel.
Add $10 for left-hand.
Subtract $25 for single trigger Hunter Model (new 1987) and smooth bore model.

RENEGADE HUNTER - .50, cal. perc. 26 in. octagon blue barrel, 1:48 in. twist, color case hardened hammer and lock, adj. rear sight, walnut stock w/recoil pad, 8 lbs. New 2003.

MSR	**$462**	**$415**	**$365**	**$300**			

SENECA - .36 or .45 cal. perc., 27 in. octagon barrel, color case hardened hammer and lock, double set triggers, American walnut, 6 lbs. Disc. 1987.

		$300	**$255**	**$200**			

Last MSR was $300.

TREE HAWK CARBINE - .50 cal. perc., 21 in. round camo barrel, camo furniture, Rynite camo stock, with swivels and sling, 6.75 lbs. Mfg. 1992-94.

		$280	**$240**	**$185**			

Last MSR was $340.

Add $135 for extra 12 ga. barrel.

WHITE MOUNTAIN CARBINE - .50 cal. flintlock or perc., 21 in. octagon tapering to round barrel, color case hardened furniture, single hunting trigger, walnut stock, 6.5 lbs. Mfg. 1989-disc.

		$295	**$265**	**$205**			

Last MSR was $350.

Add $20 for flintlock.

RIFLES: IN-LINE IGNITION

BLACK DIAMOND - .50 cal., choice of three different ignition systems, including musket cap, #11 percussion cap, or #209 shotshell primer, 22.5 in. round blue or stainless steel barrel, 1:28 in. twist, adj. Tru-Glo fiber optic sights, drilled and taped for scope mounts, Rynite stock, 6 lbs., 9 oz. New 1998.

MSR	**$317**	**$285**	**$245**	**$195**			

Add $46 for stainless steel.

BLACK DIAMOND XR - .50 cal., similar to Black Diamond, except 26 in. round blue or stainless steel barrel, 1:28 in. twist, adj. Tru-Glo fiber optic sights, drilled and taped for scope mounts, black composite, Realtree Hardwoods Camo composite, or walnut stock, recoil pad, 6.75 lbs. New 2003.

MSR	**$334**	**$300**	**$255**	**$205**			

Add $47 for stainless steel.
Add $70 for walnut stock.

Add $59 for Realtree Hardwoods Camo stock.

BLACK DIAMOND SUPER 45 XR - .45 cal., similar to Black Diamond XR, except Super .45 cal. and black composite stock only, 7.25 lbs. New 2003.

MSR	$348	$315	$270	$220

Add $47 for stainless steel.

ENCORE 209X50 MAGNUM - .50 cal. perc., #209 primer ignition, closed breech break-open action, 26 in. round blue or stainless steel barrel, 1:28 in. twist, adj. Tru-Glo fiber optic sights, drilled and taped for scope mounts, black composite, Realtree Hardwoods Camo composite, or walnut stock and forend, approx. 7 lbs.

MSR	$614	$550	$485	$395

Add $27 for walnut stock and forend.
Add $79 for stainless steel.
Add $59 for Realtree Hardwoods Camo stock.

ENCORE 209X45 SUPER MAGNUM - .45 cal. perc., #209 primer ignition, closed breech break-open action, 26 in. round blue barrel w/walnut stock and forend or stainless steel barrel w/black composite stock and forend, 1:28 in. twist, adj. Tru-Glo fiber optic sights, drilled and taped for scope mounts, approx. 7 lbs. New 2003.

MSR	$666	$595	$525	$430

Add $41 for stainless steel barrel w/black composite stock and forend.

FIRE HAWK - .50 or .54 cal. perc., 24 in. round blue steel barrel, walnut stock.

	$345	$295	$235

Last MSR was $384.

Add $50 for stainless steel barrel assembly.
Add $40 for composite stock and stainless steel barrel assembly.

FIRE HAWK DELUXE - .50 or .54 cal. perc., 24 in. round blue steel barrel, deluxe checkered walnut stock.

	$470	$400	$325

Last MSR was $520.

Add $52 for stainless steel barrel assembly.

FIRE HAWK THUMBHOLE STOCK MODEL - .50 or .54 cal. perc., 24 in. round blue steel barrel, composite thumbhole stock.

	$365	$300	$240

Last MSR was $404.

Add $50 for stainless steel barrel assembly.

FIRE HAWK BANTAM - .50 cal. perc., 21 in. round blue steel barrel, 13.25 in. LOP walnut stock.

	$345	$295	$235

Last MSR was $383.

FIRE HAWK ADVANTAGE CAMO - .50 or .54 cal. perc., 24 in. round blue steel barrel, camouflage composite stock.

	$375	$310	$250

Last MSR was $415.

G2 CONTENDER 209X45 - .45 cal. perc., #209 primer ignition, closed breech break-open action, 24 in. round blue barrel, 1:28 in. twist, walnut stock and forend, adj. Tru-Glo fiber optic sights, drilled and taped for scope mounts, approx. 5.5 lbs. New 2003.

MSR	$636	$570	$500	$410

GRADING	100%	98%	95%	90%	80%	70%	60%

OMEGA - .45 (new 2003) or .50 cal., perc., #209 primer ignition, sealed pivoting breech under lever action, 28 in. round blue or stainless steel barrel, 1:28 in. twist, adj. Tru-Glo fiber optic sights, drilled and taped for scope mounts, black composite, Realtree Hardwoods Camo composite, or gray laminated wood stock, recoil pad, approx. 7 lbs. New 2002.

MSR	$414	$370	$325	$265

Add $51 for stainless steel.
Add $30 for gray laminated wood stock.
Add $59 for Realtree Hardwoods Camo stock.
Add $14 for .45 cal.

THUNDER HAWK SHADOW CAMO - .50 cal. perc., 24 in. round blue steel barrel, camouflage composite stock.

		$285	$235	$195

Last MSR was $320.

SCOUT RIFLE/CARBINE - .50 and .54 cal. perc., 21 (carbine)or 24 in. round barrel, 7 lbs. 4 oz.

		$350	$300	$240

Last MSR was $435.

Add $135 per extra barrels.
Subtract $90 for Rynite stock model (new 1993).

SYSTEM 1 - .32, .50, .54, or .58 cal., 12 ga., perc., 26 in. round blue steel barrel, walnut stock.

		$350	$295	$235

Last MSR was $389.

Add $40 for composite stock.
Add $75 for camo composite stock.
Add $170 for .32 or .58 cal. blue steel barrel.
Add $170 for 12 ga. blue steel barrel with screw-in full choke.
Add $220 for .50 cal. or .54. cal stainless steel barrel.

THUNDER HAWK SHADOW - .50 cal. perc., 24 in. round blue steel barrel, composite stock.

		$259	$210	$175

Last MSR was $289.

Add $51 for stainless steel barrel assembly.

SHOTGUNS: PERCUSSION & IN-LINE IGNITION

BLACK MOUNTAIN MAGNUM - 12 ga., Turkey cap lock, 27 in. round barrel with special Turkey Choke Tube, blue finish, composite stock. Disc. 2002.

		$348	$296	$236

Last MSR was $387.

ENCORE MUZZLELOADING TURKEY GUN - 12 ga., perc., #209 primer In-Line ignition, closed breech break-open action, 24 in. smoothbore barrel w/screw-in Turkey choke tube, blue frame, adj. fiber optic sights, Realtree Hardwoods Camo finish barrel, Realtree Hardwoods Camo composite stock and forend, Thompson Contender styling. New 2003.

MSR	$767	$685	$600	$500

NEW ENGLANDER - 12 ga., perc., 26 or 28 in. barrel, brass furniture, 5 lbs. 2 oz.

		$280	$240	$195

Last MSR was $330.

Add $105 for extra .50 cal. barrel.

GRADING	100%	98%	95%	90%	80%	70%	60%

Add $15 for left-hand.
Add $20 for full choke.
Subtract $15 for Rynite stock.

TREE HAWK - 12 ga., similar to New Englander. Mfg. 1994-disc.

| | | $280 | $240 | $185 | | | |

Last MSR was $345.

TRADITIONS PERFORMANCE FIREARMS

Current importer located in Old Saybrook, CT. Distributor and dealer sales.

Traditions Performance Firearms imports Italian made black powder cap & ball pistols, revolvers, and longrifles, manufactured by Uberti, Pietta, and Pedersoli along with and Spanish made in-line muzzle loaders manufactured by Ardesa.

For more information and current pricing on both new and used Traditions firearms, please refer to the 24th Ed. *Blue Book of Gun Values* by S.P. Fjestad (now online also).

CANNONS: MINIATURE

NAPOLEON III - .69 cal., 14.5 in. smoothbore, fuse ignition, gold finish, wheel diameter 11.5 in., overall length 27.5 in., 15 lbs.

MSR $589 $525 $445 $355

Subtract $100 for nickel finish.

MINI NAPOLEON III - .50 cal., 7.25 in. smoothbore, fuse ignition, nickel finish, wheel diameter 6 in., overall length 14.5 in., 2 lbs. 6 oz.

MSR $209 $185 $155 $125

OLD IRONSIDES - .69 cal., 12.5 in. smoothbore, fuse ignition, black finish, wheel diameter 2 1/8 in., overall length 14 in., 9 lbs. 3 oz.

MSR $179 $155 $135 $105

MINI OLD IRONSIDES - .50 cal., 9 in. smoothbore, fuse ignition, nickel finish, wheel diameter 2 1/8 in., overall length 11.5 in., 3 lbs. 14 oz.

MSR $159 $145 $120 $98

MINI YORKTOWN - .50 cal., 7 3/8 in. smoothbore, fuse ignition, nickel finish, wheel diameter 4.5 in., overall length 13 in., 2 lbs. 6 oz.

MSR $159 $145 $120 $98

PISTOLS: IN-LINE IGNITION

BUCKHUNTER PRO - .45 (new 2002) or .50 cal. perc., 9.5 or 12.5 in. round, or 14.75 in. fluted barrel with muzzle brake, adj. sights, walnut or all weather grip and forearm, blue or nickel finish, 3 lbs. 1 oz. to 3 lbs. 11 oz.

MSR $249 $225 $195 $150

Add $20 for 12.5 in. barrel.
Add $50 for 14.75 in. fluted barrel with muzzle brake.

PISTOLS: PERCUSSION

BUCKSKINNER PISTOL - .50 cal. perc., 10 in. octagon blue barrel, color case hardened hammer and lock, black furniture, beech or laminated stock, 2.5 lbs. Mfg. 1993-disc.

$135 $115 $95

Last MSR was $146.

Add $15 for laminated stock.

GRADING	100%	98%	95%	90%	80%	70%	60%

KENTUCKY PISTOL - .50 cal. perc., 9.75 in. octagon barrel, color case hardened hammer and lock, brass trigger guard and endcap, select hardwood stock. 2.5 lbs.

MSR $149 $130 $110 $90

PIONEER PISTOL - .45 or .50 cal. perc., 9 5/8 in. octagon barrel, German silver furniture, blackened hardware, select hardwood stock, 2 lbs. 4 oz. New 1991.

MSR $149 $130 $110 $90

TRAPPER PISTOL - .45 or .50 cal. flintlock or perc., 9.75 in. octagon barrel, hooked breech, double set triggers, adj. sights, brass trim, 3 lbs. 4 oz.

MSR $189 $170 $145 $115

Add $20 for flintlock.

WILLIAM PARKER PISTOL - .50 cal. perc., 10 3/8 in. octagon polished steel barrel, hooked breech, double set triggers, checkered walnut stock, 2 lbs. 8 oz.

MSR $269 $249 $215 $175

CROCKETT PISTOL - .32 cal. perc., 10 in. octagon blue barrel, fixed tang, single trigger, select hardwood stock, 2 lbs. 4 oz. New 2000.

MSR $139 $125 $110 $90

VEST POCKET DERRINGER - .31 cal. perc., 2.25 in. brass barrel, spur trigger, simulated ivory grips.

MSR $109 $95 $80 $65

REVOLVERS: PERCUSSION

1847 COLT WALKER - .44 cal. perc., 9 in. barrel, color case hardened hammer, frame and loading lever, brass trigger guard, 3.9 lbs. Disc. 2001.

$260 $225 $180

Last MSR was $293.

1851 COLT NAVY - .36 (new 2003) or .44 cal. perc., 7.5 in. octagon barrel, color case hardened hammer and loading lever, steel or brass frame, cylinder has roll engraving.

MSR $149 $130 $110 $90

Add $30 for steel frame model.

1858 REMINGTON NEW ARMY - .44 cal. perc., 6.5 in. octagon barrel, brass or steel frame and brass trigger guard, adjustable target sights.

MSR $159 $140 $110 $85

Add $40 for steel frame.

1858 REMINGTON BISON - .44 cal. perc., 12 in. octagon barrel, brass frame and nickel trigger guard.

MSR $189 $170 $150 $125

1858 REMINGTON NEW ARMY W/TARGET SIGHTS - .44 cal. perc., 6.5 in. octagon barrel, stainless steel, adj. rear target sight.

MSR $339 $300 $250 $195

1860 COLT ARMY - .44 cal. perc., 8 in. round barrel, color case hardened steel or brass frame, brass trigger guard.

MSR $159 $140 $115 $95

Add $40 for color case hardened steel frame.
Add $60 for nickel finish and simulated ivory grips.
Add $110 for steel frame and simulated ivory grips.

GRADING	100%	98%	95%	90%	80%	70%	60%

1863 POCKET REMINGTON - .31 cal. perc., 3.5 in. octagon blue barrel, brass frame w/spur trigger, fixed sights, walnut grips, approx. 1 lbs. New 2003.

	MSR	$179	$160	$135	$115

1873 COLT PEACEMAKER - .44 cal. perc., 4.75 in. or 7.5 in. barrel, brass frame, walnut grips. Colt SAA style revolver fitted with cap and ball cylinder.

	MSR	$329	$295	$250	$195

POCKET REMINGTON - .31 cal. perc., 3.5 in. octagon barrel, brass frame, walnut grips. Disc. 2001.

		$150	$130	$100

Last MSR was $168.

REMINGTON BEALS NAVY NEW MODEL - .36 cal. perc., 6.5 in. octagon barrel, steel frame, blue finish, brass trigger guard, walnut grips, fixed sights, approx. 2.75 lbs. New 2003.

	MSR	$189	$170	$150	$120

WELLS FARGO - .31 cal. perc., 4 in. octagon barrel, 5 shot, brass frame, backstrap and trigger guard, no loading lever, 1.5 lbs. Disc. 2001.

	$125	$110	$90

Last MSR was $140.

RIFLES: FLINTLOCK & PERCUSSION

BUCKSKINNER FLINTLOCK CARBINE - .50 cal. flintlock, 21 in. octagon to round barrel, blackened hardware, select hardwood Monte Carlo stock with pistol grip, adj. TruGlo fiber optic sights (new 2000), recoil pad, 6 lbs.

	MSR	$239	$215	$185	$150

Add $70 for black laminated stock.

CREEDMOOR MATCH RIFLE - .451 cal. perc., 32 in. octagon to round blue barrel, color case hardened hammer, lock, and trigger guard, hooded front and adj. spindle diopter rear sight, checkered walnut stock, 8.5 lbs. Mfg. 1994-disc.

	$970	$865	$700

Last MSR was $1,150.

CROCKETT SMALL GAME RIFLE - .32 cal. perc., 32 in. octagon barrel, color case hardened hammer and lock, brass buttplate, trigger guard, double set trigger. 6 lbs. 7 oz. New 2000.

	MSR	$299	$270	$235	$195

DEERHUNTER RIFLE - .32, .50, or .54 cal. flintlock or perc., 24 in. octagon barrel., color case hardened hammer and lock, single trigger, black furniture, hardwood or Mossy Oak Break-Up AW synthetic stock, approx. 6 lbs.

* *Hardwood Blue* - .32 or .50 cal. flintlock or perc., blue finish with hardwood stock.

	MSR	$179	$165	$140	$105

Add $20 for flintlock, or left-hand.
Add $10 for .32 cal.

* *All Weather Synthetic Blue* - .50 or .54 cal. flintlock or perc., blue finish with black AW synthetic stock.

	MSR	$149	$130	$110	$90

Add $40 for flintlock.
Add $10 for .50 cal.

GRADING	100%	98%	95%	90%	80%	70%	60%

✳ ***All Weather Synthetic Nickel*** - .50 or .54 cal. flintlock or perc., Nickel finish with black or Mossy Oak Break-Up AW synthetic stock.

MSR	$169	$155	$130	$105

Add $20 for flintlock.
Add $40 for Mossy Oak Break-Up stock.

1853 ENFIELD (3 BAND) - .58 cal. perc., 39 in. round barrel, 3 barrel bands, color case hardened hammer, lock and barrel bands, brass buttplate, trigger guard and nosecap, full length walnut stock, 10 lbs.

	$435	$380	$300

Last MSR was $484.

FRONTIER RIFLE/CARBINE - .45 or .50 cal. perc. or flintlock, 24 (carbine) or 28 in. octagon barrel, double set triggers, adj. sights, brass trim, 6 lbs. 14 oz (6 lbs. 8 oz. carbine). Disc. 1993.

	$195	$165	$125

Last MSR was $255.

Add $15 for flintlock (.50 cal. only).

FRONTIER SCOUT RIFLE - .36, .45, or .50 cal. flintlock or perc., 26 in. octagon barrel, double set triggers, adj. sights, brass trim, 5 lbs. 8 oz., lock has adj. sear.

	$155	$135	$110

Last MSR was $215.

Add $10 for flintlock.
Add $15 for carbine.

HAWKEN RIFLE - .50, .54, or .58 cal. perc. or flintlock, 32.25 in. octagon barrel, double set triggers, adj. sights, brass trim, 8 lbs. 2 oz. Disc. 1993.

	$300	$255	$200

Last MSR was $415.

Add $10 for flintlock (.50 and .54 cal. only).
A fiberglass ramrod and deluxe rear sight were introduced in 1989.

HAWKEN MATCH RIFLE - .451 cal. perc., 32 in. octagon blue barrel, engraved brass patchbox, color case hardened hammer and lock, brass trigger guard, buttplate, and furniture, checkered walnut stock, 10 lbs.

	$450	$390	$310

Last MSR was $605.

HAWKEN WOODSMAN RIFLE - .50 or .54 cal. perc. or flintlock, 28 in. octagon blue barrel, adj. sights, color case hardened hammer and lock, double set trigger, brass furniture and patchbox, 7.5 lbs.

MSR	$249	$225	$195	$150

Add $20 for left-hand.
Add $30 for flintlock.

HAWKEN MAGNUM RIFLE - .50 cal. perc., musket cap ignition, 28 in. octagon barrel, color case hardened hammer and lock, dual wedges, fiber optic sights, double set trigger, brass furniture and patchbox, select hardwood stock. Designed for use with Pyrodex Pellets. Disc. 2001.

	$325	$275	$220

Last MSR was $259.

HENRY TARGET RIFLE - .451 cal. perc., 32 in. octagon blue barrel, color case hardened hammer and lock, hooded front and spindle diopter rear sight, blue steel trim, checkered walnut stock, 11 lbs.

	$1,000	$900	$750

Last MSR was $1,325.

GRADING	100%	98%	95%	90%	80%	70%	60%

HUNTER RIFLE - .50 or .54 cal. perc., 28 in. octagon barrel, double set triggers, adj. sights, black chrome brass trim with German silver wedge plates, lock has adj. sear, walnut stock, 8 lbs., 10 oz. Disc. 1994.

$300 $255 $200

Last MSR was $425.

A fiberglass ramrod and deluxe rear sight were introduced in 1989.

KENTUCKY RIFLE - 50 cal. perc., 33.5 in. octagon barrel, color case hardened hammer and lock, fixed sights, full length hardwood stock, brass buttplate, 7 lbs. 4 oz.

MSR $249 $225 $195 $150

KENTUCKY RIFLE - .50 cal. flintlock., 33.5 in. octagon barrel, color case hardened hammer and lock, fixed sights, full length hardwood stock, brass buttplate, 7 lbs. 4 oz. New 2002.

MSR $259 $230 $205 $170

KENTUCKY SCOUT RIFLE - .45 or .50 cal. perc. or 26 in. octagon barrel, double set triggers, adj. sights, brass trim, full length stock, lock has adj. sear, 5 lbs. 8 oz. Disc. 1989.

$185 $160 $120

Last MSR was $135.

Add $10 for flintlock.

PA PELLET FLINTLOCK - .50 cal. flintlock, 26 in. blue or nickel finish octagon barrel, adj. Tru-Glo fiber optic sights, heavy-duty lock and deep priming pan, removable breech plug, hardwood, Mossy Oak Break-Up or black AW synthetic stock, 7 lbs. New 2002.

MSR $229 $205 $180 $145

Add $10 for left-hand model.
Add $20 for nickel barrel.
Add $20 for hardwood stock.
Add $30 for Mossy Oak Break-Up stock.

PANTHER RIFLE - .50 or .54 (new 2002) cal. perc., 24 in. blue octagon barrel, adj rear sight, black AW synthetic stock, approx. 6 lbs.

MSR $119 $105 $95 $85

PENNSYLVANIA RIFLE - .50 cal. flintlock or perc., 40.25 in. blue octagon barrel, double set triggers, adj. sights, full length walnut stock, brass buttplate, brass trim, 8 lbs. 8 oz.

MSR $489 $435 $380 $310

Add $20 for flintlock version.

PIONEER CARBINE/RIFLE - .50 or .54 cal. perc., 24 (carbine) or 27.25 in., octagon barrel, color case hardened hammer, lock and furniture, German silver blade front sight, recoil pad, carbine style stock.

$175 $150 $110

Last MSR was $214.

SHENANDOAH RIFLE - .36 (new 2002) or .50 cal. flintlock or perc., color case hardened hammer and lock, 33.5 in. octagon blue barrel, double set triggers, adj. sights, full length hardwood stock, brass buttplate, brass furniture, 7 lbs. 3 oz.

MSR $379 $340 $295 $245

Add $20 for flintlock model.
Add $10 for .36 cal. (new 2002).

1861 SPRINGFIELD - .58 cal. perc., 40 in. round barrel, 3 barrel bands, full length walnut stock, all white steel. 10.25 lbs. Disc.

$470 $410 $330

Last MSR was $513.

GRADING	100%	98%	95%	90%	80%	70%	60%

TENNESSEE RIFLE - .50 cal. flintlock or perc., 24 in. octagon barrel, color case hardened hammer and lock, brass buttplate, trigger guard and nosecap, fixed sights, double set triggers, full length hardwood stock, 6 lbs.

	MSR	$309	$275	$245	$200		

Add $20 for flintlock.

THUNDER MAGNUM RIFLE - .50 cal. perc., musket cap ignition, 24 in. round barrel, blackened furniture, fiber optic sights, removable breech plug, single trigger, select hardwood stock. Designed for use with Pyrodex Pellets. Disc. 2001.

		$315	$265	$215			

Last MSR was $349.

Add $10 for all-weather model with nickel finish.

TRAPPER RIFLE - .36, .45, or .50 cal. perc., 25 in. octagon barrel, color case hardened hammer and lock, brass trim, 5 lbs. Disc. 1989.

		$200	$160	$120			

Last MSR was $200.

TROPHY RIFLE - .50 or .54 cal. perc., 27.5 in. octagon tapering to round barrel, adj. trigger, fiberglass ramrod, carbine style walnut stock, 7 lbs. Disc. 1994.

		$350	$300	$240			

Last MSR was $425.

WHITETAIL CARBINE/RIFLE - .50 or .54 cal. flintlock or perc., 21 (carbine) or 26 in. octagon to round barrel, color case hardened hammer and lock, single trigger, adj. sights, 5.75 lbs. New 1993.

		$170	$125	$100			

Last MSR was $240.

Add $10 for flintlock.
Add $60 for synthetic stock and stainless steel barrel.

RIFLES: IN-LINE IGNITION

T93 CARBINE/RIFLE - .50 cal. perc., 21 (carbine) or 28 in. round barrel, adj. sights, black furniture, modern hunting rifle style, approx. 8 lbs. Disc. 1993.

		$250	$210	$170			

Last MSR was $430.

Subtract $160 for Sporter Model.

BUCKHUNTER/BUCKHUNTER PRO - .50 or .54 cal. perc., 24 in. tapered round blue barrel, three way safety, adj. fiber optic sights, Buckhunter Pro Model was available with all-weather camo stock and nickel finish, 7 lbs. 4 oz. Disc. 2001.

		$135	$115	$95			

Last MSR was $149.

Add $10 for nickel finish.
Add $40 for Buckhunter Pro models.
Add $70 for Buckhunter Pro w/camo stock with nickel finish.

E-BOLT 209 BOLT-ACTION - .45 and .50 cal. perc., #209 primer ignition, 22 in. blue or nickel barrel, fully adj. fiber optic sights, all-weather black synthetic, AW (all-weather) synthetic Break-Up, and AW (all-weather) Advantage Timber stock, 6 lbs. 5 oz. Mfg. 2002 only.

		$150	$135	$120			

Last MSR was $169.

Add $10 for nickel barrel.

GRADING	100%	98%	95%	90%	80%	70%	60%

Add $50 for Mossy Oak Break-Up stock.
Add $60 for High Definition Advantage Timber stock.

EVOLUTION - .50 or .54 cal. perc., #209 primer ignition, bolt action, 24 in. blue, nickel, or stainless steel (fluted w/screw-on muzzle brake) round tapered barrel, 1:28 or 1:48 (.54 cal.) in. twist, Tru-Glo adj. fiber optic sights, drilled and taped for scope, all-weather black, Mossy Oak Break-Up, or High Definition Advantage Timber synthetic, beech, or walnut X-Wood stock, sling swivel studs, recoil pad, 6.75-7.5 lbs. New 2003.

MSR	$219	$195	$170	$150

Add $20 for nickel barrel.
Add $80 for stainlees steel fluted barrel w/screw-on muzzel brake.
Add $60 for beech stock.
Add $80 for walnut X-Wood stock (beech stock dipped in walnut finishing film).
Add $40 for High Definition Advantage Timber stock.
Add $30-$40 for Mossy Oak Break-Up stock.

✳ *Evolution LD* - .45 or .50 cal. perc., #209 primer ignition, bolt action, 26 in. blue or nickel fluted round tapered barrel with or without porting, 1:28 or 1:20 (.45 cal.) in. twist, Tru-Glo adj. fiber optic sights, drilled and taped for scope, all-weather black, Mossy Oak Break-Up, or High Definition Advantage Timber synthetic stock, sling swivel studs, recoil pad, 7 lbs. New 2003.

MSR	$239	$215	$185	$150

Add $10 for ported barrel.
Add $20 for nickel barrel.
Add $20 for High Definition Advantage Timber stock.
Add $30 for Mossy Oak Break-Up stock.

✳ *Evolution Premier* - .50 cal. perc., #209 primer ignition, bolt action, 26 in. blue or stainless steel round fluted and ported barrel, 1:28 in. twist, Williams steel adj. fiber optic sights, drilled and taped for scope, all-weather black or High Definition Advantage Timber synthetic, walnut X-Wood, or brown laminated stock, sling swivel studs, recoil pad, 7-7.75 lbs. New 2003.

MSR	$269	$249	$215	$175

Add $60 for walnut X-Wood stock (beech stock dipped in walnut finishing film).
Add $90 for (HD) High Definition Advantage Timber stock.
Add $170 for brown laminated stock.

LIGHTNING BOLT - .50 or .54 cal. perc., #209 primer ignition, 24 in. round barrel, fully adj. fiber optic sights, stainless steel breech plug, bolt-action, composite stock, blue, nickel, or stainless steel fluted barrel with muzzle brake (new 2000), camo finish stock, 6 lbs. 8 oz. to 7 lbs. 12 oz. Mfg. 1997-2002.

	$180	$150	$120

Last MSR was $199.

Add $130 for fluted stainless steel barrel with muzzle brake.
Add $40 for all-weather walnut stock. New 2002.
Add $30 for blue barrel with muzzle brake.
Add $160 for all-weather synthetic/Break-up with fluted stainless steel barrel and muzzle brake.
Add $80 for stainless steel barrel.
Add $20 for nickel barrel.

LIGHTNING LIGHTWEIGHT BOLT-ACTION - .50 cal. perc., #209 primer ignition, 21 in. blue or nickel fluted barrel, fully adj. fiber optic sights, all-weather Spider Web pattern composite stock, or Mossy Oak Break-Up stock, 6 lbs. 5 oz. Mfg. 2000-02.

	$195	$160	$125

Last MSR was $219.

Add $10 for nickel barrel.
Add $40 for Mossy Oak Break-Up stock.

GRADING	100%	98%	95%	90%	80%	70%	60%

LIGHTNING LD BOLT-ACTION - .45 and .50 (new 2002) cal. perc., #209 primer ignition, 26 in. blue or nickel fluted barrel, fully adj. fiber optic sights, all-weather synthetic stock, all-weather synthetic Break-Up (New 2002), and High Definition Advantage Timber stock, 7 lbs. Disc. 2002.

	100%	98%	95%
	$215	$190	$175

Last MSR was $239.

Add $10 for nickel barrel.
Add $40 for Mossy Oak Break-Up stock.
Add $60 for High Definition Advantage Timber stock.

TRACKER 209 - .45 (new 2002) and .50 cal. perc., #209 primer ignition, 22 or 24 (new 2003) in. blue or nickel barrel, fully adj. fiber optic sights, all-weather black synthetic, and all-weather Advantage Timber stock, 6 lbs. 5 oz. New 2001.

MSR	$139	$125	$110	$90

Add $20 for nickel barrel.
Add $30 for Advantage Timber stock.

THUNDER BOLT - .45 or .50 cal. perc., #209 primer ignition, bolt action, 24 in. blue or nickel cylindrical barrel, 1:28 or 1:20 (.45 cal.) in. twist, adj. Lite optic sights, drilled and taped for scope, all-weather black or Advantage Timber synthetic stock, sling swivel studs, recoil pad, 6.75 lbs. New 2003.

MSR	$179	$165	$140	$105

Add $10 for nickel barrel.
Add $30 for Advantage Timber stock.

❋ **Thunder Bolt (Youth Model)** - .50 cal. perc., #209 primer ignition, bolt action, 21 in. blue cylindrical barrel, 1:28 in. twist, adj. Lite optic sights, drilled and taped for scope, all-weather black synthetic stock, sling swivel studs, recoil pad, 6. lbs. New 2003.

MSR	$179	$165	$140	$105

SHOTGUNS: IN-LINE IGNITION

BUCKHUNTER MODEL - 12 ga. perc., 24 in. round barrel, bead sight, blackened furniture, composite black or camo stock, 6.25 lbs. Disc.

	100%	98%	95%
	$275	$230	$185

Last MSR was $313.

Add $40 for Treestand or Advantage camo stock.

BUCKHUNTER PRO - 12 ga. perc., 24 in. tapered round blue barrel with full choke, 3 way safety, bead sight, 6 lbs. 6 oz. Disc.

	100%	98%	95%
	$225	$190	$150

Last MSR was $248.

Add $44 for Comp/Advantage model.

TURKEY PRO - 12 ga. perc., #209 primer ignition, 24 in. matte blue or Mossy Oak Break-Up (new 2003) barrel, full choke, bead front sight, all-weather black, Advantage, or Mossy Oak Break-Up (new 2003) stock, 6 lbs .6 oz. New 2001.

MSR	$219	$195	$170	$150

Add $30 for Advantage stock.
Add $110 for Mossy Oak Break-Up barrel and stock.

GRADING	100%	98%	95%	90%	80%	70%	60%

SHOTGUNS: PERCUSSION

FOWLER SHOTGUN - 12 ga., perc., 32 in. octagon to round blue barrel, color case hardened hammer and lock, German silver furniture, checkered walnut stock, 5.5 lbs. Disc.

       $375   **$310**   **$250**

Last MSR was $430.

SINGLE BARREL - 12 ga. perc., 32 in. octagon tapering to round barrel, German silver wedge plate, blue furniture, scroll engraving, and polished steel furniture on deluxe version, 4 lbs. Disc. 1994.

       $260   **$225**   **$180**

Last MSR was $315.

Add $85 for deluxe model.

TRAIL GUNS ARMORY

Current importer/distributor located in Conroe, TX. All reproductions and replicas are manufactured by D. Pedersoli Co. Italy. Please refer to the Pedersoli section for current pricing and model information.

U SECTION

UBERTI, A. S.r.l.

Current manufacturer located in Serezzo, Italy, a division of P. Beretta. Previously named Aldo Uberti & Co. until 1999. Currently imported and distributed (beginning 2003) by Cabela's, located in Sidney, NE, Cimarron F.A. & Co, located in Fredricksburg, TX, Dixie Gun Works, located in Union City, TN, E.M.F., located in Santa Ana, CA, Navy Arms, located in Martinsburg, WV, Stoegers Industries located in Accokeek, MD, Taylor's & Co, located in Winchester, VA, and Tristar Sporting Arms, located in N. Kansas City, MO. Previously imported until Dec. 2002 by Uberti USA, located in Lakeville, CT.

Retail prices shown may vary according to retailer.

In 1958, company founder Aldo Uberti became the first Italian black powder manufacturer to build a reproduction Colt black powder pistol. At the time, he was an employee of Beretta, and his wife Gepi (still living), is directly related to the Beretta family. Inspection of the factory records reveals that the first black powder reproduction (1851 Navy) was returned from the proof house on Oct. 14, 1959. Mr. Uberti, who passed away in 1998, began manufacturing reproductions and replicas in quantity for Val Forgett of Navy Arms in 1959, and throughout his career produced all of the original Colt black powder designs. The company was acquired by P. Beretta in 2001.

Please refer to *Colt Blackpowder Reproductions & Replicas—A Collector's & Shooter's Guide* for color pictures of Uberti makes and models listed below. Uberti pistols can be found on pages 61 through 67, and pages 71, 79, and 96.

For more information and current pricing on both new and used A.Uberti S.r.l. firearms, please refer to the 24th Ed. *Blue Book of Gun Values* by S.P. Fjestad (now online also).

REVOLVERS: PERCUSSION

1836-39 PATERSON MODELS - .36 cal. perc., 7.5 in. octagon barrel, hidden trigger design, No. 5 Hoslter model without loading lever, 2 lbs. 9 oz. New 1998.

MSR	$350	$300	$250	$200

Add $40 for model with loading lever.
Add $85 for antique finish.

1847 WALKER - .44 cal. perc., 9 in. barrel, charcoal finish, color case hardened frame, hammer, and loading lever, brass trim, engraved cylinder, 4.4 lbs.

MSR	$305	$275	$225	$175

Add $85 for antique finish.

1848 BABY DRAGOON - .31 cal. perc., 3, 4, or 5 in. barrel, 5 shot, color case hardened frame, hammer, no loading lever, engraved cylinder, 1.4 lbs.

MSR	$255	$225	$195	$165

Add $30 for silver backstrap and trigger guard.
Add $85 for antique finish.

1848 WHITNEYVILLE HARTFORD DRAGOON AND 1ST, 2ND, 3RD MODELS - .44 cal. perc., 6 shot, steel backstrap and trigger guards, color case hardened frame, hammer, and loading lever, 3.9 lbs.

MSR	$285	$250	$215	$180

Add $55 for Whitneyville.
Add $85 for antique finish.

1849 WELLS FARGO - .31 cal. perc., 4 in. octagon barrel, 5 shot, color case hardened frame, hammer, loading lever, brass trim, 1.5 lbs.

MSR	$255	$225	$195	$165

Add $30 for silver backstrap and trigger guard.

1849 POCKET - .31 cal. perc., without loading lever, 4 in. barrel, 5 shot, color case hardened frame, hammer, brass trim, 1.5 lbs.

MSR	$255	$225	$195	$165

GRADING	100%	98%	95%	90%	80%	70%	60%

Add $30 for silver backstrap and trigger guard.

1851 NAVY - .36 cal. perc., 7.5 in. barrel, loading lever, 6 shot roll engraved cylinder, 2.8 lbs. Available with square trigger guard or round trigger guard, and in Leech & Rigdon Confederate version.

	MSR	$235	$205	$175	$150

Add $250 for detachable shoulder stock (must be ordered with revolver for proper fitting).
Add $30 for silver plated backstrap and trigger guard.
Add $15 for "London" Model w/steel backstrap and trigger guard or if cut for stock (3rd Model Navy).
Add $5 for Leech & Rigdon (round barrel) Confederate Navy.

1860 ARMY - .44 cal. perc., 8 in. barrel, 6 shot, loading lever, color case hardened frame, hammer, and loading lever, steel backstrap and brass trigger guard, 2.6 lbs.

	MSR	$255	$225	$195	$165

Add $250 for detachable shoulder stock (must be ordered with revolver for proper fitting).
Add $30 for silver plated backstrap and trigger guard.
Add $5 for fluted cylinder model.
Add $85 for antique finish.
Subtract $10 for brass backstrap and trigger guard.

1861 NAVY - .36 cal. perc., 7.5 in. barrel, color case hardened frame, hammer, and loading lever, 2.5 lbs.

	MSR	$260	$240	$200	$160

Add $30 for silver plated strap and trigger guard.
Add $250 for detachable shoulder stock (must be ordered with revolver for proper fitting).
Add $85 for antique finish.
Subtract $15 for Civilian model with brass backstrap and trigger guard.

1862 POCKET NAVY - .36 cal. perc., 5.5, or 6.5 in. barrel, color case hardened frame, hammer, and loading lever, cylinder, roll engraved cylinder, 1lb. 6 oz.

	MSR	$255	$225	$195	$165

Add $30 for silver plated backstrap and trigger guard.
Add $85 for antique finish.

1862 POLICE - .36 cal. perc., 5.5, or 6.5 in. barrel, color case hardened frame, hammer, and loading lever, semi fluted cylinder, 1lb. 6 oz.

	MSR	$255	$225	$195	$165

Add $30 for silver plated straps and trigger guard.
Add $85 for antique finish.

AUGUSTA CONFEDERATE - .36 cal. perc., 7.5 in. octagon barrel, color case hardened hammer and trigger, all brass frame, engraved cylinder, 2.5-2.75 lbs. Disc.

		$210	$180	$135

Lat MSR was $210.

GRISWOLD AND GUNNISON -.36 or .44 cal. perc., 5.5 or 7.5 in. barrel, similar to Augusta Confederate model, except has round barrel forward of lug, does not have engraved cylinder. Disc. 1994.

		$210	$180	$135

Last MSR was $220.

TEXAS CONFEDERATE DRAGOON - .44 cal. perc., 7.5 in. round barrel, color case hardened frame, hammer, and loading lever, brass trim, "Tucker, Sherrard, and Co.", 4 lbs. Disc. 1994.

		$265	$235	$180

Last MSR was $235.

Add $35 for stainless steel.

GRADING	100%	98%	95%	90%	80%	70%	60%

1858 REMINGTON NEW ARMY
- .44 cal. perc., 8 in. barrel, 6 shot, blue steel, brass trigger guard, 2.6 lbs.

	MSR	$255	$225	$195	$165

Add $35 for adj. sights.
Add $35 for color case hardened frame.
Add $50 for stainless steel model.
Add $85 for antique finish.
Add $130 for target model in stainless steel.

1858 REMINGTON NEW ARMY "MILLENNIUM FINISH"
- .44 cal. perc., 8 in. barrel, 6 shot, matte black fiish, 2.6 lbs. Disc. 2002.

$175	$150	$120

Last MSR was $195.

1858 REMINGTON NEW NAVY
- .36 cal. perc., 7.38 in. octagon barrel, 6 shot, blue frame, 2.5 lbs. Disc. 2002.

$220	$190	$150

Last MSR was $260.

1873 COLT SINGLE ACTION ARMY
- .44 cal. perc., 3.5, 4.75, 5.5 or 7.5 in. barrel, color case hardened frame, walnut grips. A special black powder percussion version of the famous Colt Peacemaker, with a custom-made cylinder designed to use percussion caps. Available in three variations: with brass backstrap and trigger guard; steel backstrap and trigger guard; and Bisley quick draw model with steel backstrap and trigger guard. Optional loading tool and spare cylinder. New 1998. Bisley Model new 2001. All disc. 2002.

$245	$210	$170

Last MSR was $275.

Add $20 for loading tool.
Add $55 for spare cylinder (requires fitting).
Add $25 for steel backstrap and trigger guard.
Add $40 for 3.5 in. model with birdhead grip.
Add $115 for Bisley Model.

REVOLVERS: CARTRIDGE CONVERSIONS

Since these are cartridge firing revolvers converted from black powder reproduction pistols, and require a FFL to transfer, these listings will be moved to the 25th *Edition Blue Book of Gun Values* by S.P. Fjestad after this edition.

COLT 1868 THUER CONVERSION TO 1860 ARMY
- .44 cal. Colt, Thuer conversion ring and cylinder, cartridge loading tool, all other specifications same as 1860 Army. Available 2002 exclusively through Cimarron F.A. Co. Disc. 2002.

$355	$300	$240

Last MSR was $418.

This model requires a special hand loaded round in .44 cal for the Thuer Conversion.

1860 ARMY RICHARDS-MASON CARTRIDGE CONVERSION
- .44 Colt, .44 Russian, 45 Schofield cal., 5.5, 7.5 or 8 in. round barrel, color case hardened frame and hammer, steel backstrap and trigger guard. New 2002. Available exclusively through Cimarron F.A. Co. Disc. 2002.

$400	$340	$275

Last MSR was $469.

1851 NAVY RICHARDS-MASON CARTRIDGE CONVERSION
- .38 Special cal., 5.5 or 7.5 in. octagonal barrel, color case hardened frame and hammer, brass backstrap and trigger guard. New 2002. Available exclusively through Cimarron F.A. Co. Disc. 2002.

$400	$340	$275

Last MSR was $469.

GRADING	100%	98%	95%	90%	80%	70%	60%

1872 OPEN TOP - .38 Colt, .38 S&W Spl., .44 Colt, .44 Russian, or .45 S&W Schofield cal., 5.5 or 7.5 in. round barrel, color case hardened frame and hammer, Navy style brass backstrap and trigger guard, or Army style steel backstrap and trigger guard. New 2000. Available exclusively through Cimarron F.A. Co. Disc. 2002.

| | | | | $400 | $340 | $275 |

Last MSR was $469.

RIFLES: FLINTLOCK & PERCUSSION

HAWKEN RIFLE - .50 or .54 cal. perc., 32 in. octagon barrel, double set triggers, approx. 9 lbs. Disc. 1994.

$405 $355 $270

Last MSR was $535.

1858 REMINGTON REVOLVING CARBINE - .44 cal. perc., 18 in. barrel, 6 shot, blue steel, brass trigger guard.

MSR $395 $350 $300 $250

1866 REVOLVING CARBINE - .44 cal. perc., 18 in. barrel, 6 shot, blue steel, brass trigger guard, walnut stock, 4.6 lbs.

$345 $300 $240

Last MSR was $420.

SANTA FE HAWKEN - .50 or .54 cal. perc., single shot, 32 in. octagon barrel, damascened finish, double set triggers, 9.5 lbs., walnut stock.

$385 $330 $265

Last MSR was $445.

ST. LOUIS RIFLE - .45, .50, .54, or .58 cal. flintlock or perc., color case hardened hammer, lock, and trigger guard, octagon barrel. Disc. 1994.

$345 $280 $210

Last MSR was $265.

Add $25 for .54 and .58 cal. percussion.
Add $15 for flintlock.
Add $30 for 54 cal. flintlock.

SQUIRREL RIFLE - .32 cal. perc. or flintlock, color case hardened hammer and lock, brass trigger guard, 28 in. octagon barrel.

$280 $225 $160

Add $15 for flintlock.

UFDA INC.

Previous manufacturer located in Scottsdale, AZ.

RIFLES: PERCUSSION

TETON RIFLE - .45, .50 cal., 12 ga. or 12 bore (.72 cal.) perc., blue chrommoly steel or stainless steel barrel, straight through ignition, Remington style heavy target action, interchangeable barrels, black or brown laminated stock. Walnut or maple upgrade available, recoil pad.

$700 $600 $500

Last MSR was $834.

Add $100 for walnut or maple stock.
Add $150 for extra barrel.

TETON BLACKSTONE - .50 cal. perc., 26 in. barrel. Same as above but in matte finish stainless steel with black epoxy coated wood stock.

$400 $300 $240

Last MSR was $534.

GRADING	100%	98%	95%	90%	80%	70%	60%

GRAND TETON - .45 or .50 cal. perc., similar to Teton Blackstone, but with 30 in. octagon barrel.

	$800	$680	$560				

Last MSR was $995.

U.S. HISTORICAL SOCIETY

Previous organization which marketed historically significant firearms and black powder reproductions until April, 1994. Located in Richmond, VA. Most firearms were manufactured by the Williamsburg Firearms Manufactory and the Virginia Firearms Manufactory.

On April 1, 1994, the Antique Arms Divison of the U.S. Historical Society was acquired by America Remembers located in Mechanicsville, VA. America Remembers' affiliates include the Armed Forces Commemorative Society, American Heroes & Legends, and the United States Society of Arms and Armor. Issues that were not fully subscribed are now available through America Remembers (please refer to listing in A section).

Please refer to *Colt Blackpowder Reproductions & Replicas—A Collector's & Shooter's Guide* for color pictures of the U.S. Historical Society pistols described below. U.S. Historical Society Colt commemoratives can be found on pages 74, 89, 92, 103, 104, 105, and 106.

The information listed below represents current information up until America Remembers acquired the Antique Arms Division of the U.S. Historical Society.

PISTOLS: LIMITED/SPECIAL EDITIONS

ANDREW JACKSON

* *Silver Edition* - 2,500 mfg.

	$2,100	$1,750	$1,400				

Last MSR was $2,100.

* *Gold Edition* - 100 mfg.

	$5,500	$3,995	$2,750				

Last MSR was $5,500.

PITCAIRN - 900 mfg.

	$2,950	$2,300	$1,750				

Last MSR was $2,950.

THOMAS JEFFERSON - 1,000 mfg.

	$3,500	$2,750	$1,995				

Last MSR was $1,900.

HAMILTON - BURR DUELING PISTOLS - 1,200 mfg. in 1981.

	$3,500	$2,750	$1,995				

Last MSR was $2,995.

WASHINGTON AND LEE FLINTLOCK PISTOLS - .69 cal., flintlock pistols with 9 15/16 in. barrels, burl walnut stocks with sterling silver fittings, engraved silver plated lock plates, trigger guard, and sideplate, firing capability, cased with accessories, limited issue of 1,000 in 1989.

	$2,700	$2,150	$1,650				

Last MSR was $2,700.

GEORGE WASHINGTON - includes pair of flintlocks, 975 mfg. 1976, cased, issue price was initially $3,000, and ended at $3,500.

	$4,250	$3,400	$2,450				

HENRY DERINGER PISTOL SET - .41 cal. perc., reproduction of Deringer's famous pistol. Available with sterling silver mounts (1,000 pair mfg. issue price $1,900), 14Kt. gold mounted (100 pair mfg.-$2,700 issue price), precious gem stone mounted (only 5 pair mfg.-$25,000 issue price). Mfg. 1978.

GRADING	100%	98%	95%	90%	80%	70%	60%

* **Silver mounted**

  $2,500 $1,750 $1,000

* **14Kt. gold mounted**

  $7,500 $5,000 $3,000

* **18Kt. jewel mounted** - too limited a supply for price evaluation.

REVOLVERS: LIMITED/SPECIAL EDITIONS

TEXAS PATERSON EDITION - reproduction of the famous Colt folding trigger model mfg. in Paterson, NJ. This hand engraved example with genuine mother-of-pearl stocks and silver bands around the barrel muzzle, cylinder and recoil shield, was a reproduction of an original Paterson, serial No. 755. Delivered in a two-drawer display case with a copy of "Paterson Colt Pistol Variations" by Philip R. Phillips and R.L. Wilson. Edition limited to 1,000 examples starting in 1988.

$2,500 $1,900 $1,450

Last MSR was $2,500.

MERRILL LINDSAY WHITNEYVILLE HARTFORD DRAGOON - .44 cal. Dragoon with gold leaf highlights on the roll engraved cylinder scene, and the legend "1915 MERRILL LINDSAY 1985" along the barrel commemorating the great author and historian, who wrote the book *One Hundred Great Guns*. Color case hardened frame, backstrap, hammer and loading lever, gold plated trigger guard. Edition of 500 cased revolvers produced in 1987.

$1,685 $1,480 $1,150

SAM HOUSTON WALKER - .44 cal., reproduction of the Colt Walker, 9 in. barrel, extensive gold etching on highly polished blue surface, smooth walnut stocks with S. Houston medallions, cased with accessories. 2,500 mfg.

$2,300 $2,000 $1,575

Last MSR was $2,300.

TEXAS RANGER DRAGOON - .44 cal., features silver plated cylinder, trigger guard, and gripstraps, color case hardened frame and loading lever, multiple 24Kt. etchings on barrel and frame front, cased with accessories, 66 oz. 1,000 mfg. in 1990 only.

$1,585 $1,050 $795

Last MSR was $1,585.

TOWER OF LONDON COL. SAM COLT DRAGOON - .44 cal., exact reproduction of the Second Model Dragoon, 7.5 in. barrel, hand engraved, Texas Ranger cylinder scene, one-piece adj. walnut grip with inscribed sterling silver plaque, case hardened frame, hammer, loading lever, and rammer, cased with accessories, limited issue of 1,000 in 1989.

$2,450 $1,950 $1,500

Last MSR was $2,450.

ROBERT E. LEE MODEL 1851 NAVY - .36 cal. only, reproduction of the 1851 Navy Colt, extensive gold etching, cylinder scene portrays historical Civil War events, walnut stocks with Robert E. Lee medallion, cased with accessories, 41 oz. 2,500 mfg. during 1984.

$2,100 $1,900 $1,450

Last MSR was $2,100.

MONITOR AND VIRGINIA MODEL 1851 NAVY REVOLVER - .44 cal., issued to commemorate the Civil War naval battle between the USS Monitor and Confederate Virginia, features gold etchings on barrel, frame, and Monitor/Virginia battle scene on cylinder, cased, 41 oz. 1,000 mfg. in 1991.

$1,250 $875 $500

Last MSR was $1,250.

GRADING	100%	98%	95%	90%	80%	70%	60%

STONEWALL JACKSON MODEL 1851 REVOLVER - .36 cal., reproduction of Colt's Model 1851 Navy, elaborate gold etching on frame and barrel, walnut grip with medallion, cased with sterling medallion and silver plated powder flask. 1988 release. 2,500 total mfg.

$2,100 $1,650 $1,250

Last MSR was $2,100.

JEFFERSON DAVIS 1851 NAVY REVOLVER - .36 cal., extensive Nimschke style engraving on barrel, loading lever, frame, and trigger, case hardened frame with silver plated brass backstrap and trigger guard, includes engraved, silver plated detachable shoulder stock, cased with accessories, 41 oz. 1,000 mfg. in 1990 only.

$2,750 $1,850 $1,250

Last MSR was $2,750.

MODEL 1851 U.S. NAVY REVOLVER - .36 cal., 7.5 in. octagon barrel, features gold etched cylinder and other embellishments, brass trigger guard and backstrap plated with 24Kt. gold, 41 oz. 1,000 mfg. in 1988 only.

$1,250 $875 $500

Last MSR was $1,250.

MODEL 1851 PONY EXPRESS REVOLVER - .36 cal., features gold plated cylinder scene, other scroll work, and barrel address, walnut grips, cased. 1,000 mfg. beginning 1992.

$1,650 $1,150 $850

Last MSR was $1,650.

U.S. CAVALRY MODEL 1860 ARMY - .44 cal., reproduction of the Colt Model 1860, stag grips, gold etched cylinder scene, cased with brass buckle. 975 manufactured 1988.

$1,450 $1,050 $800

Last MSR was $1,450.

FREDERIC REMINGTON MODEL 1860 ARMY REVOLVER - .44 cal., issued to commemorate Frederic Remington's 100th anniversary as an associate of the National Academy of Design, features gold etched barrel, cylinder (with 5 panels), trigger, frame, and gripstraps, cased with accessories, 42 oz. 1,000 mfg. in 1990 only.

$1,500 $1,000 $775

Last MSR was $1,500.

BUFFALO BILL CENTENNIAL MODEL 1860 ARMY - .44 cal., reproduction of the Colt Model 1860, bonded ivory stocks, extensive gold etchings portraying various wild west scenes, bonded ivory powder flask, brass accessories, cased. 2,500 mfg. 1983.

$1,950 $1,450 $1,100

Last MSR was $1,950.

BAT MASTERSON MODEL 1860 ARMY - .44 cal., original roll engraved pattern on cylinder, walnut grips, blue barrel decorated in 24Kt. gold. 2,500 mfg. beginning 1991.

$1,250 $875 $500

Last MSR was $1,250.

GETTYSBURG 1860 ARMY - .44 cal., blue steel with gold plated cylinder scene, backstraps, and other small parts, walnut grips, cased with belt buckle. 1,863 mfg. beginning 1994.

$1,270 $885 $500

Last MSR was $1,270.

Add $145 for case.

GRADING	100%	98%	95%	90%	80%	70%	60%

SECRET SERVICE MUSEUM EDITION - fully checkered ivory grips, silver plate, gold plate, and royal blue finish, fully engraved, includes walnut presentation case, silver plated powder flask, screwdriver, Secret Service badge, and key. 500 mfg. beginning 1988.

$995 $800 $650

Last MSR was $1,250.

REVOLVERS: MINIATURE, LIMITED/SPECIAL EDITIONS

1847 WALKER PRESIDENTIAL EDITION - miniature reproduction of 1847 Colt Walker, color case hardened receiver, all parts operational, sterling silver grips, full coverage engraving, cased. 1,500 mfg. starting 1990.

$1,575 $1,100 $825

Last MSR was $1,575.

* *1847 Walker Classic Edition* - similar to Presidential Edition, except has walnut grips and frame is not engraved, cased. 1,500 mfg. starting 1990.

$625 $450 $325

Last MSR was $625.

1851 NAVY PRESIDENTIAL EDITION - miniature reproduction of 1851 Navy Colt, color case hardened receiver, all parts operational, mother-of-pearl grips, full coverage engraving, cased. 1,500 mfg. starting 1988.

$1,575 $1,100 $825

Last MSR was $1,575.

* *1851 Classic Edition* - similar to Presidential Edition, except has walnut grips and cylinder is roll engraved, cased. 3,500 mfg. starting 1986.

$525 $400 $295

Last MSR was $525.

1860 ARMY PRESIDENTIAL EDITION - miniature reproduction of 1860 Army Colt, color case hardened engraved receiver and barrel, roll engraved cylinder scene, all parts operational, ivory grips, cherry cased. 1,500 mfg. starting 1988.

$1,575 $1,200 $875

Last MSR was $1,575.

* *1860 Classic Edition* - similar to Presidential Edition without engraving, except has rosewood grips, cased. 3,500 mfg. starting 1988.

$525 $400 $295

Last MSR was $525.

1861 NAVY PRESIDENTIAL EDITION - miniature reproduction of 1861 Navy Colt, color case hardened engraved receiver and barrel, roll-engraved cylinder scene, all parts operational, includes detachable shoulder stock, cased. 1,500 mfg. starting 1990.

$1,500 $1,150 $850

Last MSR was $1,500.

* *1861 Navy Classic Edition* - similar to Presidential Edition without engraving, cased. 1,500 mfg. starting 1990.

$750 $550 $395

Last MSR was $750.

RIFLES: LIMITED/SPECIAL EDITIONS

CONFEDERATE COMMEMORATIVE RIFLE - replicates Cook & Brother original 1861 Model Carbine, 1,500 mfg. during 1986, includes wood wall mount and velvet sleeved bag, 24Kt. gold plating and accenting.

$1,750 $1,450 $995

Last MSR was $1,900.

W SECTION

WHITE RIFLES, LLC

Current manufacturer located in Orem, UT begging 2001.

During 2001, Split Fire Sporting Goods, LLC name was changed to White Rifles LLC. Split Fire was the exclusive distributor for all White models manufactured by Muzzleloading Technologies, Inc. For information on White Rifles models produced prior to 1997, refer to the White Muzzleloading Systems section.

RIFLES: IN-LINE IGNITION

BLACKTAIL HUNTER - .504 cal. perc., standard or magnum #11 percussion caps in-line ignition, 22 in. straight tapered black Teflon coated stainless steel barrel, 1:24 in. twist, black laminate laser engraved deer scene or elk scene stock, silent double safety system, adj. White/Marble/Tru-Glo FiberOptic steel hunting sights, recoil pad, sling swivel studs, 7.7 lbs.

MSR	$600	$545	$475	$395

ELITE HUNTER - .451 or .504 cal. perc., standard or magnum #11 percussion caps in-line ignition, 24 in. straight tapered stainless steel barrel, 1:24 (.451 cal.) or 1:24 in. twist, black composite or laminate stock, silent rotary double safety system, adj. White/Marble/Tru-Glo FiberOptic steel hunting sights, recoil pad, sling swivel studs, 8.6 lbs.

MSR	$600	$545	$475	$395

THUNDER BOLT - .451 or .504 cal. perc., #209 primer in-line ignition, bolt-action, 26 in. straight tapered stainless steel barrel, 1:24 (.451 cal.) or 1:24 in. twist, black composite or laminate stock, silent rotary double safety system, adj. White/Marble/Tru-Glo FiberOptic steel hunting sights, recoil pad, sling swivel studs, 9.3 lbs. New 2002.

MSR	$700	$625	$565	$455

ULTRA-MAG - .504 cal. perc., standard or magnum #11 percussion caps and #209 primer in-line ignition, 26 in. straight tapered black Teflon coated stainless steel barrel, 1:24 in. twist, black composite or laminate stock, silent double safety system, adj. White/Marble/Tru-Glo FiberOptic steel hunting sights, recoil pad, sling swivel studs, 8.3 lbs. New 2003. Available exclusively through Sportsman's Warehouse.

MSR	$399	$355	$315	$255

WHITETAIL ADVENTURER - .451 or .504 cal. perc., standard or magnum #11 percussion caps and #209 primer in-line ignition, 26 in. straight tapered stainless steel barrel, 1:24 (.451 cal.) or 1:24 in. twist, black laminate thumbhole stock, silent rotary double safety system, adj. White/Marble/Tru-Glo FiberOptic steel hunting sights, recoil pad, sling swivel studs, 8.3 lbs. New 2003.

MSR	$800	$725	$645	$525

WHITETAIL HUNTER - .451 or .504 cal. perc., standard or magnum #11 percussion caps in-line ignition, 22 in. straight tapered stainless steel barrel, 1:24 (.451 cal.) or 1:24 in. twist, black composite or laminate stock, silent double safety system, adj. White/Marble/Tru-Glo FiberOptic steel hunting sights, recoil pad, sling swivel studs, 7.7 lbs.

MSR	$450	$395	$350	$285

WHITETAIL ODYSSEY - .451 (new 2003) or .504 cal. perc., standard or magnum #11 percussion caps and #209 primer (new 2003) in-line ignition, 24 in. straight tapered Christiansen Arms carbon fiber wrapped stainless steel barrel, 1:24 (.451 cal.) or 1:24 in. twist, glass bedded action, black laminate laser engraved Whitetail deer or Elk scene thumbhole stock, silent double safety system, drilled and tapped for scope or peep sight mounting, recoil pad, sling swivel studs, 6.7 lbs.

MSR	$1,200	$1,075	$950	$795

SHOTGUNS: IN-LINE IGNITION

WHITE'S ORIGINAL SHOTGUN - 12 ga., perc., 25 in. straight tapered stainless steel barrel, interchangeable choke tubes, custom vent rib with high visibility front bead sight, in-line ignition, black laminate or black wood stock with recoil pad and sling swivel studs, double safety system, fully-adjustable custom trigger, 5.75 lbs. Disc. 2002.

	$315	$280	$255

Last MSR was $350.

TOMINATOR SHOTGUN - 12 ga., perc., standard or magnum #11 percussion caps in-line ignition, 25 in. straight tapered blue barrel, interchangeable choke tubes, custom vent rib with high visibility front bead sight, black laminate

GRADING	100%	98%	95%	90%	80%	70%	60%

stock with recoil pad and sling swivel studs, double safety system, 6 lbs. New 2003.

MSR	$350	$315	$280	$235

WHITE MUZZLELOADING SYSTEMS

Previous manufacturer located in Roosevelt, Utah until 1997.

All White Muzzleloading Systems models were discontinued during 1997. Manufacture and distribution was changed to Muzzleloading Technologies, Inc. until 2000 when Split Fire Sporting Goods, LLC picked up distribution. During 2001 Split Fire Sporting Goods, LLC changed their name to White Rifles, LLC. For current information refer to White Rifles, LLC.

PISTOLS: IN-LINE IGNITION

CHAMPION - .41, .45, or .50 cal. perc., stainless steel barrel, SC Series lock, composite stock.

	$270	$215	$165

Last MSR was $300.

JAVELINA - .45 or .50 cal. perc., G series "Insta-Fire" in-line ignition, 14 in. barrel, double safeties, match grade trigger, adj. sights, unique two handed black composite stock.

	$425	$370	$290

Last MSR was $500.

RIFLES: IN-LINE IGNITION

BISON - .50 or .54 cal. perc., G Series "Insta-Fire" in-line ignition action, 22 in. slightly tapered non-glare blue bull barrel, fully adj. open hunting sights, drilled and tapped for scope, hardwood stock, 6.5 lbs. New 1993.

	$300	$250	$200

Last MSR was $400.

Add $50 for older model with black composite stock.

GRAND ALASKAN/GRAND ALASKAN II - .54 cal. perc., W Series "Insta Fire" in-line ignition, 24 in. stainless steel bull barrel, stainless steel hardened nipple, green laminate stock, 7.75 lbs.

	$610	$510	$410

Last MSR was $700.

ORIGINAL 68 - .45 or .50 cal. perc., W Series in-line ignition action, 24 in. round tapered blue barrel, fully adj. hunting sights, drilled and tapped for scope, black composite stock, 7.75 lbs. Mfg. 1993 only, very limited production. Disc. 1994.

	$600	$500	$400

Last MSR was $600.

This model may have more value as a collectible due to its limited production.

PRO HUNTER STAINLESS STEEL - .41, .45, or .50 cal. perc., stainless steel tapered barrel, bolt action styling, black composite or laminated stock.

	$575	$475	$350

Last MSR was $660.

Add $20 for black laminated stock.

SPORTING RIFLE - .41, .45 (.451), or .50 (.504) cal. perc., super nipple "Insta-Fire" ignition, 26 in. straight tapered barrel, GR (Green River) Series sidelock with half-cock, Manton style hooked breech, checkered crotchwood English styled composite stock, non-glare hunter's blue, 8.75 lbs. Mfg. 1994-97.

	$500	$430	$345

Last MSR was $600.

SUPER 91 - .410, .451 and .504 caliber, perc., W Series in-line ignition, "Insta-Fire" stainless steel hardened nipple, 24 in. barrel, blue steel or #416 stainless steel throughout, cleans with soap and water, walnut or composite stock, approx. 7.75 lbs.

	$480	$410	$340

Last MSR was $600.

GRADING	100%	98%	95%	90%	80%	70%	60%

Add $50 for stainless steel, and $70 for stainless steel with black laminate stock.

* **Super 91 W/Side Swing Safety** - limited mfg., disc. Oct. 1993.

	$700	$600	$500

Last MSR was $700.

This model may have more value as a collectible due to its limited production.

SUPER SAFARI/SUPER SAFARI II - .41, .45 (.451), or .50 (.504) cal. perc., W Series straight-line "Insta-Fire" ignition, 24 in. Magnum tapered barrel, straight pull cocking handle, double safety system, drilled and tapped for scope or receiver sight, full length Mannlicher style black composite stock, non-glare #416 stainless, 7.75 lbs.

$615	$535	$450

Last MSR was $800.

WHITE LIGHTNING - .50 cal. perc., "Insta Fire" in-line ignition, 22 in. tapered stainless steel barrel, recoil pad, adj. sights, black hardwood stock.

$265	$230	$190

Last MSR was $300.

WHITETAIL RIFLE - .410, .451, .504, or .54 cal. perc., "Insta-Fire" in-line ignition, 22 in. bull barrel (blue) tapered (stainless), new G series action, beech stock (blue), composite stock (stainless), 6.5 lbs. Mfg. 1992-97.

$310	$270	$215

Last MSR was $400.

Add $70 for stainless steel.
Add $100 for stainless steel with black laminate stock.
Add $160 for 1 of 1,000 Roger Ragun Signature Series with super sights and super sling factory installed.

* **The Whitetail Bull Barrel** - disc. 1992.

SHOTGUNS: IN-LINE IGNITION

DOMINATOR - 12 ga. perc., "Insta-fire" in-line ignition, 26 in. blue barrel w/vent rib, new BG series action (larger version of G series), interchangeable chokes. Part of the "Ray Eye" signature series – black laminate stock.

$415	$360	$290

Last MSR was $500.

WHITE THUNDER - 12 ga., perc., "Insta-fire" in-line-ignition, 26 in. blue barrel w/vent rib. New BG series action (larger version of G Series), interchangeable chokes, black hardwood stock.

$320	$280	$225

Last MSR was $400.

WILDERNESS RIFLE WORKS/LEMAN RIFLES

Previously manufactured by Wilderness Rifle Works located in Waldron, IN. Previously distributed by Mountain State Muzzle Loading Supplies Inc., Williamstown, WV.
For current information refer to Mowery Gun Works, Inc.

RIFLES: FLINTLOCK & PERCUSSION

CLASSIC - .50 cal. flintlock or perc., copy of early Leman-Lancaster rifle, 35 in. brown octagon barrel, high relief checkering on beautiful curly maple full stock, brass furniture, brown hammer and lock, brass buttplate and trigger guard.

* **Golden Classic**

$695	$600	$500

Last MSR was $750.

* **Silver Classic** - with nickel silver furniture.

$895	$750	$600

Last MSR was $995.

GRADING	100%	98%	95%	90%	80%	70%	60%

CUMBERLAND RIFLE - .32, .36, .40, .45, or .50 cal. flintlock or perc. 39.5 in. octagon brown barrel, brown hammer and lock, brass buttplate and trigger guard, 7.25 lbs. Mfg. 1994-disc.

	$440	$375	$300

Last MSR was $495.

Add $20 for flintlock. Mfg. 1994.

ELKHUNTER RIFLE - .50 or .54 cal. perc., 32 in. octagon brown barrel, brown furniture, hammer and lock, curly maple stock, double set triggers, adj. buckhorn rear sight, 9 lbs.

	$425	$360	$290

Last MSR was $475.

MOUNTAINEER RIFLE - .36, .40, .45, or .50 cal. flintlock or perc., 39 in. octagon brown barrel, brass or brown furniture, hammer and lock, curly maple full stock, double set triggers, adj. buckhorn rear sight, 7.25 to 8 lbs.

	$350	$300	$240

Last MSR was $425.

Add $20 for flintlock.

PLAINS RIFLE - .50 or .54 cal. perc., 32 in. octagon barrel, fancy maple stock, furniture is brass or brown steel, single set double action trigger, 9 lbs. Disc. 1993.

	$350	$300	$240

Last MSR was $495.

PRAIRIE RIFLE - .36, .40, .45, or .50 cal. perc., 32 in. barrel, brass or brown steel furniture, double set triggers, fancy figure maple stock, 8 lbs.

	$375	$315	$245

Last MSR was $425.

SUMMIT RIFLE - .50 or .54 cal. perc., 30 in. octagon barrel, brass or brown steel furniture, single set double action trigger, fancy figure maple stock, 9 lbs. Disc. 1993.

	$350	$300	$240

WINCHESTER MUZZLELOADING

Current trademark of Blackpowder Products, Inc., an importer and distributor located in Norcross, GA beginning 2002.

The Winchester name is licensed to Winchester Muzzleloading, a division of Blackpowder Products, Inc. For more information and current pricing on both new and used Winchester firearms, please refer to the 24th Ed. *Blue Book of Gun Values* by S.P. Fjestad (now online also).

RIFLES: IN-LINE IGNITION

X-150 MAGNUM 209 RIFLE - .45 and .50 cal. 209 primer perc., bolt-action, in-line ignition, 26 in. blue or stainless steel fluted barrel, 1:28 in. twist, stainless steel bolt, solid composite gray or black fleck, HD Advantage Timber or Hardwoods, or Mossey Oak Break-up (new 2003) finish stock, sling swivel studs and Winchester Muzzleloading sling, ventilated recoil pad, adj. metallic fiber optic sights, 8.2 lbs. New 2002.

MSR	$325	$275	$240	$200

Add $30 for black fleck finish stock.
Add $45 for Advantage HD Timber, Hhardwoods, or Mossey Oak Break-Up finish stock.
Add $80 for stainless steel.

APEX MAGNUM 209 RIFLE - .45 and .50 cal. 209 primer perc., swing action breech, in-line ignition, 30 in. blue or stainless steel fluted barrel, 1:28 in. twist, solid composite black fleck, or Mossey Oak Break-Up finish stock, sling swivel studs and Winchester Muzzleloading sling, ventilated recoil pad, adj. metallic fiber optic sights, 8.4 lbs. New 2003.

MSR	$340	$295	$250	$210

Add $50 for Mossey Oak Break-Up finish stock.
Add $80 for stainless steel.

Colt Black Powder
2nd Generation Serialization

Model No.	Serial # Range	Total Prod.	Prod. Began	Prod. Ended
MODEL 1851 NAVY				
C-1121	4201 - 25100	20900	1971	1978
C-1122	As above but at higher range of numbers			1978
		—	—	1978
MODEL 1851 NAVY, R. E. LEE				
C-9001	251REL - 5000REL	4750	—	1971
MODEL 1851 NAVY, U. S. GRANT				
C-9002	251USG - 5000USG	4750	—	1971
MODEL 1851 GRANT-LEE PAIR				
C-9003	01GLP - 250GLP	250	—	1971
3rd MODEL DRAGOON				
C-1770	20801 - 208 Prototype	25	1974	1978
	20901 - 24501	3601		
C-1770MN	S/N's As Above	20	1984	1984
MODEL 1851 NAVY				
F-1100	24900 - 29150	4250	5/80	10/81
F-1101	S/N's As Above W/Blank Cylinders	300	10/81	11/81
F-1110	29151S - 29640S Stainless Steel	489	6/82	10/82
MODEL 1860 ARMY				
F-1200	201000 - 212835 Rebated Cylinder	7593	11/78	11/82
F-1200EBO	S/N's As Above Butterfield	500	1979	1979
F-1200LNK	S/N's As Above Electroless Nickel	—	—	—
F-1200MN	S/N's As Above Nickel/Ivory	12	1984	1984
F-1202	S/N's As Above Limited Edition	500	1979	1979
F-1203	207330 - 211250 Fluted Cylinder	2670	7/80	10/81
F-1210	211263S - 212540S Stainless Steel	1278	1/82	4/82
1861 NAVY				
F-1300	40000 - 43165	3166	9/80	10/81

Model No.	Serial # Range	Total Prod.	Prod. Began	Prod. Ended
1862 POCKET NAVY				
F-1400	48000 - 58850 and skip odd no's.	5765	12/79	11/81
F-1400MN	S/N's As Above Nickel/Ivory	25	1984	1984
F-1401	S/N's As Above Limited Edition	500	1979	1980
1862 POCKET POLICE				
F-1500	49000 - 57300 and skip even no's.	4801	1/80	9/81
F-1500MN	S/N's As Above Nickel/Ivory	25	1984	1984
F-1501	S/N's As Above Limited Edition	500	1979	1980
1847 WALKER				
F-1600	1200 - 4120	2573	6/80	4/82
	32256 - 32500	245	5/81	9/81
1st MODEL DRAGOON				
F-1700	25100 - 34500	3878	1/80	2/82
2nd MODEL DRAGOON				
F-172	S/N's As Above and Mix at Random for 1st, 2nd, & 3rd	2676	1/80	2/82
3rd MODEL DRAGOON				
F-140	S/N's As Above and Mix at Random for 1st, 2nd & 3rd	2856	1/80	2/82
	31401 - 31450	50	10/81	11/81
F-1740EGA	Unkown (Garabaldi Model — "GCA" prefix)	200	1982	1982
BABY DRAGOON				
F-1760	16000 - 17851	1852	2/81	4/81
F-1761	S/N's As Above Limited Edition	500	1979	1980
1860 ARMY				
F-9005	US 001/001 US to US 3025/3025 US Cavalry Commemorative (Two Gun Set)	3025	9/77	1/80
HERITAGE WALKER				
F-9006	01 - 1853	1853	6/80	6/81

ITALIAN YEAR OF MFG. DATE CODES

All Dates Prior to 1943 Have Month and Year (i.e. IXXII = January 1922.) 1944 -1953 = I - IX

Code	Year	Code	Year	Code	Year	Code	Year	Code	Year	Code	Year	Code	Year	Code	Year
X =	1954	XVII =	1961	XXIV =	1968	AA =	1975	AI =	1982	AW =	1989	BH =	1996		
XI =	1955	XVIII =	1962	XXV =	1969	AB =	1976	AL =	1983	AZ =	1990	BI =	1997		
XII =	1956	XIX =	1963	XVI =	1970	AC =	1977	AM =	1984	BA =	1991	BL =	1998		
XIII =	1957	XX =	1964	XXVII =	1971	AD =	1978	AN =	1985	BB =	1992	BM =	1999		
XIV =	1958	XXI =	1965	XXVIII =	1972	AE =	1979	AP =	1986	BC =	1993	BN =	2000		
XV =	1959	XXII =	1966	XXIX =	1973	AF =	1980	AS =	1987	BD =	1994	BP =	2001		
XVI =	1960	XXIII =	1967	XXX =	1974	AH =	1981	AT =	1988	BF =	1995	BS =	2002		

PIETTA SERIALIZATION

Paterson

Year	Ser. Start	Ser. End
1984	1527	1920
1985	1921	1925
1986	1926	1991
1987	1992	2456
1988	2457	2766
1989	2767	3086
1990	2087	3336
1991	3337	3366
1992	3367	3486
1993	3487	3494
1994	3495	3569
1995	none	
1996	3570	3634
1997	3635	4051

1851 Colt Navy

Year	Ser. Start	Ser. End
1986	261770	270638
1987	270639	276146
1988	276147	281728
1989	281729	289217
1990	289218	295460
1991	295461	306404
1992	306405	320700
1993	320701	334122
1994	334123	353229
1995	353230	380047
1996	380048	396921
1997	396922	410579
1998	410579	424560
1999	424561	439794

1851 Navy Deluxe

Year	Ser. Start	Ser. End
1994	000001	001199
1995	001200	001999

1858 Remington New Model Army

Year	Ser. Start	Ser. End
1986	093517	101045
1987	101046	106063
1988	106064	110724
1989	110725	116814
1990	116815	125821
1991	125822	135274
1992	135275	149530

Year	Ser. Start	Ser. End
1993	149531	164614
1994	164615	184656
1995	184657	210677
1996	210678	235809
1997	235810	252133
1998	252134	260849
1999	R260850	R273377

Remington Target Model

Year	Ser. Start	Ser. End
1984	A0001	A0021
1985	A0022	A0255
1986	A0256	A0581
1987	A0582	A1254
1988	A1255	A1552
1989	A1553	A1816
1990	A1817	A2308
1991	A2309	A2608
1992	A2609	A2887
1993	A2888	A3093
1994	A3094	A3318
1995	A3319	A3418
1996	A3419	A3724
1997	A3725	A3893
1998	A3894	A4235

Remington Pocket Revolver

Year	Ser. Start	Ser. End
1997	H00001	H00005
1998	H00006	H001064

1860 Colt Army

Year	Ser. Start	Ser. End
1986	11745	14432
1987	14433	15913
1988	15914	17301
1989	17302	18511
1990	18512	20425
1991	20426	23307
1992	23308	26528
1993	26529	29923
1994	29924	35349
1995	35350	43464
1996	43465	50816
1997	50817	53135
1998	P53136	P57436
1999	P57437	P61353

LeMat

Year	Ser. Start	Ser. End
1985	1	131
1986	132	565
1987	566	1395
1988	1396	2109
	10001	10042
1989	2110	2488
	10043	10094
1990	2489	2719
	10095	10116
1991	10117	10146
1992	10147	10220
1993	10221	10352
1994	10353	10438
1995	10439	11208
1996	none	
1997	11209	12331
1998	L12332	L12764
1999	L12765	L12922

Spiller & Burr

Year	Ser. Start	Ser. End
1987	B0001	B0450
1988	B0451	B0912
1989	none	
1990	B0913	B1547
1991	B1548	B2188
1992	B2189	B2988
1993	B2989	B3288
1994	B3289	B3538
1995	B3539	B4048
1996	B4049	B4258
1997	B4259	B4795
1998	B4796	B4995
1999	B4996	B5195

Dance

Year	Ser. Start	Ser. End
1996	C00001	C00127
1997	C00128	C00233
1999	C00234	C00437

Starr

Year	Ser. Start	Ser. End
1999	G00001	G01508

Colt 1851 Navy
Schematic with Parts Listing

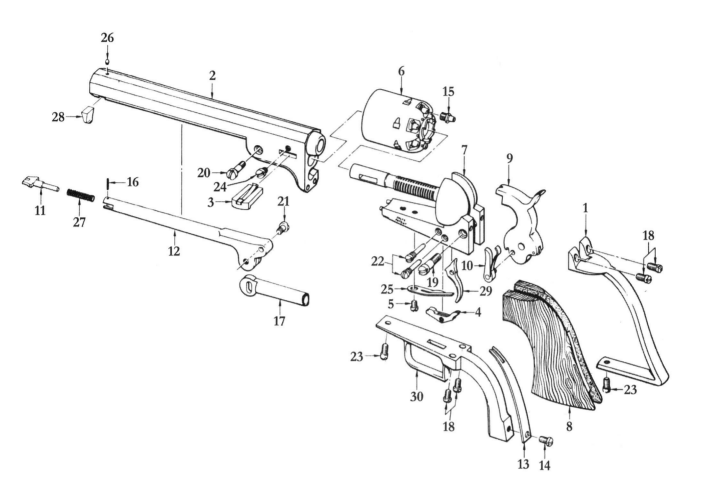

1.	Backstrap	16.	Pin, Latch Retaining
2.	Barrel	17.	Plunger, Loading
3.	Barrel Wedge Assembly	18.	Screw, Backstrap and Guard
4.	Bolt	19.	Screw, Hammer
5.	Bolt Spring Screw	20.	Screw, Loading Lever
6.	Cylinder Assembly	21.	Screw, Plunger
7.	Frame	22.	Screw, Trigger (Bolt & Trigger)
8.	Grip	23.	Screw, Trigger Guard & Butt
9.	Hammer	24.	Screw, Wedge
10.	Hand & Spring Assembly	25.	Sear and Bolt Spring
11.	Latch, Loading Lever	26.	Sight, Front
12.	Lever, Loading	27.	Spring, Latch
13.	Mainspring	28.	Stud, Barrel
14.	Mainspring Screw	29.	Trigger
15.	Nipple	30.	Trigger Guard

Remington Model 1858
Schematic with Parts Listing

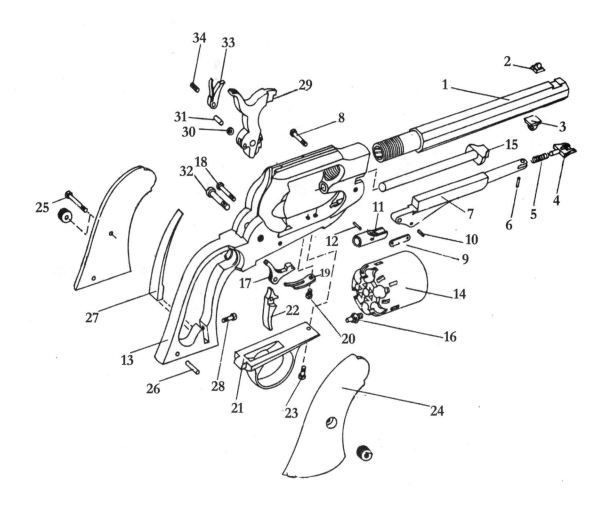

1.	Barrel	18.	Trigger & Stop Screw
2.	Front Sight	19.	Trigger & Stop Spring
3.	Loading Lever Catch	20.	Trigger & Stop Spring Screw
4.	Loading Lever Latch	21.	Trigger Guard
5.	Catch Spring	22.	Trigger
6.	Catch Pin	23.	Trigger Guard Screw
7.	Loading Lever	24.	Grips
8.	Loading Lever Screw	25.	Grip Screw
9.	Link	26.	Grip Pin
10.	Link Pin	27.	Mainspring
11.	Plunger	28.	Mainspring Screw
12.	Plunger Pin	29.	Hammer
13.	Frame	30.	Hammer Roller
14.	Cylinder	31.	Hammer Roller Pin
15.	Cylinder Pin	32.	Hammer Screw
16.	Nipple	33.	Hand & Spring
17.	Cylinder Stop	34.	Hand Screw

GLOSSARY

ACTION

The heart of a black powder arm where the barrel, trigger, and ignition system come together.

BACKSTRAP

Either brass or steel construction, the backstrap is the grip support used to attach the grips frame.

BARREL

Usually of steel construction, the barrel may vary in length and is usually either of octagonal or round design.

BARREL WEDGE

A flat metal piece which goes through the frame, barrel lug (the side of the barrel below the rifled barrel), and center pin to secure the barrel to the frame of a revolver.

BLACK POWDER

The type of propellant used in front loading arms. A superfine mix of potassium nitrate, sulphur, and charcoal. Black powder is extremely corrosive to metal surfaces and guns should be cleaned as soon after firing as possible.

BLUING

The chemical process of artificial oxidation (rusting) applied to metal to attain a dark blue or nearly black appearance.

BULLET MOLD

Usually of brass or steel construction, the bullet mold is used to cast round or conical lead bullets. Melted lead is poured into the mold and after the bullets are formed the mold can be opened and the rounds extracted.

BUTTPAD

Usually a soft rubber or other material attached to the back of the stock to protect the shooters shoulder from recoil (recoil pad).

BUTTPLATE

Usually a metal plate attached to the back of stock for protection of the stock.

BUTTSTOCK

The portion of stock that contacts the shooters shoulder when shooting.

CAMO (CAMOUFLAGE)

A patterned treatment using a variety of colors and patterns to blend into the environment.

CAPPER

Tool used to carry and fit the percussion cap to the nipple.

CASE HARDENING

A method used to strengthen metal parts by heating them up and then plunging the pieces into water. This hardens the outer metal shell.

COLOR CASE HARDENING

A method used to strengthen and apply a finish to metal parts by heating them up in a mixture of charcoal and bone meal and then plunging the pieces into water or other liquid. This hardens the metal and also produces the colorful, mottled finish seen on frames, loading levers, hammers and triggers

COMBINATION TOOL

A tool with a screw driver on one end and a nipple wrench on the other.

CYLINDER

A rotating holder of the primer, propellant and bullet on a revolver.

CYLINDER PIN

The center pin is screwed into the recoil shield and serves as both the threaded shaft upon which the cylinder rotates, and the anchor for the wedge pin securing the barrel.

DISC

A primer holding device patented by Tony Knight of Knights Rifles. The Disc provides a better ignition seal, and therefore helps eliminate both dirt and moisture.

DOUBLE ACTION

On a revolver, the ability to cock and fire the action with a single pull of the trigger.

FLUTED CYLINDER

A cylinder with concave indentations or grooves between the chambers. The fluted and semi-fluted cylinder is still the basic design for revolver cylinder manufactured in the world today.

GLOSSARY

FOREARM

A separate piece (usually made of the same material as the buttstock) forward of the action under the barrel of a two piece stock.

FOREND

The forward portion of a one-piece stock.

FRAME

The main structure around which all other components mount. The frame is usually steel but can be of brass construction as well. The frame houses the hammer and trigger mechanisms, cylinder, and on Colt revolvers the center pin through which the cylinder and barrel are attached.

FRONT SIGHT

Either a bead or blade mounted at the front of the barrel used to pinpoint the target.

GRIP

May be referred to as stock, the portion of a hand arm held on to. Typically made of wood or other material.

HAMMER

The mechanism used to cock the pistol. The hammer may also served as the rear sight on some revolvers when fully cocked, using a "V" notch in the spur that lined up with the front sight. Pulling the trigger released the hammer which came down with the force of the mainspring to strike the percussion cap and ignite the powder charge.

HINGED LOADING LEVER

Original loading lever design which was hinged to the barrel lug. The loading lever pressed the plunger into each cylinder chamber to seat the powder charge and lead ball.

IGNITION

What happens when the propellant is ignited by the priming system.

IN-LINE IGNITION

A recent technical innovation that allows a #209 primer or percussion cap to be placed in-line with the powder and projectile (in most cases, a jacketed sabot) – hence the name. This ignition system enables improved accuracy, easier cleaning, and better lock times.

LAMINATED

The process of gluing layers of wood together.

LOADING LEVER LATCH

The release pin used to retain the loading lever under the barrel when not in use.

LOADING PLUNGER

The back half of the loading lever that usually has a concave face to seat lead balls in the individual chambers.

MAINSPRING

A strip of steel to produce tension against the hammer mechanism. The mainspring is what produces the downward force for the hammer when the trigger is pulled.

NIPPLE

Used to hold the percussion cap, the nipple is a removable (replaceable) threaded tube mounted to the back of each chamber and through which the percussion cap charge is directed into the chamber to ignite the powder.

PRIMER

Small detonating cap that when struck ignites the propellant.

PYRODEX

A propellant designed by the Hodgdon Powder Company for use in muzzle loading and black powder cartridge arms found by a competent gunsmith to be in good shootable condition. Pyrodex has many advantages over black powder – more shots per pound, a much cleaner burn which alleviates fouling and the need to clean between shots, and more consistent pressures and velocities. When loaded as recommended, performance is comparable to black powder. Available in three loose grades – RS (Rifle/Shotgun) – 2F equivalent, P (Pistol) – 3F equivalent, and Select – premium 2F, in addition to three different sized pellets (30, 50, and 60 grain equivalent), in 3 calibers (.44, .50, and .54). Not recommended for flintlocks.

GLOSSARY

REBATED CYLINDER

A modified cylinder which has been increased in dimension half way forward to provide for a larger caliber round, i.e., increasing from .36 caliber to .44 caliber.

RECOIL SHIELD

The upper rounded half of the frame which supports the cylinder pin and houses the hammer and the hand. The recoil shield serves to prevent powder flashback and secure the percussion caps.

RIFLING

Spirally cut grooves cut in the bore of a barrel that stabilizes a bullet in flight.

SABOT

A plastic/synthetic sleeve or cup that surrounds and protects the bullet and barrel when fired. Upon leaving the barrel, it drops off, and lets the bullet continue accurately to its target. Saboted bullets typically allow for a higher rate of twist in the barrel.

SAFETY

A mechanism(s) which prevents ignition of the propellant.

SINGLE ACTION

On a revolver, requires the action to be cocked before it can be fired by a single pull of the trigger.

TRIGGER

The release mechanism to drop the hammer. Also secures the hammer in the half-cock position for loading.

TRIGGER GUARD

Either brass or steel construction, the trigger guard is the lower support of the frame, the anchor for the mainspring, and serves to protect the trigger.

WEDGE SCREW

The screw used to retain the barrel wedge. The wedge must be pulled all the way through the barrel, center pin and barrel lug in order to remove the barrel and cylinder for cleaning. The screw ensures that the wedge does not come completely out.

ABBREVIATIONS

Adj.	Adjustable		MSR	Manufacturers Suggested Retail
cal.	Caliber		No.	Number
DA	Double Action		Oct.	Octagon
DISC.	Discontinued		oz.	Ounce
FFL	Federal Firearms License		PG	Pistol Grip
Ga.	Gauge		perc.	Percussion
HD	High Definition		S/N	Serial Number
in.	Inch		SA	Single Action
Kt.	Karat		SAA	Single Action Army
lbs.	Pounds		SS	Stainless Steel
LOP	Length of Pull		SxS	Side by Side
Mag.	Magnum		Twist	Rate of rifling
Mfg.	Manufactured			

GUIDE TO BLACK POWDER RESOURCES

This all got started a few weeks ago when Steve came into my office and asked me to pick up line three and join him and Doug Evans of Austin & Halleck Gun Crafters in a conversation.

The first question Doug asked was, "John, you shoot black powder, don't you?"

"Yes."

"Well, what do you think of the cleanup?"

"It stinks."

"Have you checked our web site lately?"

Sinking in my chair, I answered, "Not in the last couple of weeks."

"Did you check out the *Muzzleloading Instruction Manual for Big Game Hunting* by Ralph Lemayer, at the bottom of our home page?"

"Well, no."

Doug's last comment was, "Check it out, you might learn something."

Needless to say there was a lot of learning going on, not just about what Austin & Halleck Gun Crafters has to offer for a price, but also what they are giving away for little or nothing (information). We all know how valuable good information is, but how much do we pass by without realizing it was there.

Important tips to remember when visiting web sites, don't rush, take time to read and explore areas like FAQ's (Frequently Asked Questions), Forums, and Links. Many times the new products and important information that can make life easier (cleaning your muzzleloader) is right in front of your face waiting for you to consume.

These web sites all offer products for sale, but just as importantly they offer information we can learn from. Check them out. Like Steve says "Good Information Never Sleeps," and for me it's never too late to learn.

Austin & Halleck Gun Crafters
www.austinhalleck.com
The instruction manual is located on the home page near the bottom, be sure to check out Sales & Marketing for more information and links.

Barnes Bullets, Inc.
www.barnesbullets.com
Bullet Talk, so what makes a good bullet?

Birchwood Casey
www.birchwoodcasey.com
Cleaning and finishing supplies, targets, How to Guides in PDF format.

Cabela's
www.cabelas.com
Too much to list, just cruise.

Cimarron F.A. Co.
www.cimarron-firearms.com
Links on their home page are a must.

Dixie Gun Works Inc.
www.dixiegun.com
Check out the FAQs.

Hodgdon Powder Co.
www.hodgdon.com
Something about Triple Seven and clean up.

Hornady Manufacturing Co.
www.Hornady.com
Safety, something we all can look at again, and Links on their home page are a must.

Markesbery Muzzle Loaders, Inc.
www.markesbery.com
Go to Links for a discussion on projectiles.

Shooters.com
www.shooters.com
This is a web site containing industry links from A-Z. If you can't find it here, good luck.

Thompson/Center Arms
www.tcarms.com
Go to F.Y.I. and Links for more information than can be absorbed in one day.

Traditions Performance Firearms
www.traditionsfirearms.com
Links and Tips are both full of good information.

White Rifles LLC
www.whiterifles.com
The links are a must, information on organizations, gear, and hunting just to get started.

TRADEMARK INDEX

The listings below represent the most up-to-date information currently available regarding black powder manufacturers (both domestic and international), trademarks, importers, distributors, (when applicable), to assist you in obtaining additional information from these companies or individuals. Most manufacturers of cartridge conversion and Open Top revolvers have also been included, these will be moved to the 25th Ed. *Blue Book of Gun Values* by S.P. Fjestad beginning with the next edition. Web site and email listings are provided whenever possible. More companies are offering on-line access about their products and it pays to surf the net!

If parts are needed for older, discontinued makes and models (even though the manufacturer/trademark is current), it is recommended you contact either the Numerich Gun Parts Corp. located in West Hurley, NY, or Jack First, Inc. located in Rapid City, SD for domestic availability and prices. For current manufacturers, it is recommended that you contact an authorized warranty repair center or stocking gun shop – unless a company/trademark has an additional service/parts listing.

In Canada, please refer to the Bomac Gunparts Ltd. listing. Remember, most of the people you contact for customer service questions or parts/service will probably be busy – have patience and respect their time.

As this book went to press, the information listed below represents the most up-to-date and accurate listings available. Things change every day in this industry, and a phone/fax number that is current today could be disconnected tomorrow. International fax/phone numbers may require additional overseas and country/city coding. If you should require additional assistance in "tracking" any of the current black powder manufacturers, distributors, or importers listed in this publication, please contact us and we will try to help you regarding these specific requests.

AMERICA REMEMBERS
10226 Timber Ridge Drive
Ashland, VA 23005
Phone No.: 804 550-9616
Fax No.: 804-550-9603
Web site: www.americaremembers.com
Email: America.remembers@verizon.net

AMERICAN HISTORICAL FOUNDATION, THE
1142 W. Grace St.
Richmond, VA 23220
Phone No.: 804-368-8080
Fax No.: 804-359-4895
Web site: www.ahfrichmond.com
Email: ahfrichmond@aol.com

AWA INTERNATIONAL, INC.
American Western Arms, Inc.
1450 Southwest 10th Street
Units 3 & 4B
Del Ray Beach, FL 33444-1264
Phone No.: 877 292-4867
Fax No.: 561-330-0881
Web site: www.awaguns.com
Email: info@awaguns.com
American Western Arms, Inc. Italy - srl
Branch Office
Via De Gusperi
1-25013 Carpenedolo (BS) ITALY
Fax No.: 011-390-309966322

ARM SPORT LLC
Colt and Remington cartridge conversions
P.O. Box 254
Eastlake, CO 80614
Phone No.: 303-451-7212
Web site: www.armsportllc.com
Email: RLMillington@armsportllc.com

ARMI SAN PAOLO S.r.l.
Please refer to Euroarms Italia S.r.l. listing.

ARMI SPORT SNC DI CHIAPPA SILVIA & C.
Importer - see Taylor's & Co. listing
Factory
Via Fornaci 66
25131 Brescia ITALY
Fax No.: 011-39-30-358-0109
Web site: www.armisport.com
Email: info@armisport.com

AUSTIN & HALLECK GUN CRAFTERS
2150 S. 950 E.
Provo, UT 84606-6258
Phone No.: 801-371-0412
Toll Free: 800-821-5783
Fax No.: 801-374-9998
Web site: www.austinhalleck.com
Email: ray@austinhalleck.com

BEAUCHAMP & SONS (dba FLINTLOCKS, ECT.)
Please refer to the Flintlocks, Etc. listing.

BERETTA, PIETRO
Importer - Beretta U.S.A. Corp
17601 Beretta Drive
Accokeek, MD 20607
Phone No.: 301-283-2191
Fax No.: 301-283-0435
Web site: www.berettausa.com
Factory
Fabbrica d'Armi Pietro Beretta S.p.A.
Via Pietro Beretta 18
25063 Gardone, Val Trompia
Brescia, ITALY
Fax No.: 011-39-30-8347421
Web site: www.beretta.it

BROWNING
Administrative Headquarters
One Browning Place
Morgan, UT 84050-9326
Phone No.: 801-876-2711
Sales Information No.: 800-234-2045
Product Service No.: 800-333-3288
Fax No.: 801-876-3331
Web site: www.browning.com
Browning Parts and Service
3005 Arnold Tenbrook Rd.
Arnold, MO 63010
Fax No.: 800-817-4755 (Parts only)

CABELA'S INC.
One Cabela Dr.
Sidney, NE 69160
Phone No.: 800-237-4444
Fax No.: 800-496-6329
Web site: www.cabelas.com

CHATTAHOOCHEE BPA
1795 Ivey Trace
Cummings, GA 30041
Phone No.: 770-889-3711
Fax No.: 770-889-8134

CHERRY'S
Secondary Market Colt Blackpowder Collectibles
3402-A West Wendover Avenue
P.O. Box 8768
Greensboro, NC 27419
Phone No.: 336-854-4182
Fax No.: 336-854-4184
Web site: www.cherrys.com
Email: fineguns@cherrys.com

CIMARRON, F.A. CO., INC.
105 Winding Oaks
Fredericksburg, TX 78624-0906
Phone No.: 830-997-9090
Fax No.: 830-997-0802
Web site: www.cimarron-firearms.com
Email: cimarron@fbg.net

COLT'S MANUFACTURING CO., INC.
2nd Generation (discontinued) & Custom Guns

P.O. Box 1868
Hartford, CT 06144-1868
Phone No.: 800-962-COLT
Fax No.: 860-244-1449
Web site: www.colt.com

CONNETICUT VALLEY ARMS (CVA)
Division of Blackpowder Products, Inc.

5988 Peachtree Corners East
Norcross, GA 30071
Phone No.: 770-449-4687
Fax No.: 770-242-8546
Web site: www.cva.com
Email: info@cva.com

DALY, CHARLES: CURRENT MFG.
Importer - See K.B.I., Inc. listing.

DAY, LEONARD
Handcrafted reproductions of flintlock and swivel barrel pistols and longrifles

3 Kings Highway,
West Hampton, MA 01027
Phone No.: 413-527-9627

DEER CREEK RIFLE WORKS
Refer to Mowrey Gun Works, Inc.

DIXIE GUN WORKS

P.O. Box 130
Hwy. 51 South
Union City, TN 38261
Phone No.: 901-885-0700
Fax No.: 901-885-0440
Web site: www.dixiegunworks.com

E.M.F. COMPANY
Reproductions of Colt black powder pistols

1900 E. Warner Ave., Suite 1-D
Santa Ana, CA 92705
Phone No.: 949-261-6611
Fax No.: 949-756-0133
Web site: www.emf-company.com
Email: sales@emf-company.com

EUROARMS ITALIA S.r.l.
Importer - Euroarms of America

208 East Piccadilly Street
P.O. Box 3277
Winchester, VA 22604
Phone No.: 540-662-1863
Fax No.: 504-662-4464
Web site: www.euroarms.net
Email: tell-us@euroarms.net
Factory
Via Europa, 172/A
I-25062 Concesio - Brescia - ITALY
Phone No.: 011-39-30-275-1725
Fax No.: 011-39-30-218-0365
Web site: www.euroarms.net
Email: info@euroarms.net

FABER BROTHERS

4141 S. Pulaski
Chicago, IL 60632
Phone No.: 800-366-2000
Fax No.: 312-376-0732

FEINWERKBAU
Westinger & Altenburger

Neckarstrasse 43
D-78727 Oberndorf/Neckar GERMANY
Fax No.: 011-49-7423-/814-223
Web site: www.feinwerkbau.de

FLINTLOCKS, ETC.

160 Rossiter Rd.
Richmond, MA 01254
Phone No.: 413-698-3822
Fax No.: 413-698-3866
Email: flintetc@berkshire.rr.com

FREEDOM ARMS

P.O. Box 150
Freedom, WY 83120
Phone No.: 307-883-2468
Fax No.: 307-883-2005
Web site: www.freedomarms.com
Email: freedom@freedomarms.com

GIBBS RIFLE COMPANY, INC. (G.R.C., INC.)

219 Lawn Street
Martinsburg, WV 25401
Phone No.: 304-262-1651
Fax No.: 304-262-1658
Web site: www.gibbsrifle.com
Email: support@gibbsrifle.com

GONIC ARMS

134 Flagg Rd.
Gonic, NH 03839
Phone No.: 603-332-8456
Web site: www.gonicarms.com
Email: gonicman@gonicarms.com

GUN WORKS
Custom built flintlock pistols, longrifles, American fowlers, and English sporting rifles.

247 South 2nd St.
Springfield, OR 97477
Phone No.: 541-741-4118
Fax No.: 541-988-1097
Web site: www.thegunworks.com
Email: office@thegunworks.com

HAWKEN SHOP

P.O. Box 593
Oak Harbor, WA 98277
Phone No.: 360-679-4657
Fax No.: 360-675-1114
Web site: www.thehawkenshop.com
Email: greg@thehawkenshop.com

HEGE JAGD-UND SPORTHANDELS GmbH

Seepromenade
D-88662 Überlingen GERMANY
Phone No.: 011-49-75-51-5039
Fax No.: 011-49-75-51-5209

HODGDON POWDER CO.

6231 Robinson, P.O. Box 2932
Shawnee Mission, KS 66201
Phone No.: 913-362-9455
Fax No.: 913-362-1307
Web site: www.hodgdon.com
Email: help@hodgdon.com

J.P. GUN STOCK, INC.
Distributor - please refer to Mountain States Manufacturing listing.

JACK FIRST, INC.
Gun Parts/Accessories/Service

1201 Turbine Dr.
Rapid City, SD 57701
Phone No.: 605-343-9544
Fax No.: 605-343-9420

K.B.I., INC.

P.O. Box 6625
Harrisburg, PA 17112-0625
Phone No.: 717-540-8518
Fax No.: 717-540-8567
Email: sales@kbi-inc.com
Web site: www.kbi-inc.com

KAHNKE GUN WORKS

206 West 11th
Redwood Falls, MN 56283
Phone No.: 507-637-2901

KNIGHT RIFLES

21852 Highway J46, P.O. Box 130
Centerville, IA 52544
Phone No.: 641-856-2626
Fax No.: 641-856-2628
Web site: www.knightrifles.com

YMAN PRODUCTS CORP.
475 Smith St.
Middletown, CT 06457
Phone No.: 860-632-2020
Fax No.: 860-632-1699
Web site: www.lymanproducts.com
Email: lyman@cshore.com

RANDALL SHOOTING SUPPLIES
3616 N. Scottsdale Rd.
Scottsdale, AZ 85252
Phone No.: 480-945-2553
Fax No.: 480-949-0734

MARKESBERY MUZZLE LOADERS, INC.
7785 Foundation Dr., Suite #6
Florence, KY 41042
Phone No.: 859.342.5553
Fax No.: 859-342-2380

MARLIN FIREARMS COMPANY
100 Kenna Drive
North Haven, CT 06473-0905
Phone No.: 203-239-5621
Fax No.: 203-234-7991
Web site: www.marlinfirearms.com

MID-WESTERN OUTDOOR SPECIALTIES, INC.
902 e. 4th Street
Joplin, MO 64801
Phone No.: 800-693-7455
Fax No.: 417-624-2430
Web site: www.mw-os.com

MILLENNIUM DESIGNED MUZZLELOADERS, LTD.
RR 1, Box 405
Maidstone, VT 05905
Phone No.: 802-676-3311
Fax No.: 802-676-3322
Email: MDM-muzzleloaders@outdrs.net
Web site: www.MDM-muzzleloaders.com

MITCHELL ARMS, INC. (MAUSERS)
P.O. Box 9295
Fountain Valley, CA 92728
Phone No.: 714-444-2226
Fax No.: 714-444-2220
Web site: www.mitchellsales.com
Email: custserv@mitchellsales.com

MODERN MUZZLELOADING, INC.
Please refer to Knight Rifles.

MOUNTAIN STATES MANUFACTURING
Rt 2 Box 154-1
Williamstown, WV 26187
Phone No.: 304-375-7842
Fax No.: 304-445-1776
Web site: www.msmfg.com

MOWREY GUN WORKS
P.O. Box 246
Waldren, IN
Phone No.: 765-525-6181
Fax No.: 765-525-9595

NAVY ARMS CO.
815 22nd Street
Union City, NJ 07087
Phone No.: 201-863-7100
Fax No.: 201-863-8770
Web site: www.navyarms.com
Email: info@navyarms.com

NEW ENGLAND FIREARMS
60 Industrial Rowe
Gardner, MA 01440
Phone No.: 978-632-9393
Fax No.: 798-632-2300
Web site: www.newenglandfirearms.com

NEW ULTRA LIGHT ARMS LLC
1024 Grafton Rd.
Morgantown, WV 26508
Phone No.: 304-292-0600
Fax No.: 304-292-9662
Web site: www.newultralight.com
Email: newultralightarms@cs.com

NORTH AMERICAN ARMS, INC.
2150 South 950 East
Provo, UT 84606-6285
Phone No.: 801-374-9990
Fax No.: 801-374-9998
Web site: www.naaminis.com

NORTH STAR WEST, INC.
2042 Smokey Rd.
Fremchtown, MT 59834
Phone No.: 406-626-4081
Web site: www.northstarwest.com

NUMRICH GUN PARTS CORP.
Parts supplier only
226 Williams Lane
W. Hurley, NY 12491
Phone No.: 845-679-2417
Fax No.: 845-679-5849
Web site: www.gunpartscorp.com
Email: info@gunpartscorp.com

OCTOBER COUNTRY MUZZLELOADING, INC.
P.O. Box 969
Hayden, ID 83835-0969
Phone No.: 208-762-4903
Fax No.: 208-772-9230
Web site: www.oct-country.com
Email: ocinfo@octobercountry.com

OLD DOMINION ARMS
Specializing in hand-built Virginia Longrifles, Early American rifles, restorations, repairs.
Phone No.: 804 448-1119
Web site: www.aledge.com
Email: al@aledge.com

PACIFIC RIFLE COMPANY
The Zephyr Rifle
P.O. Box 1473
Lake Oswego, OR 97035
Phone No.: 503-620-5154

PEDERSOLI, DAVIDE & C. S.n.c.
Importer please refer to Flintlocks, Etc. listing.
Importer please refer to Navy Arms Co. listing.
Factory
Via Artigiani 57
I-25063 Gardone V.T. (BS), ITALY
Fax No.: 011-39-30-8911019
Web site: www.davide-pedersoli.com
Email: commerce@davide-pedersoli.com

PEIFER RIFLE CO.
P.O. Box 192
Nokomis, IL 62075
Fax No.: 217-563-7060

PIETTA, F.lli s.n.c.
Importer please refer to Taylor's & Co. listing.
Importer please refer to Cabela's Inc. listing.
Factory
Via Mandolossa 102
I-25064 Gussago (Brescia) ITALY
Fax No.: 011-39-30-3737100
Web site: www.pietta.it
Email: fap@spidernet.it

PRAIRIE RIVER ARMS
1180 North 6th St.
Princeton, IL 61356
Phone No.: 815-875-1616
Fax No.: 815-875-1402
Web site: www.prabullpup.com
Email: service@prabullpup.com

REMINGTON ARMS CO., INC.
Attn: Consumer Services
870 Remington Drive
P.O. Box 700
Madison, NC 27025-0700
Phone No.: 800-243-9700
Fax No.: 336-548-8707
Web site: www.remington.com
Remington Arms Co., Inc. (Repairs)
14 Hoefler Ave.
Ilion, NY 13357
Phone No.: 800-243-9700

ROSSI
Importer - BrazTech International L.C.
16175 N.W. 49th Ave.
Miami, FL 33014
Phone No.: 305-474-0401
Fax No.: 305-623-7506
Web site: www.rossiusa.com
Factory
Amadeo Rossi, S.A.
Rua Amadeo Rossi, 143
B-93030-220 Sao Leopoldo-RS BRAZIL

RUMMELL, GARY/GUNMAKER
Purveyor of fine custom Pennsylvania Longrifles
1959 Quaker Valley Rd.
Fishertown, PA 15539
Phone No.: 814-839-4833

SAVAGE ARMS, INC.
100 Springfield Rd.
Westfield, MA 01085
Phone No.: 413-568-7001
Fax No.: 413-562-7764
Web site: www.savagearms.com

SHILOH RIFLE MFG. CO.
P.O. Box 279
Big Timber, MT 59011
Phone No.: 406-932-4454
Fax No.: 406-932-5627
Web site: www.shilorifle.com

SPLIT FIRE SPORTING GOODS, LLC
Please refer to White Rifles LLC.

STONE MOUNTAIN ARMS, INC.
Distributor - please refer to Conneticut Valley Arms listing.

STURM, RUGER & CO., INC.
Headquarters
1 Lacey Place
Southport, CT 06490
Phone No.: 203-259-7843
Fax No.: 203-256-3367
Web site: www.ruger.com
Service
411 Sunapee St.
New Port, NH 03773
Phone No.: 603-865-2442
Fax No.: 603-863-6165

TAYLOR'S & COMPANY, INC.
304 Lenoir Dr.
Winchester, VA 22603
Phone No.: 540-722-2017
Fax No.: 540-722-2018
Email: info@taylorsfirearms.com
Web site: www.taylorsfirearms.com

THOMPSON/CENTER ARMS CO.
P.O. Box 5002
Rochester, NH 03867
Customer Service Phone No.: 603-332-2333
Fax No.: 603-332-5133
Web site: www.tcarms.com
Email: Tech@tcarms.com

TRADITIONS PERFORMANCE FIREARMS
1375 Boston Post Rd.
P.O. Box 776
Old Saybrook, CT 06475-0776
Phone No.: 860-388-4656
Fax No.: 860-388-4657
Web site: www.traditionsmuzzle.com
Email: info@traditionsfirearms.com

TRAIL GUNS ARMORY
Route 22, Box 760
Conroe, TX 77303

UBERTI, A. & C., S.r.l.
Importer - Stoeger Industries
17603 Indian Head Highway, Suite 200
Accokeek, MD 20607-2501
Phone No.: 301-283-6300
Fax No.: 301-283-6986
Web site: www.stoegerindustries.com
Factory
Via G. Carducci, 41
I-25068 Ponte Zanano (BS) ITALY
Web site: www.ubertireplicas.com
Email: uberti@lumetel.it

U.S. HISTORICAL SOCIETY
See America Remembers listing.

WHITE RIFLES LLC
P.O. Box 1044
Orem, UT 84059-1044
Phone No.: 801-932-7950
Fax No.: 801-932-7959
Web site: www.whiterifles.com

WILDERNESS RIFLE WORKS
Please refer to Mowrey Gun Works.

WINCHESTER MUZZLELOADING
A Division of Blackpowder Products, Inc.
5988 Peachtree Corners East
Norcross, GA 30071
Phone No.: 877-892-7544
Fax No.: 770-242-8546
Web site: www.winchestermuzzleloading.com
Email: info@winchestermuzzleloading.com

INDEX

P.S.

In order to appear bigger than the other men in his village, Gustav carried a very, very small rifle.